VISCOELASTIC PROPERTIES OF POLYMERS

VISCOELASTIC
PROPERTIES
OF
POLYMERS

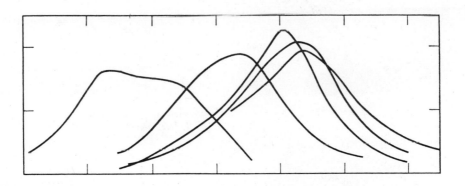

by

JOHN D. FERRY

Professor of Chemistry
University of Wisconsin

New York · London, John Wiley & Sons, Inc.

to the memory of **D. H. F.**

Preface

It is interesting to observe the evolution of science in microcosm by following the development of a highly specialized fragment of it, especially one which cuts across several conventional fields, such as the subject of this book. The familiar pattern of alternation between experimental and theoretical advances is apparent. Underlying each advance is a conceptual scheme which is an arbitrary and subjective choice of one investigator or school; in this conceptual abstraction, attention is focused on certain aspects of observed behavior that are believed to be particularly important or useful to describe, and other aspects are ignored. The conceptual scheme leads to a set of characteristic physical quantities which can be defined, measured, and correlated by theoretical relationships.

Naturally, in the spontaneous development of the subject, alternative conceptual schemes arise, each with its favored definitions, parameters, and terminology. Sometimes the languages are readily translatable, in other cases with extreme difficulty. In the course of time, a majority of the scientific community may adopt one scheme, and for a while a degree of order prevails.

The subject of the viscoelasticity of polymers has not quite reached this last stage of development, but it has matured to the point where some kind of summarizing treatment seems desirable. The phenomenological theory of linear viscoelasticity is essentially complete. The molecular origin of some aspects of the viscoelastic behavior peculiar to polymers is semi-quantitatively understood, as are their dependences on temperature, molecular weight, concentration, and other variables. Moreover, the relationships are well enough understood to permit rule-of-thumb predictions of behavior in practical situations to a far greater extent, I believe, than has been exploited up to now. Other aspects such as the effects of molecular weight distribution and the properties of highly cross-linked, glassy, and crystalline polymers are very poorly understood, but the direction which further experimental and theoretical developments should take is fairly clear.

This book was written with several objectives in view. First, I have tried to assemble the working information needed by investigators in the field, for making measurements and interpreting data—information which has hitherto been scattered in dozens of separate publications. A uniform notation has been used, most of it in accordance with the recommendations of the Society of Rheology. Second, the exposition is I hope straightforward enough so that new investigators, of whom there are many in industrial laboratories encountering the phenomena of polymer viscoelasticity without any previous experience, can use it to familiarize themselves with the subject. Third, certain needs for further theoretical and experimental advances are pointed out. Finally, a few examples of practical applications are given in the hope that these will stimulate a much wider use of approximate interconversions of viscoelastic functions, and reduced variables describing effects of temperature, pressure, and concentration, to predict viscoelastic behavior and correlate it with other properties under a wide variety of conditions.

I owe a profound debt to my former students and associates who, over the years, have participated in studies of the viscoelastic properties of polymers at the University of Wisconsin, and whose collective experience has contributed greatly to writing this book. The work cited from our own laboratory was supported by the Research Committee of the Graduate School of the University of Wisconsin; the Ordnance Corps, Department of the Army; National Science Foundation; Office of Naval Research; Allegany Ballistics Laboratory; and Union Carbide Chemicals Company.

In addition to the many citations of published investigations from other laboratories, unpublished data and theoretical calculations were generously made available by the late Professor E. Jenckel and by Drs. A. Kovacs, J. Lamb, R. S. Marvin, A. R. Payne, and K. Ninomiya.

Most of the manuscript was written during tenure of a National Science Foundation Senior Postdoctoral Fellowship at the University of Brussels in 1959. I am deeply indebted to Professor L. de Brouckère for the kind hospitality of the Laboratoire de Chimie Analytique et Minérale at the University, and to European Research Associates for the use of library facilities. Different chapters were read by Professor Edwin R. Fitzgerald of Pennsylvania State University and by Drs. Robert F. Landel, Thor L. Smith, Robert S. Marvin, Kazuhiko Ninomiya, Donald J. Plazek, Malcolm L. Williams, and André J. Kovacs; I am grateful for their constructive criticism. The proof of the entire book was painstakingly read by Professor Fitzgerald and Dr. Plazek.

JOHN D. FERRY

December, 1960

Contents

CHAPTER 1

The Nature of Viscoelastic Behavior

A. INTRODUCTION

The classical theory of elasticity deals with mechanical properties of perfectly elastic solids, for which in accordance with Hooke's law stress is always directly proportional to strain but independent of the rate of strain. The theory of hydrodynamics deals with properties of perfectly viscous liquids, for which in accordance with Newton's law the stress is always directly proportional to rate of strain but independent of the strain itself. These categories are idealizations, however; any real solid shows deviations from Hooke's law under suitably chosen conditions, and it is probably safe to say that any real liquid would show deviations from Newtonian flow if subjected to sufficiently precise measurements.

There are two important types of deviations. First, the strain (in a solid) or the rate of strain (in a liquid) may not be directly proportional to the stress but may depend on stress in a more complicated manner. Such *stress* anomalies are familiar when the elastic limit is exceeded for a solid. Second, the stress may depend on both the strain and the rate of strain together, as well as higher time derivatives of the strain. Such *time* anomalies evidently reflect a behavior which combines liquidlike and solidlike characteristics, and they are therefore called viscoelastic.

Both stress and time anomalies may of course coexist. If only the latter are present, we have *linear* viscoelastic behavior; then in a given

1

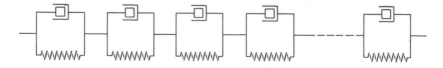

FIG. 1–1. Generalized Voigt model of springs and dashpots representing the mechanical behavior of a viscoelastic material.

experiment the ratio of stress to strain is a function of time alone, and not of the stress magnitude.

When a material exhibits linear viscoelastic behavior, its mechanical properties can be duplicated by a model consisting of some suitable combination of springs which obey Hooke's law and viscous dashpots (pistons moving in oil) which obey Newton's law. Two such models are illustrated in Figs. 1–1 and 1–2. To simulate a real material, the model may require an infinite number of units with different spring constants and flow constants, but if each unit is linear (Hookean or Newtonian respectively) the over-all behavior is linear. For most polymeric materials, linear viscoelastic response can be achieved experimentally, within a practical degree of approximation, by making the deforming stresses sufficiently small.

It is of course possible to develop the subject of viscoelasticity without recourse to mechanical models, but they are introduced here for convenience in visualizing the combination of Hookean solidlike and Newtonian liquidlike characteristics. It should be remembered, as pointed out by Poincaré,[1] that if a physical phenomenon can be represented by a mechanical model it can also be represented by an infinite number of other models. The equivalence of different viscoelastic models has been discussed by Kuhn[2] and many other writers. For example, the models of Figs. 1–1 and 1–2 are equivalent with a suitable choice of spring and flow constants (if one viscosity in 1–1 is set equal to zero and one viscosity in 1–2 is set equal to infinity). The model represents only the macroscopic behavior and does not necessarily provide any insight into the molecular basis of viscoelastic phenomena; its elements should not be thought of as corresponding directly to any molecular processes. Some other aspects of representations by models are discussed in Appendix F.

Qualitatively, the symptoms of viscoelasticity are manifested in various ways. A body which is not quite solid does not maintain a constant deformation under constant stress (even when the stress is quite small) but goes on slowly deforming with time, or creeps; obviously the model in Fig. 1–1 would behave in this manner. When such a body is constrained at constant deformation, the stress required to hold it gradually diminishes, or relaxes; in Fig. 1–2, this corresponds to the gradual release of the springs by motion of the dashpots. On the other hand, a body which is not quite liquid may while flowing under constant stress store some of the energy input, instead of dissipating all of it as heat; in Fig. 1–2, the springs are stretched (to different extents) when the dashpots are all steadily being pulled out. And when a viscoelastic body is subjected to sinusoidally oscillating stress, the strain is neither exactly in phase with the stress (as it would be for a perfectly elastic solid) nor 90° out of phase (as it would be for a perfectly viscous liquid) but somewhere in between. Some of the energy input is stored and recovered in each cycle, and some is dissipated as heat, as (in either Fig. 1–1 or Fig. 1–2) both the springs and the dashpots move back and forth in complicated fashion. In each of these examples, the material appears intermediate in character between solids and liquids.

In many of the materials of interest in classical physics, as well as of practical importance in engineering, viscoelastic anomalies are negligible or of minor significance. Though the foundations of the phenomenological theory of viscoelasticity were inspired by creep and relaxation experiments on fibers of metal and glass,[3-6] and the dissipation of energy in sinusoidally oscillating deformations has provided valuable information about the structure of metals,[7] the deviations from perfect elasticity here are small. In polymeric systems, by contrast, mechanical behavior is dominated by viscoelastic phenomena which are often truly spectacular.

The prominence of viscoelasticity in polymers is not unexpected

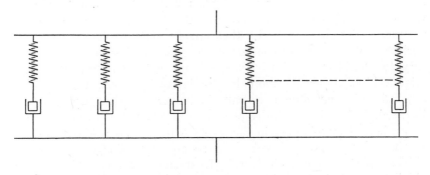

FIG. 1–2. Generalized Maxwell model of springs and dashpots representing the mechanical behavior of a viscoelastic material.

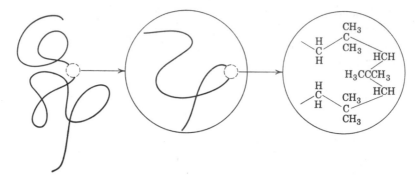

FIG. 1–3. Symbolic representation of long-range and short-range contour relationships in a flexible polymer molecule (polyisobutylene).

when one considers the complicated molecular adjustments which must underlie any macroscopic mechanical deformation. In deformation of a hard solid such as diamond, sodium chloride, or crystalline zinc, atoms are displaced from equilibrium positions in fields of force which are quite local in character; from knowledge of the interatomic potentials, elastic constants can be calculated.[8] Other mechanical phenomena reflect structural imperfections involving distances discontinuously larger than atomic dimensions.[7,8] In an ordinary liquid, viscous flow reflects the change with time, under stress, of the distribution of molecules surrounding a given molecule; here, too, the relevant forces and processes of readjustment are quite local in character, and from knowledge of them the viscosity can in principle be calculated.[9] In a polymer, on the other hand, each flexible threadlike molecule pervades an average volume much greater than atomic dimensions and is continually changing the shape of its contour as it wriggles and writhes with its thermal energy. To characterize the various configurations or contour shapes which it assumes, it is necessary to consider (qualitatively speaking) gross long-range contour relationships, somewhat more local relationships seen with a more detailed scale, and so on, eventually including the orientation of bonds in the chain backbone with respect to each other on a scale of atomic dimensions, as symbolized in Fig. 1–3. Alfrey [10] has referred to these spatial relationships, viewed over progressively longer ranges, as "kinks, curls, and convolutions." Rearrangements on a local scale (kinks) are relatively rapid, on a long-range scale (convolutions) very slow. Under stress, a new assortment of configurations is obtained;

the response to the local aspects of the new distribution is rapid, the response to the long-range aspects is slow, and all told there is a very wide and continuous range of time scale covering the response of such a system to external stress.

Every polymeric system has a glass transition temperature below which the writhing thermal motions essentially cease. Here, long-range convolutional readjustments are severely restricted; there is still a wide range of response rates to external stress, but different in nature.

From measurements of viscoelastic properties of polymers, information can be obtained about the nature and the rates of the configurational rearrangements, and the disposition and interaction of the macromolecules in both their short-range and their long-range interrelations. From the standpoint of the physical chemist, this provides a field of inquiry with unique features of interest. Investigation of viscoelastic properties of polymers has also been greatly stimulated, of course, by the practical importance of mechanical behavior in the processing and utilization of rubbers, plastics, and fibers. As a result, a very high proportion of all studies on viscoelasticity in the past two decades has been devoted to the viscoelasticity of polymers.

B. TYPES OF MECHANICAL DEFORMATIONS

In a viscoelastic as in a perfectly elastic body, the state of deformation at a given point is specified by a strain tensor which represents the relative changes in dimensions and angles of a small cubical element cut out at that position. Similarly, the state of stress is specified by a stress tensor which represents the forces acting on different faces of the cubical element from different directions. For details, the reader is referred to standard treatises.[10-12] If the strains are small, the components of the two tensors are related in a simple manner by certain moduli of elasticity which are properties of the material alone and not of the external geometry of the body. For viscoelastic materials, the moduli are time-dependent, and the nature of this dependence is the primary concern of the phenomenological study of viscoelasticity.

Experimental measurements are usually made by observing external forces and changes in external dimensions of a body with a certain shape—a cube, disc, rod, or fiber—and these must be related to the internal states of stress and strain before the moduli can be calculated. The relationships for more complicated deformations such as torsion and flexure will be taken up in the chapters on experimental measurements. There are some simple cases, however, where the strain and stress are homogeneous (the same throughout the body), and these can serve now to define the most important moduli in terms of macroscopic experiments.

In the following examples, it is assumed that the material is isotropic, that the strains are small compared with unity, and that for each type of deformation Hooke's law holds. The definitions are the same for both perfectly elastic and linear viscoelastic bodies except that for the latter the moduli and compliances will be functions of time and of the previous stress history. The notation follows that recommended by the Committee on Nomenclature of the Society of Rheology.[13]

From a physical standpoint, the two basic types of deformation are simple shear, which produces a change in shape with no change in volume, and bulk compression (or its opposite, dilatation), which produces a change in volume with no change in shape. The molecular adjustments which accompany a macroscopic response to stress must clearly be quite different in these two cases, and physical measurements of the two phenomena should yield different kinds of information about the molecular motions and interactions. Other types of deformation produce a combination of shape and volume changes, and their physical analysis is more complicated; they are often employed, nevertheless, because under certain circumstances they are much more easily measured.

1. Simple Shear

If a rectangular block as in Fig. 1–4 is deformed by a lateral force f acting parallel to its top face with area A, the shear stress is $\sigma = f/A$; the shear strain γ is the tangent of the angle of deformation α (for small strains, the angle itself). The shear modulus, or modulus of rigidity, is $G = \sigma/\gamma$; its reciprocal is the shear compliance, J. (In the experiment as illustrated, certain other forces must be acting to prevent mass motion of the sample, but these are irrelevant to the elementary definition.) This deformation represents a change in shape with no change in volume.

Simple shear is by far the most important type of deformation in studies of viscoelastic bodies, because it can be performed on liquids and solids alike, and on materials with all degrees of intermediate

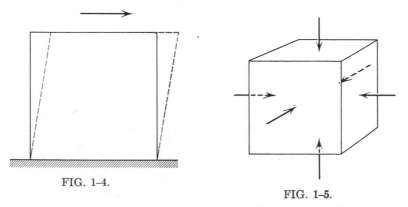

FIG. 1–4.

FIG. 1–5.

FIG. 1–4. Geometrical arrangement for deformation in simple shear.
FIG. 1–5. Geometrical arrangement for deformation in bulk compression.

character; thus, steady-state laminar flow of a liquid is simple shear with a constant rate of strain. Moreover, the absence of a volume change facilitates interpretation of the behavior in molecular terms. The majority of the experimental and theoretical discussion in this book will be formulated in terms of the shear modulus and compliance, G and J.

2. Bulk Compression

If a block as in Fig. 1–5 is subjected to a normal force on each side proportional to its area, the compressive stress everywhere is simply the pressure P and the bulk strain is the relative decrease in volume, $-\Delta V/V$. The bulk modulus is $K = -P/(\Delta V/V)$. Its reciprocal is the bulk compliance, B; if the compression is a perfectly elastic phenomenon, B is the same as the familiar thermodynamic compressibility $\beta = -(1/V)(\partial V/\partial P)_T$, but in general it will be viscoelastic so that B is time-dependent. This, of course, represents a change in volume without a change in shape.

Bulk compression would not be expected to involve changes in long-range configuration or contour shape, and hence the differences between polymers and simple liquids and solids are not so striking in compression as in shear. Nevertheless, the effects of flexible chain structure are still apparent.

The subscript T in the above partial derivative implies an isothermal measurement, and indeed all of the experimental examples given here are supposed to be carried out isothermally. The relation between isothermal and adiabatic moduli is considered in Chapter 5.

3. Simple Extension

If a rod as in Fig. 1–6 is subjected to a normal tensile force f on the ends whose area is A, leaving the sides free of external forces, the tensile stress is $\sigma = f/A$ and the strain ϵ is the relative increase in length $\Delta l/l$. Young's modulus of elasticity, E, is the ratio σ/ϵ; its reciprocal is the tensile compliance, D. This experiment, while often easy to perform, has the disadvantage that it produces changes in both shape and volume. In fact, the compliance D is related to the shear and bulk compliances by the equation

$$D = J/3 + B/9 \tag{1}$$

In polymeric systems, B is of the order of 10^{-10} cm^2/dyne or less; whereas (as will be seen in the next chapter) J may be anything from 10^{-5} to 10^{-12} cm^2/dyne, though always greater than B. Whenever J is greater than B by two orders of magnitude or more, equation 1 can be approximated by $D = J/3$; also, then, $E = 3G$. In this case, simple extension gives the same information as simple shear, and the results of the two experiments are interconvertible. Physically, this fact arises

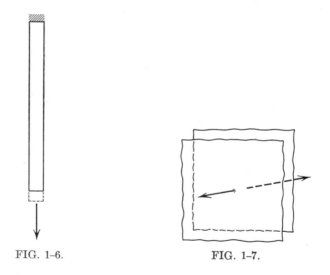

FIG. 1–6.   FIG. 1–7.

FIG. 1–6. Geometrical arrangement for deformation in simple extension.
FIG. 1–7. Geometrical arrangement for bulk longitudinal deformation.

because the change in volume caused by the extension is negligible in comparison with the change in shape. When $J \gg B$ or $G \ll K$, the material is often loosely but inaccurately called "incompressible"; a "soft elastic solid" might be better. For viscoelastic materials, the criteria for this situation involve not only the type of material but also the time scale of the experiment, since the magnitudes of J and G depend greatly on the latter.

The relations between G and E can also be written in terms of a dimensionless variable, Poisson's ratio, which is defined as $\mu = [1 - (1/V)(\partial V/\partial \epsilon)]/2$ and is a measure of the degree of lateral contraction accompanying a longitudinal extension. When $J \gg B$, there is no significant volume increase on extension and $\mu = \frac{1}{2}$. If the volume had increased sufficiently to avoid any lateral contraction of the rod in Fig. 1–5, $(1/V)(\partial V/\partial \epsilon)$ would be unity and $\mu = 0$. The minimum value of μ ordinarily observed, however, is about 0.2 for homogeneous, isotropic materials. There are 12 formulas [10, 11] connecting G, K, E, and μ, of which only two will be given here:

$$E = 2G(1 + \mu) \tag{2}$$

$$E = 3K(1 - 2\mu) \tag{3}$$

These show again that, as μ approaches $\frac{1}{2}$, E becomes equal to $3G$ and $K \gg E$.

4. One-Dimensional Extension in Infinite Medium (Bulk Longitudinal Deformation)

If a thin flat sample of infinite lateral dimensions is placed under tension or compression in the thin direction, as in Fig. 1–7, there are changes in both shape and volume, but this time the latter predominates because the constraints of the surrounding medium prevent lateral deformation. The stress/strain ratio σ/ϵ now gives a different modulus M which is related to the bulk and shear moduli by the equation

$$M = K + 4G/3 \tag{4}$$

For a soft elastic solid where $K \gg G$, this experiment evidently yields the bulk modulus alone. It cannot, of course, be readily carried out by simple application of external stresses, but it corresponds to the deformation caused by propagation of a longitudinal elastic wave in a medium all of whose dimensions are large compared with the wavelength (cf. Chapter 8).

C. FORMULATION OF TIME-DEPENDENT EXPERIMENTS

The experimental problem in any study of viscoelastic behavior is to determine the relations among stress, strain, and time for a particular type of deformation and a particular loading pattern, *i.e.*, stress history. Insofar as the viscoelastic behavior is linear, this reduces to determining the time dependence of the modulus or the compliance corresponding to the type of deformation chosen. Usually the desired simplification of linear behavior can be achieved by keeping the stresses sufficiently small. We must now summarize various possible loading patterns, each of which can in principle be applied to any of the deformations described in the previous section.

1. Transient Loading Patterns

In *creep*, the stress is suddenly applied and maintained constant, and the strain is measured as a function of time. For simple shear, this would correspond to a constant stress $\mathfrak{T}$ in Fig. 1–4; for bulk compression, to a constant confining pressure in Fig. 1–5. Conventionally, the results are expressed as a time-dependent compliance, so $J(t)$ always means the strain/stress ratio in shear creep, and $B(t)$ the strain/stress ratio in bulk creep; similarly with $D(t)$, etc. If the dimensions of the sample eventually change perceptibly, this has to be taken into account, of course, in calculating the stress and strain. For any polymeric material, the deformation is at first rapid and then progressively slower, as will be abundantly illustrated in the next chapter.

In *stress relaxation*, the sample is suddenly brought to a given deformation, and the stress required to maintain it is measured as a function of time. Conventionally, the results are expressed as a time-dependent modulus, so $G(t)$ always means the stress/strain ratio in shear stress relaxation; $K(t)$ the stress/strain ratio in bulk stress relaxation, etc. In general, $J(t) \neq 1/G(t)$, because the two loading patterns are different (although in certain special cases the two are approximately reciprocally related, as will be shown in Chapter 2).

In *deformation with constant rate of strain*, the strain is increased linearly with time and the stress is measured as a function of time. If the viscoelastic behavior is known to be linear, the results can be converted to the relaxation modulus, *e.g.*, $G(t)$; but if it is non-linear, analysis of the data is very difficult because the stress and time anomalies are combined.

In *deformation with constant rate of stress loading,* the stress is increased linearly with time and the strain is measured as a function of time. If the viscoelastic behavior is known to be linear, the results can be converted to the creep compliance, *e.g.,* $J(t)$.

To obtain complete information about viscoelastic behavior of polymer systems, and about the molecular properties which it reflects, it is necessary to make measurements over a wide range of time scale—many powers of ten. Transient measurements are limited at the short-time end by inertial effects, and moreover by the impossibility of having a truly instantaneous application of stress or strain (or onset of rate of stress or rate of strain) at the beginning of the experiment. In practice, times less than one second are rarely employed. At the long-time end, experiments with constant rate of strain or loading are limited by deviations from linear viscoelasticity at high stresses and in fact eventual rupture. But creep and stress relaxation experiments are limited only by the patience of the investigator, the precision of his apparatus, and the chemical stability of the material; they are always preferred for effects at long times.

2. Periodic or Dynamic Loading Patterns

To supplement the transient experiments and provide information corresponding to very short times, the stress is varied periodically, usually with a sinusoidal alternation at a frequency ν in cycles/sec. or ω ($= 2\pi\nu$) in radians/sec. A periodic experiment at frequency ω is qualitatively equivalent to a transient experiment at time $t = 1/\omega$. If the viscoelastic behavior is linear, the strain will also alternate sinusoidally but will be out of phase with the stress (Fig. 1–8). The stress can be decomposed vectorially into two components, one in phase with the strain and the other 90° out of phase (Fig. 1–9); when these are divided by the strain, we have separated the modulus into an in-phase (real) and out-of-phase (imaginary) component. Thus for shear the complex stress/strain ratio is

$$\mathbf{G}^* = G' + iG'' \tag{5}$$

and for bulk compression

$$\mathbf{K}^* = K' + iK'' \tag{6}$$

and similarly for the other deformation types. Thus each periodic, or dynamic, measurement at a given frequency provides *two* independent quantities. The results can be expressed in various alternative ways;

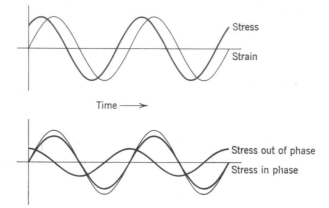

FIG. 1-8. Sinusoidally varying stress and strain for steady-state periodic deformations of a linear viscoelastic material.

for example, the ratio of the peak stress to peak strain in Fig. 1–8 is (for shear)

$$\left| \mathbf{G}^* \right| = \sqrt{G'^2 + G''^2} \tag{7}$$

and the phase angle δ is given by

$$\tan \delta = G''/G' \tag{8}$$

If the experimental data are provided in the form of $\left| \mathbf{G} \right|$ and δ, the components of the modulus can be obtained by the inverse relations

$$G' = \left| \mathbf{G}^* \right| \cos \delta \tag{9}$$

$$G'' = \left| \mathbf{G}^* \right| \sin \delta \tag{10}$$

and similar equations can be written for the complex moduli $\mathbf{K}^*$, $\mathbf{E}^*$, and $\mathbf{M}^*$ which correspond to other types of deformations.

The dynamic data can also be expressed in terms of a complex compliance:

$$\mathbf{J}^* = 1/\mathbf{G}^* = J' - iJ'' \tag{11}$$

where the real component, J', is the ratio of the strain in phase with the stress to the stress, and the imaginary component J'' is the ratio of the strain 90° out of phase with the stress to the stress. The quantities G' and J' are associated with energy storage and release in the periodic deformation and are therefore called the storage modulus and storage compliance; G'' and J'' are associated with the dissipation of energy as heat and are therefore called the loss modulus and loss compliance.

Although $\mathbf{J}^* = 1/\mathbf{G}^*$, their individual components are not reciprocally related, but are connected by the following equations:

$$J' = \frac{G'}{(G'^2 + G''^2)} = \frac{1/G'}{1 + \tan^2 \delta} \tag{12}$$

$$J'' = \frac{G''}{(G'^2 + G''^2)} = \frac{1/G''}{1 + (\tan^2 \delta)^{-1}} \tag{13}$$

$$G' = \frac{J'}{(J'^2 + J''^2)} = \frac{1/J'}{1 + \tan^2 \delta} \tag{14}$$

$$G'' = \frac{J''}{(J'^2 + J''^2)} = \frac{1/J''}{1 + (\tan^2 \delta)^{-1}} \tag{15}$$

Similar relations can of course be written for the components of $\mathbf{K}^*$, $\mathbf{E}^*$, and $\mathbf{M}^*$ and the corresponding compliances.

Periodic measurements can be made, depending on circumstances, at frequencies from 10^{-5} to 10^8 cycles/sec.; usually a given experimental method will cover only 2 to 3 powers of ten, but a great variety of methods is available, as will be seen in Chapters 5-9.

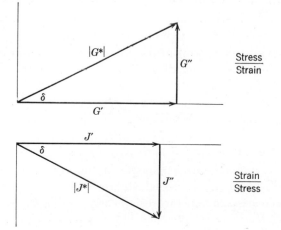

FIG. 1-9. Vectorial resolution of modulus and compliance components in sinusoidal deformations.

3. Correlation of Experimental Data to Provide Information over Wide Ranges of Time Scale

To cover a wide enough time scale to reflect the variety of molecular motions in polymeric systems, often 10 to 15 logarithmic decades, one must usually combine information from transient and dynamic experiments. It is then necessary to calculate from the results of one type of measurement what would have been observed in the other, in the same range of time (or inverse radian frequency). Fortunately, this is possible, provided the viscoelastic behavior is linear. In principle, knowledge of any one of the functions $J(t)$, $G(t)$, $G'(\omega)$, $G''(\omega)$, $J'(\omega)$, $J''(\omega)$ over the entire range of time or frequency (plus in certain cases one or two additional constants) permits calculation of all the others. Even if the values are not available over the entire range of the argument, approximation methods can be applied. These calculations are treated in detail in Chapters 3 and 4.

Since each of the preceding functions can be calculated from any other, it is an arbitrary matter which is chosen to depict the behavior of a system and to correlate with theoretical formulations on a molecular basis. In fact, two other derived functions are often used for the latter purpose—the relaxation and retardation spectra, H and L, which will be defined in Chapter 3. Actually, different aspects of the viscoelastic behavior, and the molecular phenomena which underlie them, have different degrees of prominence in the various functions enumerated above, so it is worthwhile to examine the form of several of these functions even when all are calculated from the same experimental data. A qualitative survey of their appearance will be presented in Chapter 2.

Even when only one experimental method is available, covering perhaps two or three decades of logarithmic time or frequency scale, the viscoelastic functions can be traced out over a much larger effective range by making measurements at different temperatures, and using a sort of principle of viscoelastic corresponding states. In many cases, an increase in temperature is nearly equivalent to an increase in time or a decrease in frequency in its effect on a modulus or compliance, and a temperature range of 100° may provide an effective time range of ten logarithmic decades. This scheme must be used judiciously, with regard to the reservations in the theories which support it, and to previous experimental experience; it is critically discussed in Chapter 11. When properly applied, it yields plots in terms of reduced variables which can be used with considerable confidence to deduce molecular parameters as well as to predict viscoelastic behavior in regions of time or frequency scale not experimentally accessible.

D. THE BOLTZMANN SUPERPOSITION PRINCIPLE

The relations needed for interconversion of the viscoelastic functions $J(t)$, $G(t)$, $G'(\omega)$, etc., as mentioned in the preceding section stem from a very important general principle concerning linear viscoelastic behavior. As usual, simple shear deformation will be used as an illustration, though the following remarks are of course also applicable to bulk deformation and extension.

1. Statement of the Superposition Principle

From the definition of the creep compliance, if a stress $\mathbb{T}_0$ is put on at $t = 0$, the strain as a function of time will be

$$\gamma(t) = \mathbb{T}_0 J(t) \tag{16}$$

If a higher stress, $\mathbb{T}_0 + \mathbb{T}_1$, is put on at $t = 0$, the strain will simply be proportionately larger,

$$\gamma(t) = (\mathbb{T}_0 + \mathbb{T}_1) J(t) \tag{17}$$

But if $\mathbb{T}_0$ is put on at $t = 0$ and an additional stress $\mathbb{T}_1$ is added at $t = t_1$, the total strain thereafter according to Boltzmann's superposition principle will be

$$\gamma(t) = \mathbb{T}_0 J(t) + \mathbb{T}_1 J(t - t_1), \tag{18}$$

namely, the linear superposition of the two strains at their respective elapsed times. There are innumerable possible variations of loading history, whose effects can be generalized by the basic equation

$$\gamma(t) = \sum_{u_i = -\infty}^{u_i = t} \mathbb{T}_i J(t - u_i) \tag{19}$$

or, in terms of a continuous stress variation beginning at zero time,

$$\gamma(t) = J(0) \mathbb{T}(t) + \int_0^\infty \mathbb{T}(t - s) \frac{dJ(s)}{ds} \, ds \tag{20}$$

where $s = t - u$. These equations express the strain in terms of the entire past stress history. Similar relations for the stress in terms of the past strain history are

$$\mathbb{T}(t) = \sum_{u_1=-\infty}^{u_i=t} \gamma_i G(t - u_i) \qquad (21)$$

$$\mathbb{T}(t) = G(0)\gamma(t) + \int_0^\infty \gamma(t - s) \frac{dG(s)}{ds} ds \qquad (22)$$

Any of equations 19 to 22 serves as a statement of Boltzmann's superposition principle,[3,14] and as a characterization of a linear viscoelastic material. The validity of the superposition principle for most polymeric systems under small stresses has been generally assumed with such confidence that there have not been many specific extensive experimental tests of it. There is certainly wide experience, however, to show that it is at least a close approximation. Of the various ways in which experimental tests can be carried out, perhaps the most instructive here is a comparison of measurements of creep and creep recovery.[3]

2. Illustration by Creep and Creep Recovery

If, after a creep experiment has progressed for some time, the stress is suddenly removed, the rate of deformation will change sign and the body will gradually return more or less toward its initial state (*i.e.*, for shear deformation, toward its initial shape). The course of this reverse deformation is called creep recovery. The results depend very importantly on whether the material possesses an equilibrium compliance, $J_{e.}$, In terms of the mechanical models at the beginning of this chapter, an equilibrium compliance means that none of the spring constants in the Voigt model (Fig. 1–1) is zero, or that one of the viscosities in the Maxwell model (Fig. 1–2) is infinite—so under constant stress the deformation eventually attains a constant limiting value where at least one spring is stretched to an equilibrium position. In bulk compression, an equilibrium compliance no doubt always exists —it is simply the thermodynamic compressibility. For shear and other deformations of polymers, the presence or absence of an equilibrium compliance corresponds approximately to the presence or absence of a cross-linked network in the molecular structure.

In a cross-linked polymer, shear creep followed by creep recovery is essentially as shown schematically in Fig. 1–10. If the stress $\mathbb{T}_0$ has been applied for a time t_2 long enough for the strain to reach within

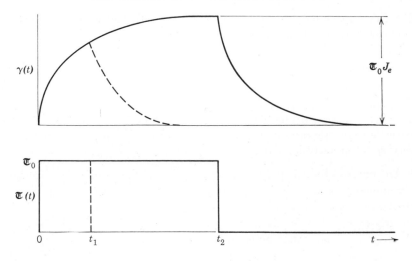

FIG. 1–10. Shear creep and creep recovery shown schematically for a cross-linked polymer.

experimental error its equilibrium value $\gamma(\infty) = \mathbb{T}_0 J_e$, then in accordance with equation 19 the course of creep recovery will be given by

$$\gamma_r(t) = \mathbb{T}_0[J_e - J(t - t_2)] \qquad (23)$$

(noting that removal of stress is equivalent to applying an additional stress of $-\mathbb{T}_0$). This is just a mirror image of the creep itself in the time axis, displaced vertically by $\gamma(\infty)$ and horizontally by t_2. If, on the other hand, the load is removed at a time t_1 before $\gamma(\infty)$ is reached, the course of recovery will be

$$\gamma_r(t) = \mathbb{T}_0[J(t) - J(t - t_1)] \qquad (24)$$

which, although not a simple mirror image, is readily susceptible of experimental test by calculating the right side of the equation from a duplicate creep run carried to longer times. The results of numerous such tests, which support the validity of the superposition principle, have been summarized by Leaderman.[3] These tests have more often been performed for deformation in simple extension than in shear; then equations 23 and 24 hold with ϵ, σ, and D substituted for γ, $\mathbb{T}$, and J.

If the deformations are not kept small, but are carried to the point where the elastic strain is non-linear (in model language, corresponding to deviations from Hookean behavior in the springs of Fig. 1–1), equations 23 and 24 do *not* hold. For soft polymeric solids, deviations from linearity appear much sooner (*i.e.*, at smaller strains) in extension than in shear, because of the characteristic features of rubberlike elasticity [15] (*cf.* Chapter 13). At substantial extensions, the relations between creep and recovery are considerably more complicated than those given above.[16]

As will be seen subsequently, precise measurements on cross-linked polymers make it seem doubtful whether a true equilibrium compliance J_e ever exists, but in many cases it is closely enough approached to make equation 23 very useful in analyzing data.

An uncross-linked polymer, whose threadlike molecules are not permanently attached to each other, has no equilibrium compliance. Ordinarily this means, in the language of models, that one of the springs in Fig. 1–1 is missing, or that all of the viscosities in Fig. 1–2 are finite. Then under constant stress the rate of strain approaches a limiting value, and a situation of steady-state flow is eventually attained, governed by a Newtonian viscosity η which is most readily visualized as the sum of all the viscosities in Fig. 1–2. Concomitantly, in this steady state, the springs of the models are stretched to a constant extent, representing elastic energy storage which is recoverable after the stress is removed. Thus, even though there is no *equilibrium* compliance, there is a *steady-state* compliance which is most readily visualized as the sum of the deformations of the springs in Fig. 1–1 divided by the stress.

For such a material the shear creep followed by creep recovery is shown schematically in Fig. 1–11. The creep is the sum of a deformation approaching a constant value $J_e \mathfrak{T}_0$ as in Fig. 1–10 plus a viscous flow contribution $\mathfrak{T}_0 t/\eta$. Hence after a sufficiently long time the creep strain is given by

$$\gamma(t) = \mathfrak{T}_0(J_e + t/\eta) \tag{25}$$

so both J_e and η can be obtained from the geometry of the linear plot in this region; whereas the recovery is given by

$$\gamma_r(t) = \mathfrak{T}_0[J_e + t/\eta - J(t - t_2)] \tag{26}$$

and it approaches a final value of $\mathfrak{T}_0 t_2/\eta$, thus providing an alternative determination of η.

One can also imagine a model with an infinite number of springs and dashpots suitably chosen in magnitude and arrangement so that neither a finite equilibrium compliance nor a condition of steady-state flow would be approached no matter how long the stress is applied. Some polymeric systems appear to have this sort of behavior.

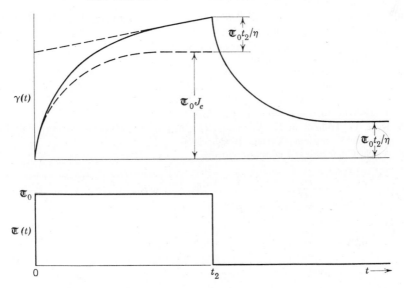

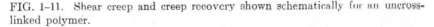

FIG. 1–11. Shear creep and creep recovery shown schematically for an uncrosslinked polymer.

The sharp dichotomy between cross-linked and uncross-linked polymers is apparent in all the time-dependent and frequency-dependent viscoelastic functions which describe their mechanical behavior in small deformations. Examples of these functions for various types of each of the two classes will be surveyed in the next chapter.

REFERENCES

1. H. Poincaré, *The Foundations of Science*, The Science Press, New York, 1929, p. 181.
2. W. Kuhn, *Helv. Chim. Acta,* **30,** 487 (1947).
3. H. Leaderman, *Elastic and Creep Properties of Filamentous Materials and Other High Polymers,* The Textile Foundation, Washington, 1943.
4. W. Weber, *Pogg. Ann.,* (2), **4,** 247 (1835).
5. R. Kohlrausch, *Pogg. Ann.,* (3), **12,** 393 (1847).
6. L. Boltzmann, *Wied. Ann.,* **5,** 430 (1878).
7. C. Zener, *Elasticity and Anelasticity of Metals,* University of Chicago Press, 1948.
8. C. Kittel, *Introduction to Solid-State Physics,* Second Edition, Wiley, New York, 1956.
9. J. G. Kirkwood, *J. Chem. Phys.,* **14,** 180 (1946); S. A. Rice and J. G. Kirkwood, *ibid.,* **31,** 901 (1959).

10. T. Alfrey, Jr., *Mechanical Behavior of High Polymers,* Interscience Publishers, New York, 1948.
11. I. S. Sokolnikoff and R. D. Specht, *Mathematical Theory of Elasticity,* McGraw-Hill, New York, 1946.
12. A. J. Staverman and F. Schwarzl, in H. A. Stuart, *Die Physik der Hochpolymeren,* Vol. IV, Chapter I, Springer-Verlag, Berlin, 1956.
13. H. Leaderman, *Trans. Soc. Rheology,* **1,** 213 (1957).
14. L. Boltzmann, *Pogg. Ann. Phys.,* **7,** 624 (1876).
15. L. R. G. Treloar, in H. A. Stuart, *Die Physik der Hochpolymeren,* Vol. IV, Chapter V, Springer-Verlag, Berlin, 1956.
16. A. N. Gent, private communication.

CHAPTER 2

Illustrations of Viscoelastic Behavior of Polymeric Systems

It seems desirable at this point to familiarize the reader with some concrete examples of the viscoelastic functions defined in the preceding chapter, and thus to provide an idea of their shapes and magnitudes as exhibited by various types of polymeric systems.

When the shear creep compliance or the shear relaxation modulus for a particular polymer is plotted against time, or any one of the dynamic functions is plotted against frequency, the most striking feature is the enormous range of magnitudes which the ordinate can assume, changing over several powers of ten. Concomitantly, a still larger range of time or frequency is required on the abscissa scale to encompass these changes. As a result, both coordinates are usually plotted logarithmically. Inspection of such logarithmic graphs reveals a pattern of certain zones on the time (or frequency) scale, where the viscoelastic functions have characteristic shapes: the transition zone from glasslike to rubberlike consistency, the plateau zone, the pseudo-equilibrium zone (in cross-linked polymers), the terminal zone (in uncross-linked polymers), etc. These regions can be associated qualitatively with different kinds of molecular responses, and appear with different degrees of prominence depending on whether the polymer is of low or high molecular weight, amorphous or crystalline, above or below its glass transition temperature, and undiluted or mixed with solvent.

Seven polymeric systems have been chosen as examples of these alternatives to illustrate the variety of viscoelastic responses and the gross correlation of behavior in different time and frequency zones

21

with molecular structure. The graphs to be portrayed here represent experimental data from the literature which have been combined by the method of reduced variables (alluded to in the preceding chapter, and discussed in detail in Chapter 11) to cover as wide a range as possible of the effective time or frequency scale. All the measurements were made on isotropic materials at sufficiently low stresses so that the viscoelastic behavior was linear, and the deformation was usually simple shear though in two cases it was simple extension (in which the shear effects predominate). It was necessary in all cases to calculate some of the viscoelastic functions indirectly from others that were directly measured, using the interconversion methods which were alluded to in the preceding chapter and will be spelled out in detail in Chapters 3 and 4. The specific calculations have been described elsewhere.[1]

A. DESCRIPTION OF THE POLYMERS CHOSEN FOR ILLUSTRATION

The first four examples are uncross-linked polymers, which do not possess any equilibrium compliance, and above the glass transition temperature exhibit viscous flow.

I. To illustrate an *amorphous polymer of low molecular weight*, a polyisobutylene of weight-average molecular weight 11,000 has been chosen. Dynamic shear data by Harper, Markovitz, and De Witt [2] and shear creep data by Leaderman, Smith, and Jones [3] were employed, after reduction to a reference temperature of 25°C. (Details are given in an earlier review.[4])

The significance of the reference temperature is that the reduced curves represent the viscoelastic functions as they would have been measured at 25°C. over a much wider range of time or frequency scale than the actual experimental measurements provided; *cf.* Chapter 11.

The molecule is a carbon chain with two methyl groups on every other chain atom, and is freely flexible except for the constraints imposed by the hindering potential to free rotation associated with the methyl groups and the fact that each molecule is entwined with many of its neighbors. For such short molecules as these (degree of polymerization about 200) the effects of the neighbors can apparently be adequately described in terms of the local frictional forces encountered by a short segment of a moving chain.

II. To illustrate an *amorphous polymer of high molecular weight,* a fractionated polyvinyl acetate of weight-average molecular weight 300,000 has been chosen. Stress relaxation data in extension, obtained by Ninomiya[5] (see Appendix D), were converted to shear deformation data by assuming Poisson's ratio to be ½ in equation 2 of Chapter 1, which is certainly justifiable in the region concerned. These data were then combined in the short-time region of the time scale with dynamic shear data of Williams and Ferry.[6] The latter had been obtained on an unfractionated sample of somewhat higher molecular weight, but in the short-time region the viscoelastic properties are unaffected by molecular weight differences. The data were all reduced to a reference temperature of 75°C.

The molecule has side groups of moderate length on every other chain carbon atom, but the principal feature differentiating it from the preceding example is its higher molecular weight. Above a critical molecular weight which for many polymers is of the order of 20,000, the effect of neighbors on molecular motion can no longer be described solely in terms of local frictional forces; the viscoelastic properties reveal a strong additional coupling to neighbors which appears to be localized at a few widely separated points along the molecular chain. This phenomenon, generally known as entanglement coupling, is poorly understood, but it clearly prolongs very greatly any molecular rearrangements which are sufficiently long-range to involve regions of a molecule separated from each other by one or more entanglement points. The term "entanglement" has come to be employed in this special sense, and is not currently applied to the short-range intermolecular entwining which must exist in all polymeric systems (other than very dilute solutions) regardless of their molecular length.

III. To illustrate an *amorphous polymer of high molecular weight with long side groups,* a fractionated poly-*n*-octyl methacrylate of weight-average molecular weight 3,620,000 has been chosen. Dynamic and shear creep data of Dannhauser, Child, and Ferry[7] and Berge, Saunders, and Ferry[8] were employed, after reduction to a reference temperature of 100°C. Some of the data are tabulated in Appendix D.

The molecule differs from the preceding in that each monomer unit, with two chain atoms, carries a flexible side ester group which now comprises nearly three-fourths of the molecular weight. Thus, in a sense, only a small proportion of the total volume is occupied by the chain backbones.

IV. To illustrate an *amorphous polymer of high molecular weight below its glass transition temperature,* a polymethyl methacrylate has been chosen; shear stress relaxation [9] and shear creep [10] data of Iwayanagi were employed, reduced to a reference temperature of $-22°C$.

The polymer has a high molecular weight, and its side groups are comparable with those of polyvinyl acetate in length. The distinguishing feature here is that the measurements are all made far below the glass transition temperature (about 100°) where the chain backbone configurations are largely immobilized. Hence the response to external stress involves primarily very local adjustments somewhat similar to those in the mechanical deformation of an ordinary hard solid (amorphous glucose, for example).

For the present, the glass transition temperature T_g of any amorphous substance, whether polymeric or not, may be defined as the point where the thermal expansion coefficient α undergoes a discontinuity. Above this temperature, α has the magnitude generally associated with liquids—6 to 10×10^{-4} deg^{-1}. Decrease in temperature is accompanied by collapse of free volume which is made possible by configurational adjustments. Eventually, the free volume becomes so small that further adjustments are extremely slow or even impossible; then it no longer decreases and the further contraction in total volume is much less, so α drops suddenly to between 1 and 3×10^{-4} deg^{-1}.

In polymers, there may be more than one discontinuity in α. The highest is usually associated with the loss of the molecular mobility which permits configurational rearrangements of the chain backbones, and it profoundly alters the viscoelastic behavior; this is "the" glass transition. Others may be associated with the loss of much more specific, local motions, such as the rearrangements of short side groups.

The subject of the glass transition temperature is discussed at greater length in Chapter 11.

The remaining three examples are cross-linked polymers, which do not exhibit viscous flow and to a first approximation possess an equilibrium compliance.

V. To illustrate a *lightly cross-linked amorphous polymer*, lightly vulcanized Hevea rubber has been chosen, cured with sulfur and an accelerator. Dynamic data, in simple extension, of Cunningham and Ivey [11] and Payne,[12] together with creep data in simple extension of Martin, Roth, and Stiehler [13] were employed, all reduced to a reference temperature of 25°C. Certain minor adjustments in the data are described elsewhere.[1] The data of Payne are tabulated in Appendix D.

The molecular structure is a network of highly flexible threadlike strands whose average molecular weight between cross-links is about

4000. Relatively short-range segmental rearrangements are oblivious of the presence of the linkage points, but of course long-range rearrangements are profoundly affected.

VI. To illustrate a *dilute cross-linked gel,* a 10% gel of polyvinyl chloride in dimethyl thianthrene has been chosen; dynamic shear data by Fitzgerald and Ferry [14] and Plazek, Vrancken, and Berge,[15] supplemented by shear creep data by Plazek [16] and stress relaxation by Heckler,[17] all reduced to 25°C.

The molecular structure is similar to that of the preceding example except that the cross-links are presumably tiny crystallites instead of chemical bonds and the network strands are interspersed by solvent molecules of very low molecular weight. The average molecular weight between cross-links is also much larger than in the preceding case.

VII. To illustrate a *highly crystalline polymer,* a linear polyethylene with a density of 0.965 g./ml. at room temperature, corresponding to a high degree of crystallinity, has been chosen. Stress relaxation data of Faucher [18] in simple extension were employed, reduced to a reference temperature of 20°C. (There was no evidence of a change in crystallinity over the temperature range within which experiments were utilized for reduction, *viz.,* −70° to 70°.)

The polymer is usually pictured as a matrix of crystallites through which the macromolecular chains thread themselves; presumably there are only very short segments with an amorphous configuration running between the crystallites. To the extent that the chains are immobile within the crystallites, each crystallite is a multiple cross-link joining many short amorphous strands in a densely linked network.

As will be seen below, each of these seven structural types has a characteristic viscoelastic behavior.

B. THE CREEP COMPLIANCE

Plotted on a linear scale, the creep compliance of an amorphous polymer of low molecular weight would look like the creep deformation as shown in Fig. 1–12, differing only by a proportionality factor of the stress. In analyzing creep experiments, such linear plots are invariably made to determine the quantities J_e and η. But in presenting the over-all aspect of $J(t)$, the ranges of both the magnitude of $J(t)$ and the time scale are so enormous (as mentioned above) that the only way to give a complete representation in a single graph is to make both coordinates logarithmic. This procedure is followed here for depicting all the viscoelastic functions. The units are cgs throughout.

In comparing different structural types of polymers, it is the shapes and the magnitudes of the functions which are important; the positions of the curves on the logarithmic time scale are in a sense irrelevant since they depend sharply on the temperature and in any case the reference temperatures for the polymers compared here are not all the same. Purely for clarity in distinguishing the curves, arbitrary shifts along the logarithmic time (or frequency) axis have been made by adding to log t (subtracting from log ω) a constant A with the following values: I, -3; II, -1; III, 0; IV, -7; V, 0; VI, 0; VII, 2. The same values of A have been used throughout this chapter. Thus the relative horizontal positions of the curves have no significance; it is their shapes and vertical positions which are to be scrutinized. The vertical positions of curves V and VII will not be directly comparable with the others, because they represent deformation in extension instead of shear; the compliances will be lower and the moduli higher by about half an order of magnitude (factor of 2.5 to 3), in accordance with equation 2 of Chapter 1.

Figure 2–1 shows the creep compliance thus plotted for the seven typical systems, with the uncross-linked ones on the left and the cross-linked on the right. The tremendous range of time scale over which response to stress is achieved is immediately apparent.

At short times, $J(t)$ approaches a value of the order of 10^{-10}

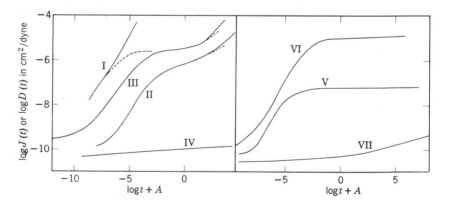

FIG. 2–1. Creep compliance for seven typical polymer systems: uncross-linked on left, cross-linked on right, identified by numbers as described in the text. Deformation is shear, $J(t)$, except for curves V and VII, which are simple extension, $D(t)$. The dashed curves represent the compliance after subtraction of the flow contribution t/η.

cm²/dyne, characteristic of a hard glasslike solid. The corresponding region of the time scale is sometimes called the glassy zone. This small compliance corresponds to the absence of any configurational rearrangements of the chain backbones within the interval of the experiment; indeed, curve IV shows that below the glass transition temperature, where the backbone configurations are immobilized, $J(t)$ has this order of magnitude throughout the time scale. Approximately, $J(t)$ may be regarded as possessing a limiting value $J(0)$ at zero time, often written J_g, the subscript standing for glass. This value is usually not very well defined operationally, however.

At long times, $J(t)$ for the uncross-linked polymers increases without limit, because it includes a contribution from viscous flow. But if the latter is subtracted, the remainder $J(t) - t/\eta$ approaches a limiting value J_e (cf. equation 25 of Chapter 1). This value has been attained in the low-molecular-weight polymer (I), but not in those of high molecular weight (II and III), because the coupling entanglements greatly prolong the time necessary for long-range configurational changes. Indeed, there is some doubt as to whether J_e can be operationally defined when the molecular weight is extremely high. The magnitude of J_e is generally of the order of 10^{-5} cm²/dyne. In terms of models, it is a measure of the energy stored in all the springs (Fig. 1–2) during steady-state flow; in molecular terms, it measures the average distortion of the polymer coils during flow, when ample time has been allowed for the interaction between Brownian motion and hydrodynamic torques to reach a steady state. For the cross-linked polymers, at long times, $J(t)$ approaches approximately a limiting value J_e which according to the theory of rubberlike elasticity [19] is proportional to the average molecular weight between cross-links in the network. This limit is evident in the soft rubber (V) and the gel (VI), although a small but perceptible positive slope exists even at the longest times; the corresponding region of the time scale may be called the pseudo-equilibrium zone. From the relative heights of the flat regions, it is clear that the gel has a much more open network than the rubber. (The need for a severe correction for loose strand ends in the polyvinyl chloride gel prevents making a quantitative comparison.) The crystalline polymer, as expected from its much tighter network, has a much lower flat region (though the theory of rubberlike elasticity cannot be literally applied to such short strands). At long times, additional deformation of the crystalline polymer sets in, the molecular origin of which is not yet certain.

At intermediate times, there is in each of the polymers except the glasslike (IV) and the highly crystalline (VII) a gradual but enormous increase of $J(t)$, rising by several powers of ten. This reflects the increasing response to external stress by configurational rearrangements, first of the relative positions of chain backbone segments near each other, then farther and farther apart, requiring more and more mutual cooperation and hence more and more time (*cf.* Fig. 1–3). In the low-molecular-weight (I) and the cross-linked polymers (V, VI) this rise occurs in a single stage, usually called the transition from glasslike to rubberlike consistency. At the end of the transition zone, the elapsed time has become long compared with the time required for the slowest rearrangement of a molecule (in the cross-linked polymers, of a strand between two cross-linking points), and the average molecular distortion has approached its maximum corresponding to the stress applied. In the uncross-linked polymers of high molecular weight (II, III) there are two stages. The first reflects relative motion of chain segments between the entanglement coupling points, and corresponds to the glass–rubber transition. At the end of this stage $J(t)$ tends to level off, and the stress can be regarded as supported by the coupling points almost as though they were crosslinks. However, the coupling points can slip, so in time relative motions of backbone segments separated by entanglements take place, and $J(t)$ enters the second stage, rising again more rapidly (on this logarithmic scale).

By analogy with the significance of J_e in the cross-linked polymers, the level attained by $J(t)$ in between the two stages of rise in curves II and III can be interpreted approximately as a measure of the average molecular weight between entanglement coupling points. Clearly this is greater for III, where the chain backbones are diluted by large side groups. We are not at present able to make quantitative calculations, however, since there is a substantial positive slope even in this intermediate region, and no definite pseudo-equilibrium value of J can be specified there.

C. THE STRESS RELAXATION MODULUS

The modulus $G(t)$, defined as the stress/strain ratio at constant deformation, is plotted against t with logarithmic scales in Fig. 2–2. In certain regions, $G(t)$ is approximately $1/J(t)$, so that the logarithmic plots have roughly the appearance of mirror images of those in Fig. 2–1 reflected in the time axis. The more slowly $J(t)$ changes with

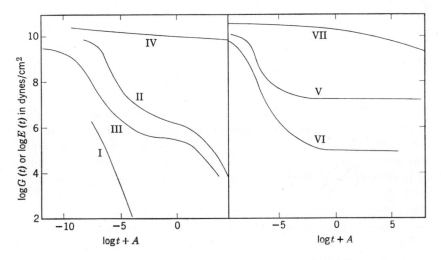

FIG. 2–2. Stress relaxation modulus for the seven systems identified as in Fig. 2–1.

time, the more nearly is the reciprocal relation approached. Thus, at short times, $G(t)$ appears to approach a limiting value which (if it exists) is $G_g = 1/J_g$, of the order of 10^{10} dynes/cm², and represents the rigidity in the absence of backbone rearrangements. At long times, $G(t)$ for the lightly cross-linked networks V and VI approaches values which are again nearly constant, written $G_e = 1/J_e$ and representing the equilibrium shear modulus as treated by the theory of rubberlike elasticity.

At long times for the uncross-linked polymers, however, $G(t)$ falls rapidly and eventually vanishes. In terms of models, this corresponds to the complete relaxation of all springs in an array such as Fig. 1–2; in molecular terms, it corresponds to the resumption of random average configurations by the macromolecular coils, which have completely freed themselves from the constraints originally imposed on them, even though the external dimensions of the sample remain deformed. (The final residual deformation corresponds to the flow contribution to a creep experiment.) The region of time scale in which $G(t)$ falls sharply is often called the terminal zone. If the viscoelastic behavior is represented by a finite mechanical model such as Fig. 1–2, the decay of $G(t)$ must at the end become exponential, proportional to e^{-t/τ_1} where τ_1 is the terminal relaxation time. However, there might be cases which could be only represented by an infinite model with constants suitably chosen such that the exponential law would never be reached.

At intermediate times, the stress gradually falls as the distortion of the chain backbones adjusts itself through Brownian motion, first of segments with respect to closely neighboring segments, then with respect to those farther removed along the backbone contour, and so on (*cf.* Fig. 1–3). The drop occurs in two stages for the uncross-linked polymers of high molecular weight II and III, and in one stage for the others, just as the creep compliance rises in either one or two stages, and for the same reasons. Between the transition and terminal zones of II and III, $G(t)$ flattens somewhat at a level which again is associated with the average spacing between entanglement coupling points along these very long polymeric molecules. From the Boltzmann superposition principle it can be shown that $J(t)G(t) \leqq 1$ for all values of t, so each drop in $G(t)$ always occurs at somewhat shorter times than the corresponding rise in $J(t)$.

In the glassy polymer, IV, there is very little stress relaxation over many decades of logarithmic time, since no backbone contour changes occur; in the densely crystalline polymer, VII, there is some relaxation at very long times through whatever mechanism is responsible for the creep which also occurs in this region.

D. THE STORAGE MODULUS

The modulus $G'(\omega)$ is defined as the stress in phase with the strain in a sinusoidal deformation divided by the strain; it is a measure of the energy stored and recovered per cycle, when different systems are compared at the same strain amplitude. It is plotted against the radian frequency ω with logarithmic scales in Fig. 2–3. Since both $G(t)$ and $G'(\omega)$ are measures of stored elastic energy, and a dynamic measurement at frequency ω is qualitatively equivalent to a transient one at $t = 1/\omega$, these graphs are approximately mirror images of those for the relaxation modulus, reflected in the modulus axis. In particular, when $G(t)$ is changing very slowly, $G(t) \cong G'(1/t)$, so the values G_g and G_e characteristic of high and low frequencies are the same as those characteristic of short and long times respectively.

At long times for the uncross-linked polymers, $G'(\omega)$ approaches 0 with decreasing frequency, just as $G(t)$ does with increasing t; macroscopically, this means that the phase angle between stress and strain approaches 90° as the stored energy per cycle of deformation becomes

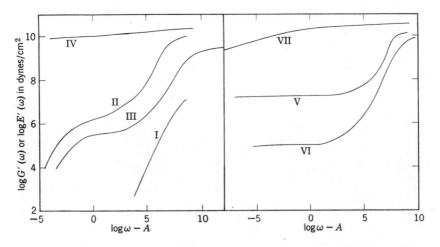

FIG. 2–3. Storage modulus plotted against frequency, with logarithmic scales, for the seven systems identified as in Fig. 2–1.

negligible compared with that dissipated as heat. However, the shape of the curve is somewhat different and $G'(1/t) > G(t)$ at all times. For a system representable by a mechanical model, at the end of the terminal zone G' becomes proportional to $\omega^2\tau_1^2$ instead of exponentially dependent on τ_1. To the writer's knowledge, however, measurements have never been carried to low enough frequencies to attain this square law, corresponding to a slope of 2 on a plot against frequency with logarithmic scales.

At intermediate times, the behavior is very similar to what has already been described for $G(t)$, except that $G'(1/t)$ always exceeds $G(t)$ to some extent. On a molecular basis, the magnitude of G' depends on what contour rearrangements can take place within the period of the oscillatory deformation.

E. THE LOSS MODULUS

The modulus $G''(\omega)$ is defined as the stress 90° out of phase with the strain divided by the strain; it is a measure of the energy dissipated or lost as heat per cycle of sinusoidal deformation, when different systems are compared at the same strain amplitude. It is plotted with logarithmic scales in Fig. 2–4.

Observation of these curves reveals a feature which can be stated

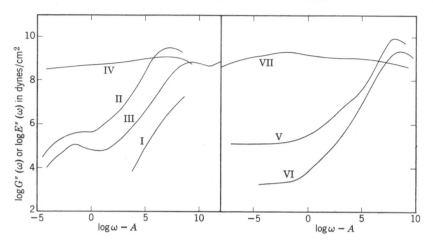

FIG. 2–4. Loss modulus plotted logarithmically for the seven systems identified as in Fig. 2–1.

qualitatively as follows. In frequency regions where $G'(\omega)$ changes slowly (undergoes little dispersion), corresponding to very little stress relaxation in the equivalent plot of $G(t)$, the behavior is more nearly perfectly elastic; hence comparatively little energy is dissipated in periodic deformations. Thus in such regions G'' tends to be considerably less than G'. This effect is prominent in the locations of G'' for the glass (IV) and the crystalline polymer (VII), whose G' curves are relatively flat throughout; G'' is so low that it intersects some of the other curves. Also, the flattening of G' between the transition and terminal zones of the polymers which exhibit entanglement coupling (II and III) is accompanied by a minimum in G''.

At high frequencies, a mechanical model such as Fig. 1–2 would be expected to approach perfect elastic behavior, as the motion of the dashpots became negligible with that of the springs; then G'' should approach zero. On a molecular basis, this would correspond to the absence of any molecular or atomic adjustments capable of dissipating energy within the period of deformation. This situation is not in fact achieved for high polymers or any other solids of simpler structure; however, maxima in G'' appear for the soft polymers II, III, V, and VI at rather high frequencies beyond which the losses due to backbone configurational changes diminish. Other maxima, in IV and VII, represent peaks in other dissipative processes.

At very low frequences, a system corresponding to a finite mechanical model should exhibit direct proportionality of G'' to ω, or a slope of 1 on a logarithmic plot. This is in fact approached by the low-molecular-weight polyisobutylene (I); for II and III, the data would have to be carried to lower frequencies.

F. THE DYNAMIC VISCOSITY

The dissipative effects of alternating stress can be described just as well by another quantity, the ratio of stress in phase with rate of strain divided by the strain. This has the dimensions of a viscosity, and is the real part η' of a complex viscosity, $\boldsymbol{\eta}^* = \eta' - i\eta''$, defined in the same manner as $\mathbf{G}^*$ in Chapter 1. In sinusoidal deformations, if the strain is $\gamma(t) = \gamma_0 e^{i\omega t}$, the rate of strain $\dot{\gamma}(t)$ is $i\omega\gamma_0 e^{i\omega t} = i\omega\gamma(t)$. Hence $\boldsymbol{\eta}^* = \mathbf{G}^*/i\omega$, and the individual components are related by

$$\eta' = G''/\omega \tag{1}$$

$$\eta'' = G'/\omega \tag{2}$$

The real component η', often for simplicity called just the dynamic viscosity, is useful especially in discussing uncross-linked polymers because for these systems at very low frequencies η' approaches η, the ordinary steady-flow viscosity. With increasing frequency, η' falls monotonically as shown in Fig. 2–5, reaching values many orders of magnitude smaller than η.

As is obvious from equation 1, in regions where G'' is flat, η' is inversely proportional to frequency; whereas when G'' rises steeply, on the left side of a maximum, η' may flatten out, as seen particularly in the lightly cross-linked polymers V and VI.

The low-frequency limiting value of η is approached by the low-molecular-weight polyisobutylene (I), corresponding to the fact that G'' is directly proportional to ω here, but for the other uncross-linked polymers η is extremely high and η' is evidently far below it even at the lowest frequencies shown. For a cross-linked polymer, η is of course infinite, but if the viscoelastic behavior can be represented by a finite mechanical model, η' should approach a finite limiting value at low frequencies; for example, in Fig. 1–2, if one of the viscosities is infinite, there is no finite steady-flow viscosity, but the low-frequency limit of η' is finite and equal to the sum of all the other viscosities. To the author's knowledge, this situation has never been experimentally observed in a cross-linked polymer.

An alternative frequency–dependent viscosity, which could also be called the dynamic viscosity, is the absolute value $|\eta^*| = (\eta'^2 + \eta''^2)^{1/2} = (G'^2 + G''^2)^{1/2}/\omega$.

G. THE STORAGE COMPLIANCE

The compliance $J'(\omega)$ is defined as the strain in a sinusoidal deformation in phase with the stress divided by the stress; it is a measure of the energy stored and recovered per cycle, when different systems are compared at the same *stress* amplitude. It is plotted with the usual logarithmic scales in Fig. 2–6. For the same reason that $G'(\omega)$ resembles $G(t)$ plotted backwards, $J'(\omega)$ resembles $J(t)$ reflected in the compliance axis. An important distinction, however, appears in the uncross-linked polymers: the elastic (recoverable) part of the creep is obtained only after subtracting t/η, and it is the difference $J(t) - t/\eta$ which approaches a limiting value J_e if the molecular weight is not too high; but for J' the

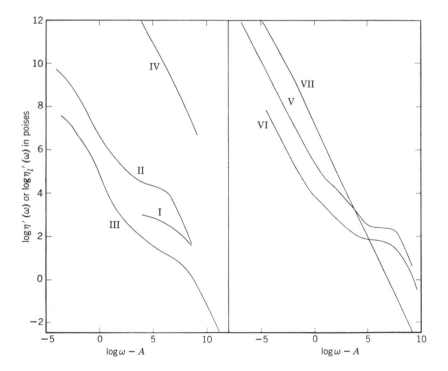

FIG. 2–5. Real part of the complex dynamic viscosity, plotted logarithmically for the seven systems identified as in Fig. 2–1.

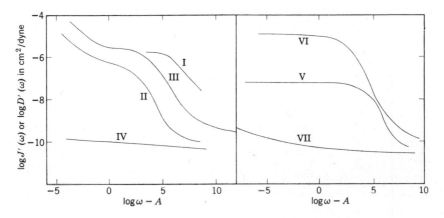

FIG. 2–6. Storage compliance plotted logarithmically for the seven systems identified as in Fig. 2–1.

phase specification automatically eliminates any flow contribution, so J' itself approaches J_e at low frequencies.

In the transition zone and other regions where J' changes rapidly, the shapes of $J'(\omega)$ and $J(t)$ differ such that $J'(1/t) < J(t)$ at all times. From equation 12 of Chapter 1 it is evident also that $J'(\omega) < 1/G'(\omega)$. The magnitudes of the two compliances and reciprocal moduli fall in the following order: $J'(1/t) < J(t) - t/\eta < 1/G'(1/t) < 1/G(t)$. It is also evident from equations 7 and 11 of Chapter 1 that $J' < |J^*| = 1/|G^*| < 1/G'$. In practice $J(t)$ often lies quite close to $|J^*|$.

H. THE LOSS COMPLIANCE

The compliance $J''(\omega)$ is defined as the strain 90° out of phase with the stress divided by the stress; it is a measure of the energy dissipated or lost as heat per cycle of sinusoidal deformation, when different systems are compared at the same stress amplitude. It is plotted with logarithmic scales in Fig. 2–7.

This function is characterized by a broad maximum which appears in the cross-linked and the uncross-linked polymers of high molecular weight, at a point corresponding to the low-frequency end of the transition zone. It is presumably characteristic of a network structure, whether of permanently bonded strands or strands coupled by entanglement. In the latter case, the maximum is associated with a minimum on the low-frequency side.

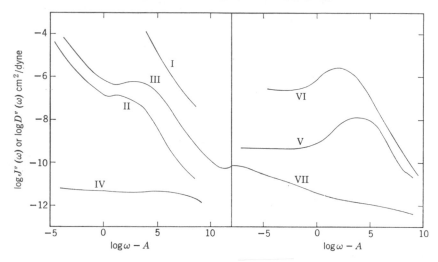

FIG. 2–7. Loss compliance plotted logarithmically for the seven systems identified as in Fig. 2–1.

At very low frequencies, J'' according to a finite mechanical model should become inversely proportional to ω, in fact equal to $1/\omega\eta$. As usual, it is only the low-molecular-weight polyisobutylene (I) which approaches this limiting behavior.

I. THE LOSS TANGENT

A useful parameter which is dimensionless and conveys no physical magnitude but is a measure of the ratio of energy lost to energy stored in a cyclic deformation is the loss tangent, $\tan\delta = G''/G' = J''/J'$ (equation 8, Chapter 1). The logarithmic plots in Fig. 2–8 reveal several characteristic levels of $\tan\delta$. First, the uncross-linked polymers approach very high values at low frequencies, and indeed $\tan\delta$ should become eventually inversely proportional to the frequency. Second, all the amorphous polymers, whether cross-linked or not, have values in the transition zone which are in the neighborhood of $\tan\delta = 1$, ranging perhaps from 0.2 to 3. Third, the glassy and crystalline polymers, IV and VII, have values in the general neighborhood of 0.1; and, finally, the soft cross-linked polymers attain extremely small values at low frequencies, of the order of 0.01.

In the transition zone between glasslike and rubberlike consistency,

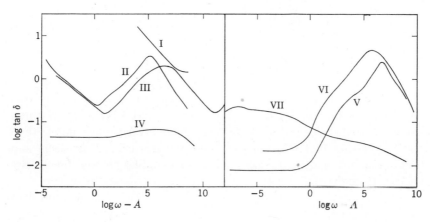

FIG. 2–8. Loss tangent plotted logarithmically for the seven systems identified as in Fig. 2–1.

the loss tangent goes through a pronounced maximum in cross-linked and uncross-linked polymers alike. It is of interest that the maxima in J'' occur to the left of those in tan δ, and the maxima in G'' occur to the right of those in tan δ on the frequency scale; the differences amount to several logarithmic decades. Each of these three functions is a measure of elastic losses or heat dissipation, but it is clear that the frequency region in which the "loss" occurs depends on the choice of function by which the loss is specified.

Smaller maxima occur in the curves for the glassy and highly crystalline polymers, reflecting other dissipative mechanisms.

The loss tangent determines such macroscopic physical properties as the damping of free vibrations, the attenuation of propagated waves, and the frequency width of a resonance response. It can often be more conveniently measured than any other viscoelastic function, by observations of these phenomena, and is of considerable practical interest. It is less susceptible of direct theoretical interpretation than the other functions, however.

J. VISCOELASTIC BEHAVIOR IN OTHER TYPES OF DEFORMATION

As explained in Chapter 1, shear and bulk deformations are essentially different in character, one involving a shape change and the other a volume change; and they are accompanied by quite different molecular processes. Other deformations, such as the two types of one-dimensional extensions portrayed in Figs. 1–6 and 1–7, can be regarded as combinations of shear and bulk effects.

All the viscoelastic phenomena portrayed graphically in this chapter are dominated by the behavior in shear. Bulk effects enter only into the data obtained in extension (polymers V and VII) at short times (or high frequencies) where $J(t)$ is no longer very much larger than $B(t)$ (equation 1 of Chapter 1). The features of the transition and terminal zones, and the manifestations of coupling entanglements, are all due to molecular processes associated with shear distortion.

For bulk compression, there is also a pattern of time-dependent mechanical behavior with a set of viscoelastic functions describing volume creep, $B(t)$, pressure relaxation, $K(t)$, dynamic bulk moduli K' and K'', and dynamic bulk compliances B' and B''. It is not possible to assemble a set of representative graphs for these functions, however, because too little information is available.

When a hard, glasslike polymer is deformed in simple extension (or any other manner combining volume change and shear), the viscoelastic properties will reflect both time-dependent shape and time-dependent volume changes. The creep, relaxation, and dynamic functions $D(t)$, $E(t)$, E', E'', etc., will be given by certain combinations of the corresponding shear and bulk functions. For creep the relation is very simple, corresponding to equation 1 of Chapter 1:

$$D(t) = J(t)/3 + B(t)/9 \qquad (3)$$

where now the two terms on the right are of similar magnitude, though the second is always smaller. For the dynamic properties, the relations have the same form as those for perfect elastic solids with complex moduli substituted for the constant moduli, and a complex Poisson's ratio; thus, equation 2 of Chapter 1 becomes

$$E^* = 2G^*(1 + \mu^*) \qquad (4)$$

where μ', the real part of μ^*, is that part of the lateral contraction in phase with a sinusoidally oscillating linear extension, etc. For further details, papers by Schwarzl [20,21] may be consulted; the subject will be taken up again in Chapter 8.

K. CONCLUSIONS

The foregoing examples are intended to provide some familiarity with the character and scope of the time-dependent viscoelastic behavior in polymeric systems, and a rough qualitative idea of its origin in molecular processes. Before returning in later chapters to a more detailed discussion of theoretical interpretations and correlations with molecular structure, we shall digress to consider the purely phenomenological theory of interrelations among the different viscoelastic functions, and also methods of experimental measurements.

It should be emphasized again that all the remarks in this chapter, as well as those in the two to follow, refer to isotropic systems whose properties are the same in all directions, and to small deformations.

REFERENCES

1. J. D. Ferry and K. Ninomiya, in J. T. Bergen, *Viscoelasticity—Phenomenological Aspects*, Academic Press, New York, 1960, p. 55.
2. R. C. Harper, H. Markovitz, and T. W. De Witt, *J. Polymer Sci.*, **8**, 435 (1952).
3. H. Leaderman, R. G. Smith, and R. W. Jones, *J. Polymer Sci.*, **14**, 47 (1954).
4. J. D. Ferry, in H. A. Stuart, *Die Physik der Hochpolymeren*, Vol. IV, Chapter VI, Springer-Verlag, Berlin, 1956.
5. K. Ninomiya, *J. Colloid Sci.*, **14**, 49 (1959).
6. M. L. Williams and J. D. Ferry, *J. Colloid Sci.*, **9**, 479 (1954).
7. W. Dannhauser, W. C. Child, Jr., and J. D. Ferry, *J. Colloid Sci.*, **13**, 103 (1958).
8. J. W. Berge, P. R. Saunders, and J. D. Ferry, *J. Colloid Sci.*, **14**, 135 (1959).
9. S. Iwayanagi, *J. Sci. Research Inst. Japan*, **49**, 4 (1955).
10. K. Sato, H. Nakane, T. Hideshima, and S. Iwayanagi, *J. Phys. Soc. Japan*, **9**, 413 (1954).
11. J. R. Cunningham and D. G. Ivey, *J. Applied Phys.*, **27**, 967 (1956).
12. A. R. Payne, in P. Mason and N. Wookey, *Rheology of Elastomers*, Pergamon Press, London, 1958, p. 86.
13. G. M. Martin, J. L. Roth, and R. D. Stiehler, *Trans. Inst. Rubber Ind.*, **32**, 189 (1956).
14. E. R. Fitzgerald and J. D. Ferry, *J. Colloid Sci.*, **8**, 1 (1953).
15. D. J. Plazek, M. N. Vrancken, and J. W. Berge, *Trans. Soc. Rheology*, **2**, 39 (1958).
16. D. J. Plazek, unpublished measurements.
17. J. D. Ferry, D. J. Plazek, and G. E. Heckler, *J. chim. phys.*, **55**, 152 (1958)
18. J. A. Faucher, *Trans. Soc. Rheology*, **3**, 81 (1959).

19. L. R. G. Treloar, in P. Mason and N. Wookey, *Rheology of Elastomers,* Pergamon Press, London, 1958.
20. F. Schwarzl, *Kolloid-Z.,* **148,** 47 (1956).
21. A. J. Staverman and F. Schwarzl, in H. A. Stuart, *Die Physik der Hochpolymeren,* Vol. IV, Chapter I, Springer-Verlag, Berlin, 1956.

CHAPTER 3

Exact Interrelations among the Viscoelastic Functions

Without attempting for the present to extend the molecular interpretation of viscoelastic phenomena in polymers beyond the very qualitative allusions in the preceding chapter, it is possible now to review the phenomenological theory of linear viscoelasticity and to derive exact relations by which each of the functions described in the preceding chapter (as well as others) can be calculated from any other function. A considerable literature has accumulated on this subject, interest in which stems from several sources. In the first place, such calculations are usually necessary to map out the behavior of any one function over the complete panorama of time or frequency scale, by combining the results of different sorts of measurements. Most of the curves in Chapter 2 were in fact obtained in this manner. Second, the calculations are of practical value in permitting prediction of the behavior of a plastic or rubber in a certain situation, perhaps inaccessible to direct experiment, from measurements made under other more readily realizable conditions. Finally, the phenomenological theory offers some mathematical challenges and its structure can be summarized in a rather elegant and attractive form. Moreover, it is a special case of the more general theory of linear transformations, which is widely used in the analysis of electrical circuits. In the present chapter, the concepts and results of the theory will be presented without going into its more abstract aspects, involving Fourier and Laplace transforms, for which the reader is referred elsewhere.[1-6] Specific references to derivations of equations are given only for a few of the less well-known cases. As usual, everything is

41

formulated in terms of shear deformation, but analogous relations exist for bulk compression, simple extension, etc.

A. THE RELAXATION AND RETARDATION SPECTRA

In discussing the relations among the various viscoelastic functions, it has proved useful to introduce two additional derived functions, the relaxation and retardation spectra. To explain the significance of these spectra, we shall again bring in some mechanical models; although they are quite unnecessary for the purposes of mathematical definition and some purists find them objectionable, they are useful for visualization and have neither more nor less significance than the equations which correspond to their behavior.

1. The Maxwell Element

A single spring-dashpot pair in series, such as those arrayed in Fig. 1–2, is called a Maxwell element (Fig. 3–1). If the spring corresponds to a shear rigidity $G_i = 1/J_i$ (we choose shear as the type of deformation to be worked out in detail, though any other deformation would do as well) and the dashpot to a viscosity η_i, then the *relaxation time* of the element is defined as $\tau_i = \eta_i/G_i$, and is a measure of the time required for stress relaxation. If η_i is in poises and G_i in dynes/cm^2, τ_i is in seconds.

The viscoelastic functions exhibited by the Maxwell element can be easily derived (see Appendix F) and are summarized as follows:

$$J(t) = J_i + t/\eta \tag{1}$$

$$G(t) = G_i e^{-t/\tau_i} \tag{2}$$

$$G'(\omega) = G_i \omega^2 \tau_i^2 / (1 + \omega^2 \tau_i^2) \tag{3}$$

$$G''(\omega) = G_i \omega \tau_i / (1 + \omega^2 \tau_i^2) \tag{4}$$

$$\eta'(\omega) = \eta_i / (1 + \omega^2 \tau_i^2) \tag{5}$$

$$J'(\omega) = J_i \tag{6}$$

$$J''(\omega) = J_i/\omega\tau_i = 1/\omega\eta_i \tag{7}$$

$$\tan \delta = 1/\omega\tau_i \tag{8}$$

2. The Voigt Element

A single spring-dashpot pair in parallel, such as those arrayed in Fig. 1–1, is called a Voigt element (Fig. 3–2). If the spring and dashpot have the same significance as before, their ratio τ_i is defined as the *retardation time* and is a measure of the time required for the extension of the spring to its equilibrium length while retarded by the dashpot.

The model of Fig. 3–2 was introduced by Kelvin before Voigt, and is sometimes called the Kelvin element, but the name of Voigt has come to be more generally used.

The viscoelastic functions exhibited by the Voigt element are as follows:

$$J(t) = J_i(1 - e^{-t/\tau_i}) \tag{9}$$

$$G(t) = G_i \tag{10}$$

$$G'(\omega) = G_i \tag{11}$$

$$G''(\omega) = G_i\omega\tau_i = \omega\eta_i \tag{12}$$

$$\eta'(\omega) = \eta_i \tag{13}$$

$$J'(\omega) = J_i/(1 + \omega^2\tau_i{}^2) \tag{14}$$

$$J''(\omega) = J_i\omega\tau/(1 + \omega^2\tau_i{}^2) \tag{15}$$

$$\tan \delta = \omega\tau_i \tag{16}$$

Graphs of these functions have been given in many places,[7-9] but will not be reproduced here because they are too drastically simplified to correspond to any real viscoelastic behavior (with rare possible exceptions). It may be noted that the creep of the Voigt element and the stress relaxation of the Maxwell element are exponential functions of time. All observed creep and relaxation processes in polymers progress more gradually than specified by these simple equations. The

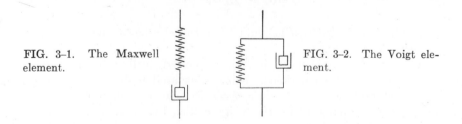

FIG. 3–1.   The Maxwell element.

FIG. 3–2.   The Voigt element.

components of the complex modulus for the Maxwell element, and those of the complex compliance for the Voigt element, depend on frequency in a manner reminiscent of the Debye dispersion of the complex dielectric constant. Again, all observed moduli and compliances change with frequency more gradually than this.

The time-dependent behavior of the Maxwell and Voigt elements is in fact exactly analogous to the time-dependent electrical behavior of combinations of resistances and capacities or resistances and inductances. There are several possible ways of setting up the analogy. In particular, if capacities are equated to springs and dashpots to resistances, the storage and dissipative units correspond correctly physically, but the topology is backwards—*i.e.*, parallel mechanical connections correspond to series electrical connections. If resistances are equated to springs and capacities to dashpots, the two topologies are identical but the physical analogy is less satisfactory. A large literature has been devoted to this subject.[10-12] The analog of the Boltzmann superposition principle in the electrical case is known as the Hopkinson superposition principle.

3. Discrete Viscoelastic Spectra

Any number of Maxwell elements in series have the properties of a single Maxwell element with $J = \Sigma J_i$ and $1/\eta = \Sigma(1/\eta_i)$; any number of Voigt elements in parallel have the properties of a single Voigt element with $G = \Sigma G_i$ and $\eta = \Sigma \eta_i$. However, Maxwell elements in parallel or Voigt elements in series, as in Figs. 1–1 and 1–2, obviously have much more complicated properties.

A group of Maxwell elements in parallel represents a discrete spectrum of relaxation times, each time τ_i being associated with a spectral strength G_i. Since in a parallel arrangement the forces (or stresses) are additive, it can readily be shown that for the Maxwell model, Fig. 1–2, the viscoelastic functions $G(t)$, $G'(\omega)$, $G''(\omega)$, and $\eta'(\omega)$ are obtained simply by summing the expressions in equations 2 to 5 over all the parallel elements; thus, if there are n elements,

$$G(t) = \sum_{i=1}^{n} G_i e^{-t/\tau_i} \tag{17}$$

etc. The functions $J(t)$, $J'(\omega)$, and $J''(\omega)$ can also be calculated, but not in a simple manner.

A group of Voigt elements in series represents a discrete spectrum of retardation times, each time τ_i being associated with a spectral compliance magnitude J_i. Since in a series arrangement the strains are additive, it turns out that for the Voigt model, Fig. 1–1, the viscoelastic functions $J(t)$, $J'(\omega)$, and $J''(\omega)$ are obtained by summing the expressions in equations 9, 14, and 15 over all the series elements; thus

$$J(t) = \sum_{i=1}^{n} J_i(1 - e^{-t/\tau_i}) \tag{18}$$

(to which a term t/η must be added if one of the springs has zero rigidity, as must be the case for an uncross-linked polymer), etc. The functions $G(t)$, $G'(\omega)$, $G''(\omega)$, and $\eta'(\omega)$ cannot be simply expressed for this model.

Any experimentally observed stress relaxation curve which decreases monotonically can in principle be fitted with any desired degree of accuracy to a series of terms as in equation 17 by taking n sufficiently large, and this would amount to determining the discrete spectrum of "lines," each with a location τ_i and intensity G_i. Similarly, fitting creep data to equation 18 would amount to experimental determination of the discrete retardation spectrum. Certain molecular theories, as described in Chapter 10, do indeed predict discrete spectra corresponding to equations 17 and 18. In the analysis of experimental data, however, it is impossible in practice to resolve the lines, which are too closely spaced; the empirical choice of parameters τ_i and G_i (or J_i) would be largely arbitrary. Although an arbitrary set of parameters would suffice to predict macroscopic behavior, it would not be unique and would be of little value for theoretical interpretation. This difficulty can be avoided, however, by substituting continuous spectra.

4. The Relaxation Spectrum

If the number of elements in the Maxwell model of Fig. 1–2 is increased without limit, the result is a continuous spectrum in which each infinitesimal contribution to rigidity $F\,d\tau$ is associated with relaxation times lying in the range between τ and $\tau + d\tau$. Actually, experience has shown that a logarithmic time scale is far more convenient; accordingly the continuous relaxation spectrum is defined as $H\,d\ln\tau$, the contribution to rigidity associated with relaxation times whose logarithms lie in the range between $\ln\tau$ and $\ln\tau + d\ln\tau$. (Evidently, $H = F\tau$.) For the continuous spectrum, equation 17 becomes

$$G(t) = G_e + \int_{-\infty}^{\infty} H e^{-t/\tau}\,d\ln\tau \tag{19}$$

which may alternatively be taken as a mathematical definition of H without recourse to the language of mechanical models. Here the constant G_e is added to allow for a discrete contribution with $\tau = \infty$ ($G_e = 0$ for uncross-linked polymers).

Here we continue to follow the notation recommended by Committee on Nomenclature of the Society of Rheology. Various other symbols have been used for H, and in some cases a spectrum has been defined by an equation analogous to 19 with $d \log_{10} \tau$ instead of $d \ln \tau$, thereby differing by a factor of 2.303.

Plots of H for the seven polymer types surveyed in Chapter 2 are shown in Fig. 3–3. The constant A has the same significance as before. Their shapes are rather similar to those of G'', reflected in the modulus axis. Their maxima represent concentrations of relaxation processes in certain regions of the logarithmic time scale. At long times, in uncross-linked systems, when steady-state flow is reached, H should vanish (after all the springs in the model of Fig. 1–2, for example, have relaxed). It is in fact falling steeply at the longest times visible here, representing the terminal zone. For cross-linked systems, H attains quite low values at long times but gives no evidence of approaching zero; this behavior is associated with the persistence of a small negative slope in stress relaxation (Fig. 2–2), showing that some degree of relaxation continues apparently indefinitely. At very short times, if the mechanical behavior approaches perfect elasticity, H should also vanish; actually, it remains finite, and in

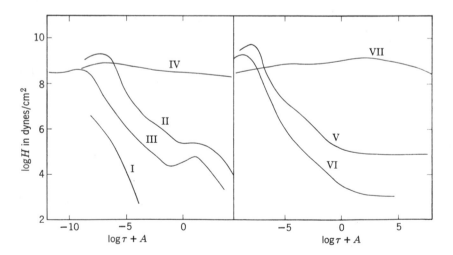

FIG. 3–3. The relaxation spectrum, plotted with logarithmic scales for the seven typical polymer systems described in Chapter 2, uncross-linked on left, cross-linked on right, identified by numbers as described in the text.

polymers at a rather high level, since some relaxation processes occur even at the shortest times (dissipative processes at the highest frequencies).

The characteristic zones of the viscoelastic time scale are clearly apparent in H: the glassy zone to the left of the principal maximum, the transition zone where H drops steeply, the terminal zone where it approaches zero, and the pseudo-equilibrium zone for cross-linked polymers where it is approximately horizontal. For uncross-linked polymers of high molecular weight (II and III), there is a region between the transition and terminal zones where H is also relatively flat (in some polymers, quite horizontal), often called the plateau zone.

5. The Retardation Spectrum

In an entirely analogous manner, if the Voigt model in Fig. 1–1 is made infinite in extent, it represents a continuous spectrum of retardation times, L, alternatively defined by the continuous analog of equation 18:

$$J(t) = J_g + \int_{-\infty}^{\infty} L(1 - e^{-t/\tau})\, d\ln\tau + t/\eta \qquad (20)$$

In this case an instantaneous compliance J_g must be added to allow for the possibility of a discrete contribution with $\tau = 0$. (Although J_g may be inaccessible experimentally, its presence must be inferred or else instantaneous deformation would require infinite stress.[1])

Plots of L for the seven polymer types are shown in Fig. 3–4. Their shapes, correspondingly, resemble those of J'' reflected in the compliance axis. Their maxima represent a concentration of retardation processes, measured by their contributions to compliance rather than modulus, in certain regions of the logarithmic time scale; they occur at quite different locations from the maxima in H.

At long times, L, like H, should vanish when an uncross-linked polymer reaches the state of steady flow. This condition is approached only for the example of low molecular weight (I). The polymers of high molecular weight have elastic compliance mechanisms persisting beyond the longest times for which data are available, and in this zone L is relatively flat, rising slowly. The plateau zone in the spectrum H corresponds roughly to the maximum in the spectrum L.

The two spectra are of the nature of distribution functions, although they have the dimensions of a modulus (H) and a compliance (L) respectively, rather than the dimensionless character of the usual distribution function.

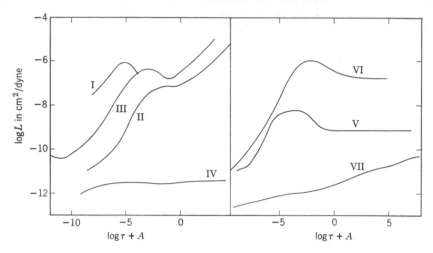

FIG. 3–4. The retardation spectrum, plotted logarithmically for the seven systems, identified as in Fig. 3–3 and Chapter 2.

In some treatments of linear viscoelastic behavior, normalized dimensionless distributions are employed:

$$h = H/G_g$$

$$l = L/(J_e - J_g)$$

where G_g is the stress/strain ratio for an instantaneous deformation and J_e is the equilibrium compliance (for a cross-linked polymer) or the steady-state compliance (for an uncross-linked polymer). Although these functions have mathematical convenience (their integrals over $d \ln \tau$ from $-\infty$ to ∞ are unity), they are less practical to apply to experimental data, because the normalizing factors are usually known only with poor precision or else are operationally inaccessible. Hence the non-normalized functions H and L will be used throughout this book.

As defined in the preceding equations, the spectra H and L refer to deformation in shear. Similar spectra can of course be used for other types of deformation, and are specified by subscripts, *e.g.*, H_v for bulk compression and H_l for simple elongation; thus, curves V and VII in Fig. 3–3 are actually H_l. Often in the literature H and H_l are not clearly distinguished.

6. Interrelations between the Spectra

If one spectrum is known over the entire range of time scale, together with certain limiting values such as G_e, J_g, and η, the other spectrum can be calculated.[1] The necessary equations are:

$$L = \frac{H}{\left[G_e - \int_{-\infty}^{\infty} \frac{H(u)}{\tau/u - 1} \, d \ln u \right]^2 + \pi^2 H^2} \qquad (21)$$

$$H = \frac{L}{\left[J_g + \int_{-\infty}^{\infty} \frac{L(u)}{1 - u/\tau} \, d \ln u - \frac{\tau}{\eta} \right]^2 + \pi^2 L^2} \qquad (22)$$

For an uncross-linked polymer, $G_e = 0$; for a cross-linked one, $\eta = \infty$. The fact that J_g is generally not known with any degree of accuracy is unimportant, since it ordinarily makes a negligible contribution to the denominator of equation 22.

To calculate L from H, for example, it is necessary for each point desired to evaluate the integral in the denominator of equation 21 graphically or numerically from knowledge of H over its entire range. A graph of the integrand is shown in Fig. 3–5 for a representative case. The integration is carried up to within a small distance of the singularity, and the positive and negative contributions within the interval $\ln \tau - \delta$ to $\ln \tau + \delta$ will cancel if H is changing slowly. (A closer approximation can be made by assuming H to be linear in the interval with the slope of its tangent at $u = \tau$, as illustrated by Silva and Gross [13] for a similar integration relating dielectric properties.) Although this calculation is not particularly difficult, it involves two areas of similar magnitude and opposite sign, with attendant loss of precision. The reader may be assured that far simpler approximation methods exist, adequate for most situations, which will be introduced in Chapter 4.

Interconversion formulas for the corresponding discrete viscoelastic spectra have also been given by Gross.[1]

The existence of equations 21 and 22 raises the question as to why one should bother to deal with both spectra since they are interrelated and they present in principle the same information. But the viscoelastic behavior is seen differently in the two, since H weights contributions to modulus and L contributions to compliance. Generally,

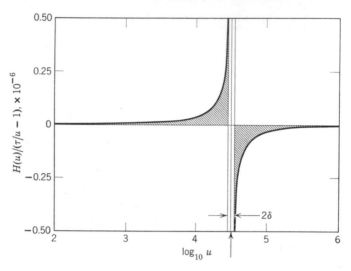

FIG. 3–5. Graphical evaluation of integral in equation 21, for polyvinyl acetate (polymer II of the series in Chapter 2) at log $\tau = 4.5$. For convenience, logarithms to the base 10 are used, and the net area is multiplied by 2.303. At the arrow, $u = \tau$. The integral is the difference between the positive and negative contributions, $(6.9 - 5.6) \times 10^4 = 1.3 \times 10^4$; $H = 0.51 \times 10^5$; $G_e = 0$; thence $L = 1.9 \times 10^{-6}$ cm²/dyne. The calculation was carried out by K. Ninomiya for reference 1 of Chapter 2.

short-time processes are revealed in more detail in H, and long-time processes in L. Accordingly, it is worthwhile to examine both spectra.

B. CALCULATION OF VISCOELASTIC FUNCTIONS AND CONSTANTS FROM THE SPECTRA

Equation 19 permits calculation of the relaxation modulus $G(t)$ when H is known. Similarly, the other moduli can be obtained by integrations which are equivalent to summing over all the elements of an infinite Maxwell model:

$$G' = G_e + \int_{-\infty}^{\infty} [H\omega^2\tau^2/(1 + \omega^2\tau^2)] \, d \ln \tau \tag{23}$$

$$G'' = \int_{-\infty}^{\infty} [H\omega\tau/(1 + \omega^2\tau^2)] \, d \ln \tau \tag{24}$$

$$\eta' = \int_{-\infty}^{\infty} [H\tau/(1 + \omega^2\tau^2)] \, d \ln \tau \tag{25}$$

The compliances cannot be calculated from H in a simple manner, but they can be obtained from L by integrations which are equivalent to summing over all the elements of an infinite Voigt model. Equation 20 provides $J(t)$; the dynamic compliances are given by

$$J' = J_g + \int_{-\infty}^{\infty} [L/(1 + \omega^2\tau^2)] \, d\ln\tau \qquad (26)$$

$$J'' = \int_{-\infty}^{\infty} [L\omega\tau/(1 + \omega^2\tau^2)] \, d\ln\tau + 1/\omega\eta \qquad (27)$$

Each of these equations requires in principle knowledge of the spectrum over a wide range of time scale, depending on how fast the integrand converges. The kernel (that part of the integrand exclusive of H or L) approaches zero at low τ in equations 19 and 23; at high τ in 20 and 26; and at both ends in 24, 25, and 27. The spectra themselves approach zero rather rapidly in certain regions: L at low τ, and H at high τ for uncross-linked polymers.

An example of graphical integration of equations 19, 23, and 24 for a favorable case of convergence, near the terminal zone of the spectrum H, is shown in Fig. 3-6.

Some of the preceding equations can be expressed in more compact form by using $z = \ln\tau$ as the variable of integration.[14] For example, equation 27 becomes

$$J'' = \frac{1}{2} \int_{-\infty}^{\infty} L \operatorname{sech}(N - z) \, dz + 1/\omega\eta$$

where $N = -\ln\omega$.

Certain viscoelastic constants can also be obtained by integration over the spectra. Thus for an *uncross-linked* polymer, by setting $\omega = 0$ in equation 25, we obtain for the steady-flow viscosity

$$\eta = \int_{-\infty}^{\infty} H\tau \, d\ln\tau \qquad (28)$$

For cross-linked polymers, it is an open question as to whether the above integral is finite. The steady-flow viscosity η is of course infinite, but if H vanishes at long times, the integral should represent a finite low-frequency limiting value of η'. Experimental data relating to this question will be discussed in Chapter 13.

By setting $\omega = \infty$ in equation 23 we obtain for the instantaneous modulus

$$G_g = \int_{-\infty}^{\infty} H \, d \ln \tau + G_e \qquad (29)$$

It will be recalled that there is some operational uncertainty in the definition of G_g and its reciprocal J_g, since H usually does not drop rapidly enough at the shortest times experimentally accessible to provide a converging integral in equation 29. Even if it does, there may be further contributions from some other viscoelastic mechanism at still shorter times which would be reflected in a further rise in G_g with extension of the time scale.

From equation 26, setting $\omega = 0$, we have for the equilibrium compliance in a cross-linked material or the steady-state compliance in one uncross-linked:

$$J_e = \int_{-\infty}^{\infty} L \, d \ln \tau + J_g \qquad (30)$$

where J_g is ordinarily negligible in comparison with the integral. From the fact that L persists to very long times without vanishing, in all but uncross-linked polymers of very low molecular weight (Fig. 3–4), it is evident that the integral in equation 30 may not strictly converge either, corresponding to the fact that $J'(\omega)$ and $J(t) - t/\eta$ sometimes appear to continue increasing indefinitely with decreasing ω or increasing t (Figs. 2–1 and 2–6). However, a point is reached

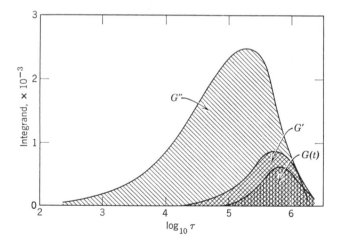

FIG. 3–6. Graphical evaluation of equations 19, 23, and 24, for a polyvinyl acetate in the terminal zone, at log $t = 6.0$ for $G(t)$, log $\omega = -6.0$ for $G'(\omega)$ and $G''(\omega)$. The integrals give $G(t) = 1.06 \times 10^3$, $G' = 1.96 \times 10^3$, $G'' = 1.00 \times 10^4$ (Calculations by K. Ninomiya).

beyond which further contributions to the integral are relatively small and for some purposes J_e may be considered to have attained a limiting value.

The steady-state compliance J_e can also be calculated from H by a relation obtained by equating the expressions for stored energy in a Maxwell and a Voigt model during steady-state flow:

$$J_e = \int_{-\infty}^{\infty} H\tau^2\, d \ln \tau \bigg/ \left[\int_{-\infty}^{\infty} H\tau\, d \ln \tau \right]^2 \qquad (31)$$

C. CALCULATION OF RELAXATION AND RETARDATION SPECTRA FROM EXPERIMENTALLY DETERMINED VISCOELASTIC FUNCTIONS

Although it is relatively easy to obtain the viscoelastic functions from the spectra, the reverse process is difficult, and usually involves successive approximations of some kind as described in Chapter 4. However, if the dynamic viscoelastic functions can be expressed by mathematical formulas, the spectra can be obtained directly therefrom by a substitution involving complex algebra,[1,2] derived for the analogous case of dielectric properties by Fuoss and Kirkwood.[15] To obtain H from G' or G'':

$$H(\tau = 1/\omega) = \pm \frac{1}{\pi} \lim_{\varepsilon \to 0} \mathbf{G}^*(-\omega \pm i\varepsilon) = \pm \frac{1}{\pi} \operatorname{Im} \mathbf{G}^*(\omega e^{\pm i\pi}) \qquad (32)$$

$$H(\tau = 1/\omega) = \pm \frac{2}{\pi} \lim_{\varepsilon \to 0} \operatorname{Im} G'(\varepsilon \pm i\omega) = \pm \frac{2}{\pi} \operatorname{Im} G'(\omega e^{\pm i\pi/2}) \qquad (33)$$

$$H(\tau = 1/\omega) = \frac{2}{\pi} \lim_{\varepsilon \to 0} \operatorname{Re} G''(\varepsilon \pm i\omega) = \frac{2}{\pi} \operatorname{Re} G''(\omega e^{\pm i\pi/2}) \qquad (34)$$

Correspondingly, to obtain L from $\mathbf{J}^*$:

$$L(\tau = 1/\omega) = \pm \frac{1}{\pi} \lim_{\varepsilon \to 0} \operatorname{Im} \mathbf{J}^*(-\omega \mp i\varepsilon) = \pm \frac{1}{\pi} \operatorname{Im} \mathbf{J}^*(\omega e^{\mp i\pi}) \qquad (35)$$

The validity of the above expressions, as well as equations 21 and 22, is based on taking certain integrals as their Cauchy principal values. In practice, the functional forms of $\mathbf{G}^*$ and $\mathbf{J}^*$ are so complicated, as seen in Chapter 2, that usually no attempt is made to represent them by analytical expressions, and the data remain in tabular or graphical form. Even if they were fitted by an empirical equation within the range of experiments, it would not be certain that the equation would have the analytic continuation outside that range which the calculation implies. Thus equations 32 to 35 are rarely used for experimental data. They may be valuable, however, for manipulating the results of theories (Chapter 10).

D. CALCULATION OF ONE EXPERIMENTALLY OBSERVABLE VISCOELASTIC FUNCTION FROM ANOTHER

1. Interrelation of the Two Transient Functions

The creep compliance and the relaxation modulus are connected by the relations

$$\int_0^t G(\tau)J(t - \tau)\, d\tau = t \tag{36}$$

and

$$\int_0^t J(\tau)G(t - \tau)\, d\tau = t \tag{37}$$

from which it follows [16] that $J(t)G(t) \leqq 1$ as mentioned in Chapter 2. An efficient method for numerical evaluation of this convolution integral has been outlined and illustrated by Hopkins and Hamming; [17] values of $G(t)$ spaced at log t intervals of 0.2 are used, for example, to calculate $J(t)$, by a progressive operation starting at $t = 0$.

Alternatively, the Laplace transforms of $J(t)$ and $G(t)$ are reciprocally related:

$$p\mathcal{L}\{J(t)\} = 1/p\mathcal{L}\{G(t)\} \tag{38}$$

from which, in principle, if one function is given analytically, the other can be calculated.

2. Interrelation of a Transient with the Corresponding Dynamic Functions

The components of the complex dynamic modulus are obtainable from the relaxation modulus by the Fourier transforms

$$G'(\omega) = G_e + \omega \int_0^\infty [G(t) - G_e] \sin \omega t\, dt \tag{39}$$

$$G''(\omega) = \omega \int_0^\infty [G(t) - G_e] \cos \omega t\, dt \tag{40}$$

and the relaxation modulus from G' or G'' by the inverse transforms

$$G(t) = G_e + \frac{2}{\pi} \int_0^\infty [(G' - G_e)/\omega] \sin \omega t \, d\omega \tag{41}$$

$$G(t) = G_e + \frac{2}{\pi} \int_0^\infty (G''/\omega) \cos \omega t \, d\omega \tag{42}$$

In all these equations, $G_e = 0$ for an uncross-linked polymer; it is the equilibrium modulus in cases where the latter exists. In principle, these integrals can be performed numerically or graphically if the starting function is known over a sufficiently wide range of time or frequency.

For relating the real component G' to $G(t)$, a far more convenient formulation can be made utilizing the fact that the difference $G'(\omega)$ — $G(t)$ for $t = 1/\omega$ is relatively small, and can be expressed in terms of the relaxation spectrum by equations 19 and 23, as pointed out by Marvin: [18]

$$G'(\omega)\big|_{1/\omega=t} - G(t) = \int_{-\infty}^\infty H \left(\frac{\tau^2}{t^2 + \tau^2} - e^{-t/\tau} \right) d \ln \tau \tag{43}$$

Even though this still contains an integral to be evaluated graphically or numerically, and moreover another function H which must also be determined approximately from whichever of the moduli is known at the start of the problem, the right side of equation 43 represents a minor correction which need not be calculated with great precision. With it, $G'(\omega)$ can be obtained from $G(t)$ or vice versa.

Analogous relations to equations 39 to 43 connect the creep compliance with the components of the complex dynamic compliance. As formulated by Dr. R. S. Marvin, they are:

$$J'(\omega) = J_e - \omega \int_0^\infty [J_e - J(t) + t/\eta] \sin \omega t \, dt \tag{44}$$

$$J''(\omega) = \omega \int_0^\infty [J_e - J(t) + t/\eta] \cos \omega t \, dt + 1/\omega\eta \tag{45}$$

$$J(t) = J_g + \frac{2}{\pi} \int_0^\infty [(J' - J_g)/\omega] \sin \omega t \, d\omega + t/\eta \tag{46}$$

$$J(t) = J_g + \frac{2}{\pi} \int_0^\infty (J''/\omega - 1/\omega^2\eta)(1 - \cos \omega t) \, d\omega + t/\eta \tag{47}$$

$$J'(\omega)\big|_{1/\omega=t} - J(t) + t/\eta = \int_{-\infty}^\infty L \left(e^{-t/\tau} - \frac{\tau^2}{t^2 + \tau^2} \right) d \ln \tau \tag{48}$$

In applications of these equations, J_g is often relatively so small that it does not matter whether it is known accurately. Although the integral in equation 43 is always positive, that in equation 48 is always negative, confirming the relative magnitudes $J'(1/t) < J(t) - t/\eta < 1/G'(1/t) < 1/G(t)$, as stated in Chapter 2.

3. Interrelations between the Components of a Complex Dynamic Function

If both components of **G*** are known at a single frequency, both components of **J*** can be very simply calculated by equations 12 to 15 of Chapter 1. On the other hand, if *one* component is known over the whole frequency range, the other can be obtained from it by mechanical analogs of the Kronig-Kramers relations.[19, 20, 21] Thus, for the compliances,

$$J'(\omega_1) = J_g + \frac{2}{\pi} \int_{-\infty}^{\infty} [(J''\omega^2 - \omega/\eta)/(\omega^2 - \omega_1^2)] \, d \ln \omega \qquad (49)$$

$$J''(\omega_1) = \frac{2}{\pi} \int_{-\infty}^{\infty} [(J' - J_g)\omega_1\omega/(\omega_1^2 - \omega^2)] \, d \ln \omega + 1/\omega_1\eta \qquad (50)$$

To calculate J' from J'', for example, it is necessary for each point desired (ω_1) to evaluate the integral of equation 49 graphically or numerically. The integration has features similar to those of equations 21 and 22 which connect the relaxation and retardation spectra.[13]

4. Evaluation of Viscoelastic Constants

There are some interesting relations which can be obtained from equations 23 to 31 to connect the steady-flow viscosity and the steady-state compliance, for uncross-linked polymers, with experimentally measured functions: [1, 17, 22]

$$\eta = \int_{-\infty}^{\infty} tG(t) \, d \ln t \qquad (51)$$

$$\eta = \frac{2}{\pi} \int_{-\infty}^{\infty} \frac{G'(\omega)}{\omega} \, d \ln \omega \qquad (52)$$

$$J_e = J_g + \frac{2}{\pi} \int_{-\infty}^{\infty} (J''(\omega) - 1/\omega\eta) d \ln \omega \qquad (53)$$

$$J_e = \frac{1}{\eta^2} \int_{-\infty}^{\infty} t^2 G(t) \, d \ln t \qquad (54)$$

These equations are principally useful as sensitive tests of the accuracy of the experimental functions $G(t)$, $G'(\omega)$, etc., near the limits of the range of measurement, provided η and J_e are known from other sources.

E. CALCULATION OF MORE COMPLICATED EXPERIMENTAL FUNCTIONS

There are other more complicated experimental situations where viscoelastic behavior can also be predicted in terms of the relaxation and retardation spectra or other functions. In Chapter 1, deformations at constant rate of strain and at constant rate of stress increase were cited as examples. Another is stress relaxation after cessation of steady-state flow.

1. Deformation at Constant Rate of Strain

If, starting from the undeformed state, the strain is made to increase at a constant rate $\dot{\gamma}$, its value at time t will be $\gamma = \dot{\gamma}t$, and the stress $\mathfrak{T}$ will represent the superposition of a series of partially relaxed stresses up to that instant. In terms of the relaxation spectrum, two alternative formulations can be given: [23]

$$\mathfrak{T} = \dot{\gamma} \int_{-\infty}^{\infty} \tau H(1 - e^{-t/\tau}) \, d\ln\tau + G_o\dot{\gamma}t \tag{55}$$

$$\mathfrak{T} = \dot{\gamma} \int_{0}^{t} \int_{-\infty}^{\infty} He^{-u/\tau} \, d\ln\tau \, du + G_e\dot{\gamma}t \tag{56}$$

A plot of $\mathfrak{T}$ against γ (equivalent with a change of scale to plotting $\mathfrak{T}$ against t) gives a so-called stress-strain curve at constant rate of strain.

Stress-strain curves are commonly obtained in simple extension rather than in shear, and, sometimes involve large strains where the viscoelastic behavior may not be linear as assumed in equations 55 and 56. For soft solids in which moderate extensions are not accompanied by large stresses or changes in internal structure, the above equations may be used with σ, $\dot{\epsilon}$, and H_l substituted for $\mathfrak{T}$, γ, and H. At high extensions, however, linear theory cannot be applied and the whole problem must be reformulated (cf. Chapter 13).

Differentiation of the stress-strain curve yields the relaxation modulus:

$$d\mathfrak{T}/d\gamma = (1/\dot{\gamma}) \, d\mathfrak{T}/dt = \int_{-\infty}^{\infty} He^{-t/\tau} \, d\ln\tau + G_e = G(t) \tag{57}$$

and calculations of this sort have been successfully made by Smith,[24] the results agreeing with direct measurements.

2. Deformation at Constant Rate of Stress Loading

If the stress is increased linearly starting from zero, on the other hand, the resulting strain will reflect the superposition of a series of retarded compliances. Then, if $\dot{\mathfrak{C}}$ is the rate of stress increase,

$$\gamma = \dot{\mathfrak{C}} t J_g + \dot{\mathfrak{C}} \int_0^t \int_{-\infty}^\infty L(1 - e^{-u/\tau}) \, d \ln \tau \, du + \frac{\dot{\mathfrak{C}} t^2}{2\eta} \tag{58}$$

$$\gamma = \dot{\mathfrak{C}} t J_g + \dot{\mathfrak{C}} \int_{-\infty}^\infty L[t - \tau(1 - e^{-t/\tau})] \, d \ln \tau + \frac{\dot{\mathfrak{C}} t^2}{2\eta} \tag{59}$$

In extension, the analogous equations will not have the same form for constant rate of *force* loading, which corresponds to constant increase of stress calculated on *original* cross-section area rather than the actual cross-section as implied here.

When the strain-stress curve obtained under these conditions is differentiated, the result is the creep compliance:

$$d\gamma/d\mathfrak{C} = (1/\dot{\mathfrak{C}}) \, d\gamma/dt = J_g + \int_{-\infty}^\infty L(1 - e^{-t/\tau}) \, d \ln \tau + t/\eta = J(t) \tag{60}$$

If there is any suspicion of non-linear viscoelastic behavior, however, it is better to measure the relaxation modulus and creep compliance directly rather than to obtain them from equations 57 and 60, since the criteria for linearity are more apparent in the simpler experiments.

3. Stress Relaxation after Cessation of Steady-State Flow

If an uncross-linked polymeric system is subjected to constant stress until steady-state flow has been established, and then the flow is stopped and the system held at constant strain, the stress will decay differently from its course in the ordinary stress relaxation experiment. Qualitatively, in the language of models, this arises because of a different distribution of stress across the elements in Fig. 1–2, for example. In instantaneous loading, the stress is distributed in proportion to the stiffnesses of the individual springs; this gives rise to the usual relaxation modulus, $G(t)$. In steady-state flow, the stress is distributed in proportion to the viscosities of the individual dashpots, and a different stress relaxation $\mathfrak{T}_{ss}(t)$ ensues after cessation of flow; it does not depend on the magnitude of γ attained, but only on the value of $\dot{\gamma}$ during flow. It is given by [25]

$$\mathfrak{T}_{ss}(t) = \dot{\gamma} \int_{-\infty}^{\infty} H\tau e^{-t/\tau} d\ln \tau \tag{61}$$

and reflects a heavier weighting of the longest relaxation times. Deviations from linear viscoelastic behavior may be apparent at lower stresses in $\mathfrak{T}_{ss}(t)$ than in $G(t)$. Equation 61 can be inverted to obtain H from $\mathfrak{T}_{ss}(t)$ by approximation procedures.

F. OTHER ASPECTS OF THE PHENOMENOLOGICAL THEORY

All the relations in this chapter are derivable from the Boltzmann superposition principle, as stated in Chapter 1, which is equivalent to representation by a linear mechanical model such as Figs. 1-1 or 1-2. They provide a variety of possible experimental tests for the superposition principle, such as, for example, comparison of the results of transient and dynamic data by equations such as 43 and 48. In the few cases where sufficient data have been available for a critical comparison, any discrepancies have generally been found to be small and insufficient to cast serious doubt on the postulates of the theory.[27,28] One puzzling case of a larger discrepancy has been reported.[29]

It has been pointed out by Meixner [6,30] that certain other postulates besides the superposition principle are needed for the strict development of the theory; these are ordinarily taken for granted.

The features of linear viscoelastic behavior also follow from the principles of linear irreversible thermodynamics.[31,32]

REFERENCES

1. B. Gross, *Mathematical Structure of the Theories of Viscoelasticity,* Hermann et Cie., Paris, 1953.
2. J. Schrama, Ph.D. Dissertation, Leiden, 1957.
3. S. Kästner and E. Schlosser, *Kolloid-Z.,* **152,** 116 (1957).
4. J. R. Macdonald and M. K. Brachman, *Rev. Modern Phys.,* **28,** 393 (1956).
5. S. Goldman, *Transformation Calculus and Electrical Transients,* Prentice-Hall, Englewood Cliffs, New Jersey, 1949.

6. J. Meixner and H. König, *Rheol. Acta*, **1**, 190 (1958).
7. A. J. Staverman and F. Schwarzl, in H. A. Stuart, *Die Physik der Hochpolymeren*, Vol. IV, Chapter I, Springer-Verlag, Berlin, 1956.
8. T. Alfrey, Jr., *Mechanical Behavior of High Polymers*, Interscience Publishers, New York, 1948.
9. J. D. Ferry, W. M. Sawyer, and J. N. Ashworth, *J. Polymer Sci.*, **2**, 593 (1947).
10. H. F. Olson, *Dynamical Analogies*, Van Nostrand, New York, 1943.
11. G. Kegel, *Kolloid-Z.*, **135**, 125 (1954).
12. B. Gross, *J. Polymer Sci.*, **20**, 371 (1956).
13. H. Silva and B. Gross, *Phys. Rev.*, **60**, 684 (1941).
14. H. Leaderman, *J. Applied Phys.*, **25**, 294 (1954).
15. R. M. Fuoss and J. G. Kirkwood, *J. Amer. Chem. Soc.*, **63**, 385 (1941).
16. C. Zener, *Elasticity and Anelasticity of Metals*, Chicago University Press, 1948, p. 21.
17. I. L. Hopkins and R. W. Hamming, *J. Applied Phys.*, **28**, 906 (1957).
18. R. S. Marvin, *Phys. Rev.*, **86**, 644 (1952).
19. R. de L. Kronig, *J. Opt. Soc. Amer.*, **12**, 547 (1926).
20. H. A. Kramers, *Atti Cong. dei Fisici*, Como, 1927, p. 545.
21. J. H. Van Vleck, in *Properties of Short Radio Waves*, Edited by D. E. Kerr, McGraw-Hill, New York, 1951, p. 641.
22. H. Fujita, personal communication.
23. R. Sips, *J. Polymer Sci.*, **5**, 69 (1950).
24. T. L. Smith, *J. Polymer Sci.*, **20**, 89 (1956).
25. F. W. Schremp, J. D. Ferry, and W. W. Evans, *J. Applied Phys.*, **22**, 711 (1951).
26. T. L. Smith, *J. Polymer Sci.*, **14**, 37 (1954).
27. E. Catsiff and A. V. Tobolsky, *J. Colloid Sci.*, **10**, 375 (1955).
28. D. J. Plazek, *J. Colloid Sci.*, **15**, 50 (1960).
29. W. Sommer, *Kolloid-Z.*, **167**, 97 (1959).
30. J. Meixner, *Z. Physik.*, **139**, 30 (1954).
31. J. Meixner, *Kolloid-Z.*, **134**, 3 (1953); *Z. Naturf.*, **9a**, 654 (1954).
32. A. J. Staverman, *Kolloid-Z.*, **134**, 189 (1953).

Additional References

33. W. Kuhn, *Z. Phys. Chem.*, **B42**, 1 (1939).
34. K. Bennewitz and H. Rötger, *Physik. Z.*, **40**, 416 (1939).
35. T. Alfrey and P. Doty, *J. Applied Phys.*, **16**, 700 (1945).
36. T. Alfrey and E. F. Gurnee, in F. R. Eirich, *Rheology*, Vol. I, Chapter 11 (1956).
37. R. Sips, *J. Polymer Sci.*, **5**, 69 (1950).
38. R. Sips, *J. Polymer Sci.*, **6**, 285 (1951).
39. E. R. Love, *Austr. J. Phys.*, **9**, 1 (1956).
40. H. König and J. Meixner, *Math. Nachr.*, **19**, 265 (1959).
41. E. A. Hiedemann and R. D. Spence, *Z. Phys.*, **133**, 109 (1952).
42. R. S. Marvin, in J. T. Bergen, *Viscoelasticity—Phenomenological Aspects*, Academic Press, New York, 1960, p. 27.

CHAPTER 4

Approximate Interrelations among the Viscoelastic Functions

Many of the equations in the preceding chapter, although accurate within the assumptions of linear viscoelasticity, fail to meet practical needs for converting one viscoelastic function into another. Usually, an integration from $-\infty$ to ∞ is required, and the function which is known initially may not be available over a wide enough range of time or frequency to give convergence of the integral; or even if it is, the integration may be tedious, and sensitive to errors through addition of terms of opposite sign as in Fig. 3–5. For these reasons, a variety of approximation methods have been developed for performing such calculations.

Most of the approximation procedures involve taking derivatives either of the initial function or of related functions, either graphically or by a numerical differencing process. Some can be extended in principle to utilize second and higher derivatives, but it is rare (except in isolated cases where curvature changes sharply) that experimental data are sufficiently precise to make any derivatives beyond the second worthwhile. For measuring slopes, graphical methods are in the writer's opinion usually preferable, although they are not entirely objective. Differencing procedures are subject to fluctuations unless the original data are smoothed to an extra significant figure beyond the requirements of the calculations; they do, however, have the advantage of being amenable to routine processing.

Generally, the approximation methods have an analytical foundation based on the properties of the integrands of the corresponding exact equations. Such an integrand is usually the product of the viscoelastic function initially known and an additional dimensionless intensity function. For example, in equation 19 of Chapter 3,

$$G(t) = G_e + \int_{-\infty}^{\infty} H e^{-t/\tau} \, d \ln \tau \tag{1}$$

the initial function H is multiplied by the intensity function $e^{-t/\tau}$ which goes from 0 at $\tau = 0$ to 1 at $\tau \to \infty$. If the latter were approximated by a step function going from 0 to 1 at $\tau = t$, we would have

$$G(t) \cong G_e + \int_{\ln t}^{\infty} H \, d \ln \tau \tag{2}$$

and the integral would not be grossly different. Moreover, by differentiating equation 2 with respect to the limit $\ln t$, we obtain

$$- \frac{dG(t)}{d \ln t}\bigg|_{t=\tau} \cong H(\tau) \tag{3}$$

so the relaxation spectrum at $\tau = t$ is obtainable in first approximation as the negative slope of the relaxation modulus. This is Alfrey's rule.[1]

Equations 2 and 3 are not sufficiently accurate unless H changes very slowly with time. To achieve a better approximation, there are two approaches: to develop the problem analytically [2-6] or to proceed semi-empirically [7,8] with a set of correction factors based on an assumed form for H. If the assumed form fits H over a relatively limited region of time scale, this is ordinarily sufficient.

In other cases, simple explicit solutions can be obtained for integrals in equations such as 21 and 22 of Chapter 3 if the viscoelastic function in the integrand is assumed to have a certain form and the intensity function is retained without approximation. Again, it may be sufficient for the form assumed for the viscoelastic function to be valid over perhaps two decades of logarithmic time scale.

In the following summary of approximation methods, no derivations will be given; these are in the original literature. Some comments on utility will be made, however. Methods involving graphical differentiation are usually outlined in terms of slopes measured on logarithmic plots like those in Chapter 2.

A. CALCULATION OF SPECTRA FROM EXPERIMENTAL FUNCTIONS

This is the most important application of approximation methods, since exact methods are of such limited use.

1. Relaxation Spectrum from Relaxation Modulus

The method of Ferry and Williams [7] provides

$$H(\tau) = -M(m)G(t) \, d \log G(t)/d \log t \big|_{t=\tau} \qquad (4)$$

where $M(m) = 1/\Gamma(m+1)$ and $-m$ is the slope of a doubly logarithmic plot of H against τ. (The method is limited to positive values of m.) The procedure is to make a tentative (first approximation) calculation of H by setting $M = 1$ in equation 4. Ordinarily, a series of points equally spaced on the logarithmic time scale is chosen, each providing a value of H at $\tau = t$. Then from a tentative logarithmic plot of H against τ, the slope $-m$ is measured at each point; the corresponding value of M is obtained and multiplied by the provisional value of H. Tables of M and other useful correction factors are given at the end of this chapter. Graphs of $\log M$ against m are also very convenient.

The second approximation method of Schwarzl and Staverman [2] provides

$$H(\tau) = -dG(t)/d \ln t + d^2 G(t)/d(\ln t)^2 \big|_{t=2\tau}$$

or, in terms of log-log plots,

$$H(\tau) = -G(t)[d \log G(t)/d \log t - (d \log G(t)/d \log t)^2$$
$$- (1/2.303) \, d^2 \log G(t)/d(\log t)^2] \big|_{t=2\tau} \qquad (5)$$

Here both first and second derivatives of $G(t)$ must be measured, and the calculated value of H corresponds not to $\tau = t$ but to $\tau = t/2$. The two methods really use equivalent information, since the first derivative of H, needed for m in equation 4, is closely related to the second derivative of $G(t)$.

A potentially more accurate, but much more complicated method has been outlined by Roesler,[9] involving expansion of $G(t)$ in Fourier series.

64   VISCOELASTIC PROPERTIES OF POLYMERS

2. Retardation Spectrum from Creep Compliance

The analog of the Ferry-Williams calculation, as shown by Stern,[10] is:

$$L(\tau) = M(-m)[J(t) - t/\eta]\, d \log [J(t) - t/\eta]/d \log t\big|_{t=\tau} \qquad (6)$$

where M is the same function as before and $+m$ is the slope of a doubly logarithmic plot of L against τ. The calculation is carried out in two stages as with equation 4.

The second approximation method of Schwarzl and Staverman gives

$$L(\tau) = dJ(t)/d \ln t - d^2J(t)/d(\ln t)^2\big|_{t=2\tau} \qquad (7)$$

or $$L(\tau) = (d/d \ln t)[J(t) - dJ(t)/d \ln t]\big|_{t=2\tau} \qquad (8)$$

and has the advantage, not possessed by equation 6, that the flow term t/η need not be subtracted from $J(t)$ before making the calculation. (Actually, equations 7 and 8 are unchanged [11] by substituting $J(t) - t/\eta$ for $J(t)$.) When creep experiments on uncross-linked polymers have not been carried far enough to determine η with confidence, the Ferry-Williams method cannot be applied.

3. Relaxation Spectrum from Storage Modulus

The method of Williams and Ferry provides two formulas depending on whether m, the negative slope of H on a doubly logarithmic plot, is greater or less than 1. Almost invariably, $m < 1$, in which case:

$$H(\tau) = AG'\, d \log G'/d \log \omega\big|_{1/\omega=\tau} \qquad (9)$$

where $A = (2 - m)/2\Gamma\left(2 - \frac{m}{2}\right)\Gamma\left(1 + \frac{m}{2}\right)$. If, on the other hand, $1 < m < 2$, the corresponding formula is

$$H(\tau) = A'G'(2 - d \log G'/d \log \omega)\big|_{1/\omega=\tau} \qquad (10)$$

where $A' = m/2\Gamma\left(1 + \frac{m}{2}\right)\Gamma\left(2 - \frac{m}{2}\right)$. As with equation 4, the calculation is carried out in two stages; first A is set equal to unity, and a preliminary calculation is made with each point at a given value of ω yielding a value of H at $\tau = 1/\omega$. From a tentative graph of H, the value of m is measured at each point, and the appropriate correction factor A is applied. Values of A are also given at the end of the chapter.

The method of Schwarzl and Staverman (third approximation) provides

$$H(\tau) = dG'/d \ln \omega - \tfrac{1}{4} d^3 G'/d(\ln \omega)^3 \big|_{1/\omega=\tau} \qquad (11)$$

and the first approximation of Okano [4] and Fujita: [5]

$$H(\tau) = \frac{e^2}{2\pi} \left[\frac{dG'}{d \ln \omega} - \frac{1}{2} \frac{d^2 G'}{d(\ln \omega)^2} \right] \bigg|_{1/\omega=\tau} \qquad (12)$$

or in terms of log-log plots,

$$H(\tau) = \frac{e^2}{2\pi} G'[d \log G'/d \log \omega - \tfrac{1}{2}(d \log G'/d \log \omega)^2$$
$$- (1/4.606) \, d^2 \log G'/d(\log \omega)^2] \big|_{1/\omega=\tau} \qquad (13)$$

where e is the base of natural logarithms. (These authors also give higher approximations requiring derivatives which would ordinarily not be available with sufficient accuracy.)

The method of Ninomiya and Ferry [6] involves measuring no slopes but instead certain values of G', spaced at equal intervals on a logarithmic frequency scale above and below the frequency $\omega - 1/\tau$ corresponding to the value of τ for which H is desired: viz., at ω/a^2, ω/a, $a\omega$, and $a^2\omega$, with a suitable choice of a. Then

$$H(\tau) = \frac{G'(a\omega) - G'(\omega/a)}{2 \ln a}$$
$$- \frac{a^2}{(a^2 - 1)^2} \cdot \frac{G'(a^2\omega) - G'(\omega/a^2) - 2G'(a\omega) + 2G'(\omega/a)}{2 \ln a} \bigg|_{1/\omega=\tau} \qquad (14)$$

In practice $\log a = 0.2$ to 0.4 is a reasonable choice; with larger values the approximation is poorer, and with smaller values the limitations in accuracy of the experimental values of G' may cause serious fluctuations in the differencing. The calculation can be easily performed with perforated guide cards as illustrated at the end of the chapter.

Finally, Roesler and Twyman [13] have outlined an iterative numerical method by which, starting with a first approximation such as equation 9 with $A = 1$, successive corrections are applied point by point.

4. Retardation Spectrum from Storage Compliance

These are analogs to equations 9 to 14, as follows. By the method of Williams and Ferry, when m, the (positive) slope of a doubly logarithmic plot of L, is less than 1:

$$L(\tau) = -AJ' \, d \log J'/d \log \omega|_{1/\omega=\tau} \tag{15}$$

and in the rare event that $m > 1$

$$L(\tau) = A'J'(2 + d \log J'/d \log \omega)|_{1/\omega=\tau} \tag{16}$$

with A and A' defined in terms of m as above. By the method of Schwarzl and Staverman,

$$L(\tau) = -dJ'/d \ln \omega + \tfrac{1}{4} d^3J'/d(\ln \omega)^3|_{1/\omega=\tau} \tag{17}$$

and that of Fujita

$$L(\tau) = -\frac{e^2}{2\pi} \left[\frac{dJ'}{d \ln \omega} - \frac{1}{2} \frac{d^2J'}{d(\ln \omega)^2} \right] \Bigg|_{1/\omega=\tau} \tag{18}$$

and that of Ninomiya and Ferry

$$L(\tau) = \frac{J'(\omega/a) - J'(a\omega)}{2 \ln a}$$
$$- \frac{a^2}{(a^2 - 1)^2} \frac{J'(\omega/a^2) - J'(a^2\omega) - 2J'(\omega/a) + 2J'(a\omega)}{2 \ln a} \Bigg|_{1/\omega=\tau} \tag{19}$$

where a perforated card may again be employed.

5. Relaxation Spectrum from Loss Modulus

In zero approximation, the loss modulus at ω is directly the relaxation spectrum at $\tau = 1/\omega$, but there is no need to use such a crude approximation when very simple methods are available to improve it.

The method of Williams and Ferry again provides two alternative formulas depending on whether m is positive or negative, but these can be readily synthesized by using the absolute values of m and of the slope $d \log G''/d \log \omega$:

$$H(\tau) = BG''(1 - |d \log G''/d \log \omega|)|_{1/\omega=\tau} \tag{20}$$

where $B = (1 + |m|)/2\Gamma\left(\dfrac{3}{2} - \dfrac{|m|}{2}\right)\Gamma\left(\dfrac{3}{2} + \dfrac{|m|}{2}\right)$. The calculation

proceeds in two steps as in the other Williams-Ferry methods; values of B are given at the end of the chapter.

The method of Schwarzl and Staverman (second approximation) gives

$$H(\tau) = (2/\pi)[G'' - d^2G''/d(\ln \omega)^2]|_{1/\omega=\tau} \tag{21}$$

and that of Fujita (first approximation)

$$H(\tau) = (e^2/4\pi)[G'' - d^2G''/d(\ln \omega)^2]|_{1/\omega=\tau} \tag{22}$$

or in terms of logarithmic plots

$$H(\tau) = (e^2/4\pi)G''[1 - (d \ln G''/d \ln \omega)^2 - d^2 \ln G''/d(\ln \omega)^2]|_{1/\omega=\tau} \tag{23}$$

The numerical factors in equations 21 and 22 are closely similar—0.637 and 0.588 respectively. The value of B for $m = 0$ (and $d \ln G''/d \ln \omega = 0$) is also $2/\pi = 0.637$, so for this case equations 20 and 21 agree except for the second derivative in the latter. Experience has shown that when the second derivative is substantial (a rare circumstance) equations 21 and 22 are preferable. Further approximations with higher derivatives are also given by these authors, but their use is rarely permitted by the accuracy of experimental data.

The method of Ninomiya and Ferry (first approximation) for this calculation involves three values of G'', equally spaced on the logarithmic frequency scale with a spacing of log a:

$$H(\tau) = \frac{2}{\pi}\left[G''(\omega) - \frac{a}{(a-1)^2}\left\{G''(a\omega) + G''(\omega/a) - 2G''(\omega)\right\}\right]\Bigg|_{1/\omega=\tau} \tag{24}$$

The perforated card for this operation is also shown at the end of the chapter.

There are also the iterative numerical methods of Roesler and Pearson [14] and Roesler and Twyman,[13] which avoid derivatives and in principle can be carried to any degree of approximation desired.

6. Retardation Spectrum from Loss Compliance

The Williams-Ferry formula for this calculation is

$$L(\tau) = BJ''(1 - |d \log J''/d \log \omega|)|_{1/\omega=\tau} \tag{25}$$

with B the same function of $|m|$ as before. For an uncross-linked polymer, at very low frequencies, J'' approaches $1/\omega\eta$; hence the calculation becomes numerically uncertain, with J'' increasing without limit and the quantity in parentheses approaching zero. Mathematically, of course, L approaches zero at low frequencies as it must if there is a finite number of relaxation mechanisms. The numerical uncertainty can be avoided, or shifted to an earlier stage in the data processing, if η is known and $J'' - 1/\omega\eta$ is substituted for J'' in the formula.

The Schwarzl-Staverman second approximation is

$$L(\tau) = (2/\pi)[J'' - d^2J''/d(\ln \omega)^2]\big|_{1/\omega=\tau} \qquad (26)$$

where, for an uncross-linked polymer, $J'' - 1/\omega\eta$ can alternatively be substituted for J''. The Fujita first approximation is

$$L(\tau) = (e^2/4\pi)J''[1 - (d\ln J''/d\ln \omega)^2 - d^2\ln J''/d(\ln \omega)^2]\big|_{1/\omega=\tau}$$

$$(27)$$

The Ninomiya-Ferry first approximation, with no derivatives, gives

$$L(\tau) = (2/\pi)\left[J''(\omega) - \frac{a}{(a-1)^2}\left\{J''(a\omega) + J''(\omega/a) - 2J''(\omega)\right\}\right]\Bigg|_{1/\omega=\tau}$$

$$(28)$$

identical in form with equation 24. Here, also, subtraction of the flow term $1/\omega\eta$ from J'' makes no difference in the final result.

7. Criteria of Applicability of Various Approximations

The degree of error in an approximate calculation of a relaxation or retardation spectrum can be gauged in various ways. The original experimental function from which it was derived can be reconstructed by an integration such as equation 1, and compared with the initial data; this is not a very critical test and has rarely been undertaken. An iterative method such as that of Roesler and Pearson can be carried to convergence and used to check a simpler method; in one test of this sort,[14] the Williams-Ferry equation 20 was rather closely confirmed except near the maximum in H. More commonly, the values of H obtained by approximations from different experimental functions are compared. This is almost always possible in analyzing dynamic measurements, where G' and G'' (or J' and J'') are determined simultaneously. Failure of the spectra calculated from the storage and loss components to agree indicates that at least one is in error, whereas agreement is reasonable evidence of a satisfactory calculation since both would not be expected to deviate in the same manner.

For sharp peaks in spectra, none of the approximations is satisfactory, but such peaks rarely occur. In regions where m changes slowly (corresponding to small second derivatives of G'', J'', H, or L, or small third derivatives of G', J', $G(t)$ or $J(t)$), the Williams-Ferry formulas have repeatedly given agreement between the calculations from storage and loss components to 0.05 log unit (10%) or better, which is probably as much as can be expected from most experimental data. These formulas are susceptible of rapid and easy calculation, although some judgment is needed in measuring slopes graphically. They cannot be relied upon, however, under circumstances where the correction factors (M, A, B, etc.) are smaller than ½. They fail where there is sharp curvature in H and L, such as near the maxima and minima in Curves III of Figs. 3–3 and 3–4. In such regions, the Schwarzl-Staverman or Fujita methods appear to be preferable. The Ninomiya-Ferry method lends itself to routine calculation with no exercise of judgment needed, but it requires carefully smoothed original data.

B. INTERRELATIONS BETWEEN THE SPECTRA

Equations 21 and 22 of Chapter 3 can be modified in various ways for simpler calculation of H from L and vice versa. Most of the resulting formulas have been given by Smith,[15] and are based on two principles: (a) if H is known, it has ordinarily been obtained from either $G(t)$ or G' and G'', so these latter functions can be utilized to aid in the calculation of L, and *mutatis mutandis* compliances can be utilized in the calculation of H from L; (b) over a limited range of logarithmic time scale, H can be assumed proportional to τ^{-m}, and L proportional to τ^m, *viz.* they can be characterized by the logarithmic slope m as used in the Williams-Ferry approximation methods.

1. One Spectrum and Transient Known

To obtain L from H and $G(t)$, the formula is

$$L(\tau) = \frac{H(\tau)}{\left\{ G(t) + H(\tau) \left[\frac{\pi}{2} \left(\csc \frac{m\pi}{2} - \sec \frac{m\pi}{2} \right) - \Gamma(m) + 1.37 \right] \right\}^2 + \pi^2 H^2}$$

(29)

where m is the negative slope of a logarithmic plot of H, measured of course separately point by point; and to obtain H from L and $J(t)$,

$$H(\tau) = \frac{L(\tau)}{\left\{ J(t) - 2t/\eta + L(\tau) \left[\frac{\pi}{2} \left(\csc \frac{m\pi}{2} - \sec \frac{m\pi}{2} \right) + \Gamma(-m) + 1.37 \right] \right\}^2 + \pi^2 L^2}$$

(30)

where m is the positive slope of a logarithmic plot of L. These formulas are limited to $-1 < m < 1$.

2. One Spectrum and Dynamic Data Known

In this case, the slopes m are not necessary. To obtain L from H, G', and G'', we have

$$L(\tau) = \frac{H(\tau)}{[G'(1/\tau) - G''(1/\tau) + 1.37H(\tau)]^2 + \pi^2 H^2(\tau)} \quad (31)$$

and to obtain H from L, J', and J'', the corresponding approximation is

$$H(\tau) = \frac{L(\tau)}{[J'(1/\tau) - J''(1/\tau) + 1.37L(\tau)]^2 + \pi L^2(\tau)^2} \quad (32)$$

3. One Spectrum Known with Constant Logarithmic Slope

There are two cases of interest where additional data are not required for the interconversion provided the given spectrum has a constant logarithmic slope over a wide range of time scale. When this is so, the exponents m in the expressions $H \propto \tau^{-m}$ and $L \propto \tau^m$ are equal. If $m = \frac{1}{2}$,

$$H(\tau)L(\tau) = 1/\pi^2 \quad (33)$$

which is approximately applicable in the transition zone from rubberlike to glasslike consistency where $\log H$ has a slope near $-\frac{1}{2}$ and $\log L$ near $\frac{1}{2}$ (Figs. 3–3 and 3–4, Curves II, III, V, and VI). Thus in such a zone $H(\tau) \cong 0.1/L(\tau)$.

If, on the other hand, $m \ll 1$, so that H falls very slightly and L rises very slightly, as in Curves IV and V at long times, Figs. 3–3 and 3–4,

$$H(\tau)L(\tau) = m^2 \quad (34)$$

so that in such extended plateau regions $H(\tau) \ll 1/L(\tau)$, as observed for the curves cited.

C. CALCULATION OF VISCOELASTIC FUNCTIONS FROM THE SPECTRA

Simplified methods for this type of calculation have not been widely developed, partly because the problem seldom arises in practice and partly because the exact formulas, involving integrals such as equation 1 with reasonably rapid convergence, are not difficult to evaluate.

However, Smith [15] has quoted two formulas, obtained by rearranging equations 29 and 30, from which the transient experimental functions can be calculated if both spectra are known:

$$G(t) = [H/L - \pi^2 H^2]^{\frac{1}{2}} - H \left[\frac{\pi}{2} \left(\csc \frac{m\pi}{2} - \sec \frac{m\pi}{2} \right) - \Gamma(m) + 1.37 \right]$$

(35)

where m refers to the negative logarithmic slope of H; and

$$J(t) = [L/H - \pi^2 L^2]^{\frac{1}{2}}$$

$$- L \left[\frac{\pi}{2} \left(\csc \frac{m\pi}{2} - \sec \frac{m\pi}{2} \right) + \Gamma(-m) + 1.37 \right] + \frac{2t}{\eta} \quad (36)$$

where m refers to the (positive) logarithmic slope of L. For these formulas, m must be measured separately at each value of τ corresponding to the value of t at which the transient function is desired.

Two experimental functions which are quite easily derivable from the spectra are the closely related dynamic loss functions. Equations 20 and 25 can be rearranged to give

$$G''(\omega) = H/B(1 - |m|)|_{\tau=1/\omega} \quad (37)$$

$$J''(\omega) = L/B(1 - |m|) + \tau/\eta|_{\tau=1/\omega} \quad (38)$$

where m has its usual significance and at each point B is determined by the value of m. Some alternative equations have been given by Smith: [15]

$$G''(\omega) = (H\pi/2) \sec (m\pi/2)|_{\tau=1/\omega} \quad (39)$$

$$J''(\omega) = (L\pi/2) \sec (m\pi/2) + \tau/\eta|_{\tau=1/\omega} \quad (40)$$

D. CALCULATION OF ONE EXPERIMENTALLY OBSERVABLE VISCOELASTIC FUNCTION FROM ANOTHER

1. Interrelation of the Two Transient Functions

From equation 36 of Chapter 3, an approximate relation can be derived by assuming, for example, that $\log J(t)$ is a linear function of $\log t$ over a moderate interval of time scale, the slope of the function being as usual denoted by m. Then [11]

$$G(t) = (\sin m\pi)/m\pi J(t) \quad (41)$$

The same equation may be used to obtain $J(t)$ from $G(t)$, with m the slope of the doubly logarithmic plot of $G(t)$. A table of $(\sin m\pi)/m\pi$ is given at the end of the chapter.

It may be noted that with $m \ll 1$, $G(t)$ becomes simply the reciprocal of $J(t)$, as mentioned in Chapter 2; otherwise, $G(t) < 1/J(t)$. Moreover, when an uncross-linked polymer reaches a steady-state condition of flow, $m \rightarrow 1$ (since $J(t) = t/\eta +$ other terms which eventually become negligible by comparison); then according to equation 41, $G(t) \rightarrow 0$, as it must (Chapter 2).

2. Interrelation of a Transient with the Corresponding Dynamic Storage Function

The approximate equations for these calculations are of two types, depending on whether additional information is available in the form of the dynamic loss function or the spectrum.

If both dynamic components are known, the transient function can be calculated by the method of Ninomiya and Ferry. Thus, for relaxation:

$$G(t) = G'(\omega) - 0.40G''(0.40\omega) + 0.014G''(10\omega)\big|_{\omega=1/t} \qquad (42)$$

requiring G' at the corresponding frequency $\omega = 1/t$ and G'' at two other frequencies. Similarly, for creep:

$$J(t) = J'(\omega) + 0.40J''(0.40\omega) - 0.014J''(10\omega)\big|_{\omega=1/t} \qquad (43)$$

The calculations can be performed routinely with perforated cards similar to those shown at the end of the chapter. Alternatively, if $G(t)$ and G'' are known, G' can be calculated.

If either $G(t)$ or G' is known together with H, the other experimental function can be calculated by a simplification of equation 42 of Chapter 3 which avoids performing the integration, as introduced by Catsiff and Tobolsky: [16]

$$G'(\omega)\big|_{\omega=1/t} - G(t) = H(\tau)\psi(m)\big|_{\tau=t} \qquad (44)$$

where H can be obtained from equation 4 or 9, depending on which of the experimental functions is given initially; m is as usual the negative slope of a plot of $\log H$ against $\log \tau$ at the point $\tau = t$, and $\psi(m) = (\pi/2)$ csc $(m\pi/2) - \Gamma(m)$. A table of $\psi(m)$ is given at the end of the chapter. With equation 44, $G'(\omega)$ can be calculated from $G(t)$ or vice versa.

The analogous equation connecting the compliance functions is [15]

$$J'(\omega)\big|_{\omega=1/t} - J(t) + t/\eta = L(\tau)\psi'(m)\big|_{\tau=t} \qquad (45)$$

where m is the (positive) slope of a plot of $\log L$ against $\log \tau$ at the point $\tau = t$, and $\psi'(m) = (\pi/2)$ csc $(m\pi/2) + \Gamma(-m)$. A table of $\psi'(m)$

is also given at the end of the chapter; it is negative, as required by the fact that $J(t) > J'(1/t)$, even after subtraction of t/η.

If $G'(\omega)$ is very flat, H (which reflects the slope of G') is small by comparison, and as a result G' and $G(t)$ are almost identical, as seen in Chapter 2. Similarly, if J' is very flat, it is almost identical with $J(t) - t/\eta$. Another specific case of some interest occurs when $G' = G''$ and both are proportional to $\omega^{\frac{1}{2}}$, as specified in certain theories (Chapter 10) and roughly fulfilled in the transition region between glasslike and rubberlike consistency (especially in gels of cellulose derivatives—Chapter 17); then equation 44 reduces to $G(t) = 0.79G'(1/t)$. Still another example is given by the so-called Andrade creep behavior of cross-linked systems at long times (Chapter 13), where the compliance can be represented by the empirical equation $J(t) = J_A + \beta t^{\frac{1}{3}}$. At an equivalent frequency $\omega = 1/t$, the dynamic compliances are then given by [17]

$$J'(\omega) = J_A + [\beta\Gamma(\tfrac{1}{3})/2\sqrt{3}]\omega^{-\frac{1}{3}} = J_A + 0.773\beta\omega^{-\frac{1}{3}} \quad (46)$$

$$J''(\omega) = [\beta\Gamma(\tfrac{1}{3})/6]\omega^{-\frac{1}{3}} = 0.446\beta\omega^{-\frac{1}{3}} \quad (47)$$

and at frequencies sufficiently low that the term J_A in equation 46 can be neglected,

$$J''/J' = 1/\sqrt{3} = 0.577 \quad (48)$$

If the slope m of the creep function $J(t)$ on a doubly logarithmic plot is quite small (precluding the presence of viscous flow, of course), it is related to the loss tangent J''/J' by the equation [18]

$$\tan\delta = J''/J' = G''/G' = m\pi/2, \qquad m\pi/2 \ll 1 \quad (49)$$

Thus under certain circumstances $\tan\delta$ is independent of frequency, as seen in Fig. 2–8 (Curves IV and V at low frequencies).

Finally, a numerical method has been outlined by Benbow [19] for calculating the components of the dynamic compliance from the creep compliance, based on a Fourier analysis of the latter.

3. Interrelations between the Components of a Complex Dynamic Function

Two relations have been given by Staverman and Schwarzl [20] relating the values of G' at two frequencies ω_1 and ω_2:

$$G'(\omega_2) - G'(\omega_1) \cong \frac{2}{\pi} \int_{\ln\omega_1}^{\ln\omega_2} G''(\omega) \, d\ln\omega \quad (50)$$

$$\ln G'(\omega_2)/G'(\omega_1) \cong \frac{2}{\pi} \int_{\ln\omega\cdot}^{\ln\omega_2} \tan\delta \, d\ln\omega \quad (51)$$

4. Criteria of Applicability

It is difficult to generalize in appraising the possible errors in the various approximations given here, which can range from within the experimental error of any measurements to deviations of 25% or more, depending on the features of the functions employed. Smith[15] has compared approximate with exact calculations in a number of cases and found that over a wide range of circumstances the respective logarithms did not differ by more than 0.1. In general, results which involve subtraction of two numbers similar in magnitude, or the product of one quantity which is rapidly increasing and another which is approaching zero, should be regarded with skepticism; they can be distinguished by arithmetic common sense.

E. CALCULATION OF SPECTRA FROM MORE COMPLICATED EXPERIMENTAL FUNCTIONS

In Section E of Chapter 3, some more complicated viscoelastic experiments were formulated. The stress-strain curves can provide spectra through first differentiating to give the transient functions and then applying formulas such as equations 4 to 8. The stress relaxation after cessation of steady-state flow can provide the spectrum H through the following approximation relation

$$H(\tau) = -(N/\dot{\gamma}t) \, d\mathcal{T}_{ss}/d \ln t \big|_{t=\tau} \qquad (52)$$

where $\dot{\gamma}$ is the rate of shear during flow and $N = 1/\Gamma(m)$. A table of N is also given at the end of the chapter. It should be remarked that corrections for the non-Newtonian character of the flow and relaxation may be necessary in this case,[21] even when the stresses are fairly small.

Once again, the reader is reminded that, although all the equations in this chapter refer to deformation in shear, they are equally applicable to other types of deformation if the shear moduli, compliances, and spectra are replaced by the corresponding functions appropriate to extension or bulk compression, etc.

F. NUMERICAL EXAMPLES OF APPROXIMATION CALCULATIONS

Two illustrations of numerical calculations are given here, and demonstrate the simplicity of some of the methods. The first, Table 4–I, is the calculation of the relaxation spectrum of poly-n-octyl methacrylate [22] (Curve III of Fig. 3–3) from the storage modulus and loss modulus by equations 9 and 20. The values from the two dynamic components are almost all in very good agreement. (At lower frequencies, however, the curvature in H made it necessary to use other methods.[23]) The second, Table 4–II, is a calculation of the stress relaxation function in extension, $E(t)$, for polyisobutylene from the creep compliance $D(t)$, using the analog of equation 41, performed

Table 4–I

CALCULATION OF RELAXATION SPECTRUM OF POLY-n-OCTYL METHACRYLATE FROM STORAGE MODULUS AND LOSS MODULUS BY EQUATIONS 9 AND 20

From Storage Modulus

$\log \omega$	$\log G'$	$\dfrac{d \log G'}{d \log \omega}$	$\dfrac{\log}{\dfrac{d \log G'}{d \log \omega}}$	Prov. $\log H$	m	$\log A$	$\log H$	$\log \tau$
1.5	5.56	0.065	−1.19	4.37	0.40	−0.03	4.34	−1.5
2.0	5.61	0.110	−0.96	4.65	0.40	−0.03	4.62	−2.0
2.5	5.68	0.16	−0.80	4.88	0.40	−0.03	4.85	−2.5
3.0	5.77	0.21	−0.68	5.07	0.40	−0.03	5.04	−3.0
3.5	5.89	0.29	−0.54	5.35	0.55	−0.06	5.29	−3.5
4.0	6.05	0.33	−0.48	5.57	0.50	−0.05	5.52	−4.0
4.5	6.20	0.40	−0.40	5.80	0.50	−0.05	5.75	−4.5
5.0	6.45	0.46	−0.34	6.11	0.55	−0.06	6.05	−5.0
5.5	6.67	0.51	−0.29	6.38	0.60	−0.07	6.31	−5.5
6.0	6.98	0.64	−0.19	6.79	0.75	−0.11	6.68	−6.0
6.5	7.31	0.72	−0.14	7.17	0.80	−0.12	7.05	−6.5
7.0	7.68	0.76	−0.12	7.56	0.85	−0.14	7.44	−7.0
7.5	8.06	0.81	−0.092	7.97	0.80	−0.12	7.85	−7.5
8.0	8.49	0.76	−0.12	8.37	0.65	−0.08	8.29	−8.0
8.5	8.82	0.55	−0.26	8.56	0.40	−0.03	8.53	−8.5
9.0	9.03	0.39	−0.41	8.62	0.14	0	8.62	−9.0
9.5	9.20	0.28	−0.55	8.65	0	0	8.65	−9.5
10.0	9.31	0.19	−0.72	8.59	0	0	8.59	−10.0
10.5	9.39	0.12	−0.92	8.47	0	0	8.47	−10.5
11.0	9.44	0.088	−1.06	8.38	0	0	8.38	−11.0

Table 4–I (continued)

From Loss Modulus

$\log \omega$	$\log G''$	$\dfrac{d \log G''}{d \log \omega}$	$1 - \left\| \dfrac{d \log G''}{d \log \omega} \right\|$	Prov. $\log H$	$\|m\|$	$\log B$	$\log \bar{H}$	$\log \tau$
1.5	4.82	0.28	−0.14	4.68	0.40	−0.07	4.61	−1.5
2.0	4.97	0.37	−0.20	4.77	0.40	−0.07	4.70	−2.0
2.5	5.19	0.45	−0.26	4.93	0.40	−0.07	4.86	−2.5
3.0	5.42	0.49	−0.29	5.13	0.40	−0.07	5.06	−3.0
3.5	5.68	0.56	−0.36	5.32	0.55	−0.04	5.28	−3.5
4.0	5.98	0.58	−0.38	5.60	0.50	−0.05	5.55	−4.0
4.5	6.22	0.61	−0.41	5.81	0.50	−0.05	5.76	−4.5
5.0	6.58	0.66	−0.47	6.11	0.55	−0.04	6.07	−5.0
5.5	6.90	0.67	−0.48	6.42	0.60	−0.03	6.39	−5.5
6.0	7.26	0.71	−0.54	6.72	0.75	−0.01	6.71	−6.0
6.5	7.63	0.73	−0.57	7.06	0.80	−0.01	7.05	−6.5
7.0	7.98	0.65	−0.46	7.52	0.85	0	7.52	−7.0
7.5	8.28	0.49	−0.29	7.99	0.80	−0.01	7.98	−7.5
8.0	8.55	0.44	−0.25	8.30	0.65	−0.02	8.28	−8.0
8.5	8.71	0.26	−0.13	8.58	0.40	−0.07	8.51	−8.5
9.0	8.81	0.12	−0.06	8.75	0.14	−0.14	8.61	−9.0
9.5	8.83	−0.05	−0.02	8.81	0	−0.20	8.61	−9.5
10.0	8.77	−0.14	−0.07	8.70	0	−0.20	8.50	−10.0
10.5	8.73	−0.10	−0.05	8.68	0	−0.20	8.48	−10.5
11.0	8.67	−0.03	−0.01	8.66	0	−0.20	8.46	−11.0
11.5	8.74	0.19	−0.09	8.65	0	−0.20	8.45	−11.5
12.0	8.87	0.36	−0.19	8.68	0	−0.20	8.48	−12.0

by K. Ninomiya. The $D(t)$ had been derived from measured values [24] of $E(t)$ by Hopkins and Hamming [25] with an exact calculation based on equation 36 of Chapter 3. The values of $E(t)$ obtained by the approximation can thus be compared with the original measured values, and are in most cases in very good agreement.

G. TABLES OF CORRECTION FACTORS AND PERFORATED CARDS

For convenience in calculation, Table 4–III gives values of the correction factors M, A, A', B, N, ψ, ψ', and $(\sin m\pi)/m\pi$ as functions of m. It will be recalled that, depending on the equation used, m is the negative slope of $\log H$ against $\log \tau$, the positive slope of $\log L$ against

Table 4–II

CALCULATION OF RELAXATION MODULUS OF POLYISOBUTYLENE FROM CREEP COMPLIANCE

The creep compliance in Column 2 has been derived by an exact calculation, using equation 36 of Chapter 3, from measured stress relaxation data (Column 7), which are compared with the results of the approximate calculations (Column 6).

1	2	3	4	5	6	7
			$\dfrac{\sin m\pi}{m\pi}$	$\dfrac{-\log}{}$ $\dfrac{\sin m\pi}{m\pi}$		$\log E(t)$
$\log t$	$-\log D(t)$	m			$\log E(t)$	Original
−14.0	10.47	0.048	0.995	0.002	10.46	10.46
−13.5	10.44	0.069	0.991	0.004	10.43	10.43
−13.0	10.40	0.101	0.982	0.008	10.39	10.39
−12.5	10.33	0.158	0.960	0.018	10.31	10.32
−12.0	10.23	0.224	0.919	0.037	10.19	10.20
−11.5	10.09	0.346	0.813	0.090	10.00	10.02
−11.0	9.90	0.438	0.712	0.147	9.75	9.77
−10.5	9.65	0.513	0.619	0.208	9.44	9.46
−10.0	9.38	0.566	0.549	0.260	9.12	9.12
−9.5	9.08	0.606	0.495	0.305	8.78	8.79
−9.0	8.77	0.630	0.462	0.335	8.44	8.47
−8.5	8.45	0.646	0.440	0.356	8.09	8.12
−8.0	8.13	0.634	0.456	0.341	7.79	7.80
−7.5	7.82	0.610	0.490	0.310	7.51	7.52
−7.0	7.52	0.546	0.578	0.238	7.28	7.29
−6.5	7.27	0.431	0.720	0.143	7.13	7.11
−6.0	7.08	0.294	0.862	0.064	7.02	7.00
−5.5	6.97	0.162	0.957	0.019	6.95	6.95
−5.0	6.92	0.074	0.990	0.004	6.91	6.91
−4.5	6.90	0.021	0.999	0.001	6.90	6.90
−4.0	6.89	0.024	0.999	0.001	6.89	6.89
−3.5	6.87	0.047	0.996	0.002	6.87	6.87
−3.0	6.84	0.069	0.991	0.004	6.84	6.84
−2.5	6.80	0.078	0.989	0.005	6.80	6.80
−2.0	6.76	0.087	0.987	0.006	6.75	6.75
−1.5	6.71	0.113	0.979	0.009	6.70	6.70
−1.0	6.64	0.156	0.960	0.018	6.62	6.62
−0.5	6.55	0.205	0.933	0.030	6.52	6.53
0	6.43	0.270	0.883	0.054	6.38	6.39
0.5	6.28	0.337	0.821	0.086	6.19	6.21
1.0	6.09	0.432	0.719	0.143	5.95	5.97
1.5	5.84	0.553	0.568	0.246	5.60	5.61
2.0	5.54	0.690	0.381	0.419	5.12	5.15

Table 4–III

FUNCTIONS OF THE LOGARITHMIC SLOPE m USED IN
APPROXIMATION CALCULATIONS

m	M	A	A'	B	N	ψ	ψ'	$\dfrac{\sin m\pi}{m\pi}$	m
−1.1							−0.639		−1.1
−1.0		0.637		1.000			−0.571		−1.0
−0.9		0.699		0.996			−0.521		−0.9
−0.8		0.757		0.984			−0.487		−0.8
−0.7		0.810		0.963			−0.464		−0.7
−0.6		0.858		0.936	1.757		−0.453		−0.6
−0.5		0.900		0.900	1.324		−0.449		−0.5
−0.4	0.672	0.936		0.858	1.052		−0.454		−0.4
−0.3	0.771	0.963		0.810	0.868		−0.468		−0.3
−0.2	0.859	0.984		0.757	0.737		−0.492		−0.2
−0.1	0.935	0.996		0.699	0.645		−0.527		−0.1
0	1.000	1.000		0.637	0.577	−0.577		1.000	0
0.1	1.051	0.996		0.699	0.527	−0.649		0.984	0.1
0.2	1.089	0.984		0.757	0.493	−0.737		0.935	0.2
0.3	1.114	0.963		0.810	0.470	−0.864		0.859	0.3
0.4	1.127	0.936		0.858	0.454	−1.050		0.756	0.4
0.5	1.128	0.900		0.900	0.449	−1.323		0.637	0.5
0.6	1.119	0.858		0.936	0.672	0.454	−1.755	0.499	0.6
0.7	1.101	0.810		0.963	0.771	0.465		0.368	0.7
0.8	1.074	0.757		0.984	0.859	0.488		0.234	0.8
0.9	1.040	0.699		0.996	0.935	0.523		0.109	0.9
1.0	1.000	0.637	0.637	1.000	1.000	0.571			1.0
1.1	0.956		0.699	0.996	1.050	0.640			1.1
1.2	0.908		0.757	0.984	1.089	0.732			1.2
1.3	0.857		0.810	0.963	1.114	0.866			1.3
1.4	0.805		0.858	0.936	1.127	1.057			1.4
1.5	0.753		0.900	0.900	1.128	1.336			1.5
1.6	0.700		0.936	0.858	1.119	1.783			1.6
1.7	0.647		0.963	0.810	1.100				1.7
1.8	0.597		0.984	0.757	1.074				1.8
1.9	0.547		0.996	0.699	1.040				1.9
2.0	0.500		1.000	0.637	1.000				2.0
Used in equations:	4	9 15	10 16	20 25 37 38	52	44	45	41	

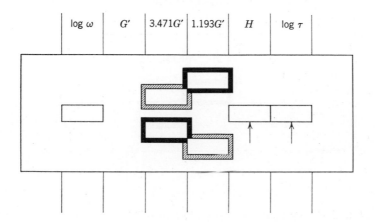

FIG. 4–1. Perforated guide card for calculating H from G' by equation 14, with a **log** a spacing of 0.2. Adding the numbers in the black-bordered holes and subtracting those in the shaded-bordered holes gives H, whereas $\log \tau = -\log \omega$.

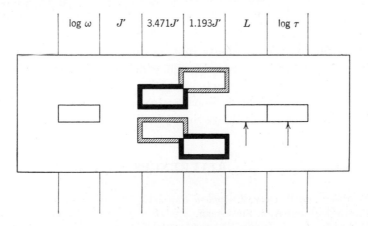

FIG. 4–2. Perforated guide card for calculating L from J' by equation 19, with a **log** a spacing of 0.2. Addition and subtraction as in Fig. 1–1.

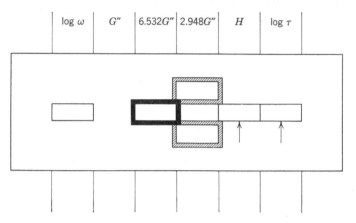

FIG. 4–3. Perforated guide card for calculating H from G'' or L from J'' (for the latter, J'' is substituted for G'' throughout) by equations 24 and 28 respectively, with a $\log a$ spacing of 0.2. Addition and subtraction as in Fig. 1–1.

$\log \tau$, the positive slope of $\log J(t)$ against $\log t$, or the negative slope of $\log G(t)$ against $\log t$.

The Ninomiya-Ferry calculations can be expedited by preparing tables of the initial data at frequencies spaced on the logarithmic scale by the interval $\log a$, with parallel columns multiplied by the constant factors which appear in the equations, and covering them with perforated guide cards through which certain numbers are revealed to be added or subtracted, together with a blank for recording the result. The cards corresponding to equations 14 and 19, and 24 and 28 which are identical, are shown in Figs. 4–1 to 4–3.

REFERENCES

1. T. Alfrey and P. Doty, *J. Applied Phys.*, **16,** 700 (1945).
2. F. Schwarzl and A. J. Staverman, *Appl. Sci. Research*, **A4,** 127 (1953).
3. H. Leaderman, *J. Applied Phys.*, **25,** 294 (1954).
4. M. Okano, *Busseiron Kenkyu*, **3,** 493 (1958).
5. H. Fujita, *J. Applied Phys.*, **29,** 943 (1958).
6. K. Ninomiya and J. D. Ferry, *J. Colloid Sci.*, **14,** 36 (1959).
7. R. D. Andrews, *Ind. Eng. Chem.*, **44,** 707 (1952).
8. J. D. Ferry and M. L. Williams, *J. Colloid Sci.*, **7,** 347 (1952).
9. F. C. Roesler, *Proc. Phys. Soc.*, **B68,** 89 (1955).
10. D. M. Stern, Ph.D. Thesis, University of Wisconsin, 1957.

11. H. Leaderman, in F. R. Eirich, *Rheology,* Vol. II, Academic Press, New York, 1958.
12. M. L. Williams and J. D. Ferry, *J. Polymer Sci.,* **11,** 169 (1953).
13. F. C. Roesler and W. A. Twyman, *Proc. Phys. Soc.,* **B68,** 97 (1955).
14. F. C. Roesler, private communication, "The Relaxation Spectrum of Polyvinyl Acetate," 1955.
15. T. L. Smith, *Trans. Soc. Rheology,* **2,** 131 (1958).
16. E. Catsiff and A. V. Tobolsky, *J. Colloid Sci.,* **10,** 375 (1955).
17. D. J. Plazek, *J. Colloid Sci.,* **15,** 50 (1960).
18. C. Zener, *Elasticity and Anelasticity of Metals,* Chicago University Press, 1948.
19. J. J. Benbow, *Proc. Phys. Soc.,* **B69,** 885 (1956).
20. A. J. Staverman and F. Schwarzl, in H. A. Stuart, *Die Physik der Hochpolymeren,* Vol. IV, Chapter 1, Springer-Verlag, 1956.
21. F. W. Schremp, J. D. Ferry, and W. W. Evans, *J. Applied Phys.,* **22,** 711 (1951).
22. W. Dannhauser, W. C. Child, Jr., and J. D. Ferry, *J. Colloid Sci.,* **13,** 103 (1958).
23. J. W. Berge, P. R. Saunders, and J. D. Ferry, *J. Colloid Sci.,* **14,** 135 (1959).
24. A. V. Tobolsky and E. Catsiff, *J. Polymer Sci.,* **19,** 111 (1956).
25. I. L. Hopkins and R. W. Hamming, *J. Applied Phys.,* **28,** 906 (1957).

CHAPTER **5**

Experimental Methods for Viscoelastic Liquids

We now devote several chapters to the experimental determination of the viscoelastic functions whose general forms have been surveyed in Chapter 2 and whose interrelationships, according to the linear phenomenological theory, have been summarized in Chapters 3 and 4.

The viscoelastic functions relate stresses to strains. Experiments, however, do not measure stresses and strains directly but rather forces and displacements. The calculation of a modulus or compliance therefrom always involves a form factor which depends on the size and shape of the sample and the distribution of stresses and strains within it; the absolute accuracy of the results is often limited by this form factor or sample coefficient.

Experimental methods depend greatly on the consistencies of the materials to be studied, and are classified accordingly in the next five chapters. Strictly, a category such as "viscoelastic liquids," the subject of the present chapter, is meaningless since viscoelastic bodies are neither liquid nor solid; but it serves to identify materials which are sufficiently liquidlike that they must be supported in containers to avoid flowing under the action of gravity during an experiment. Such materials include polymers of quite low molecular weight above their glass transition temperatures, concentrated polymer solutions, and also very dilute polymer solutions whose properties are only slightly different from those of the corresponding pure solvents. Some of the methods are transient, others dynamic in character. In this chapter, they all deal with deformation in shear.

A. CREEP

1. Apparatus Geometry

The usual geometry for creep measurements on a viscoelastic liquid is shear between coaxial cylinders [1,2] or between a cone and plate,[3] as shown in Fig. 5–1. If a constant torque $\mathcal{S}$ is applied and the angle of rotation α is measured as a function of time, then

$$J(t) = b\alpha(t)/\mathcal{S} \tag{1}$$

where the form factor b (units cm^3) is given approximately by $4\pi L/ (1/R_1^2 - 1/R_2^2)$ for coaxial cylinders and $2\pi R^3/3\theta$ for cone and plate. Here L is the depth of liquid between cylinders, and R_1 and R_2 their radii; R is the radius of the cone-plate assembly, and θ the angle of the gap. Corrections for end effects in coaxial cylinders [4] and for various types of misalignment of the cone and plate [3] have been considered by various authors in considerable detail.

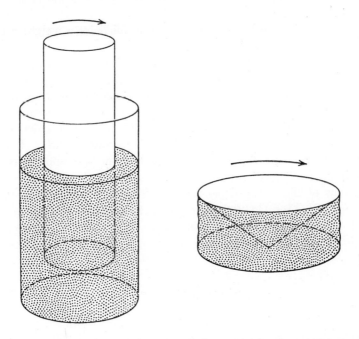

FIG. 5–1. Coaxial cylinder and cone-and-plate geometry for measurements on viscoelastic liquids.

A table of form factors b, relating experimentally measured quantities (force, torque, displacement, angular displacement, etc.) to viscoelastic functions for a variety of sample geometries is given in Appendix C at the end of the book. Formulas for the maximum strain and stress within the sample are also included.

The coaxial cylinder geometry has the disadvantage that the strain and rate of strain are not homogeneous throughout the sample, but decrease from the inner cylinder outwards; for example, for a Newtonian liquid the rate of strain at radius r ($R_1 < r < R_2$) is $(d\alpha/dt)(2/r^2)/(1/R_1{}^2 - 1/R_2{}^2)$. For non-Newtonian liquids, the distribution of rate of strain is more complicated.[5] As long as the stresses are very small, this disadvantage is not particularly serious, but of more concern is the normal stress effect, which distorts the sample geometry (see the following section). A coaxial cylinder apparatus is also difficult to fill if the steady-flow viscosity of the liquid is very high (*e.g.*, $> 10^5$ poises). In the cone and plate geometry, the strain and rate of strain are homogeneous throughout the sample, and distortions due to the normal stress effect are less serious. However, the sample is exposed on its periphery, and, if its composition includes a volatile solvent, evaporation is difficult to control.

A constant torque is most commonly applied by a weight attached to a pulley, and the rotation is followed by light reflected from a mirror on the rotating cylinder to a scale, photoelectric cell, or other measuring device.[1,6] The instantaneous application of torque as implied in the definition of $J(t)$ cannot of course be strictly achieved, and if it requires a time t_1 for the torque to reach its maximum value then the measurements are not significant for direct calculation of $J(t)$ until somewhat later, perhaps of the order of $10t_1$. If sudden application of torque produces oscillations in the apparatus, these must be allowed to die out before measurements begin.

In view of the strong dependence of viscoelastic properties on temperature (Chapter 11), control of temperature is important in this as in all other viscoelastic measurements. In particular, heat must not be allowed to leak into the system through the mechanical connection used to apply the torque.

2. Non-Linear Effects

In steady-state flow of polymeric systems, significant deviations from Newtonian behavior occur at moderate stresses; they may often be roughly gauged as of the order of a few per cent when the stress in dynes/cm^2 is 10^4c, c being the concentration in g. polymer per cc. solution (for an undiluted polymer, equal to the density). The apparent viscosity, or ratio of stress to rate of strain, falls steadily with increasing stress and can be in general represented by a power series in even powers of the stress.[7] (Empirically, the first power sometimes enters in the fitting of data,[8] although odd powers are physically inadmissible.) In model language, the dashpots of Fig. 1–2 are non-Newtonian dashpots whose rates of deformation increase more rapidly with stress than directly proportional. In molecular terms, the flexible polymer molecules rotate during flow and are subjected to periodic hydrodynamic distortions which resemble to some extent those imposed by periodic macroscopic deformations with *small* strains. At high rates of rotation, the failure of some modes of configurational rearrangements to keep pace with the periodic changes in hydrodynamic forces causes relatively less energy to be dissipated, just as there is less dissipated per cycle at high frequencies in a dynamic experiment. Accordingly, the apparent viscosity falls with increasing rate of shear. At the same time, the directions of the principal macroscopic stresses change.[9]

It is evident from a variety of experiments [10–12] that the steady-flow apparent viscosity as a function of shear rate, $\dot{\gamma}$, closely resembles the real part of the complex dynamic viscosity, η', as a function of radian frequency, ω. It is perhaps even closer [13] to the reciprocal of the dynamic fluidity, $1/\omega J''(\omega)$, or [14] to the absolute value, $|\eta^*| = (\eta'^2 + \eta''^2)^{1/2}$, as a function of ω. Thus non-linear steady-flow viscosity measurements appear to reflect qualitatively the same molecular phenomena which underlie *linear* time-dependent or viscoelastic measurements. However, the theory of non-Newtonian flow of polymers [13, 15–17] has not advanced to the stage where molecular parameters can be obtained from such measurements with certainty.

For present purposes, it is sufficient to note that the stresses in creep experiments should be sufficiently small to keep non-Newtonian deviations negligible, in order to have not only the steady-flow viscosity η but also the whole course of the function $J(t)$ independent of applied stress. These requirements can be tested, of course, by successive experiments with the constant torque chosen at different values.

Not only may the flow be non-Newtonian, but the steady-state elastic compliance J_e may be non-Hookean at larger stresses. Indeed, at finite elastic strains in polymeric systems, substantial deviations from Hooke's law arise (Chapter 13). But these can also be avoided, in general, in creep experiments again by keeping the maximum stresses ($\mathfrak{T}$) below the order of 10^4c in dynes/cm². (Between coaxial cylinders, the maximum stress will be at the inner cylinder wall, given by $S/2\pi LR_1^2$.) The maximum elastic strain will be given by $\mathfrak{T}J_e$ and this is what determines deviations from Hookean elasticity; it should not exceed perhaps 0.1. The total strain, $\mathfrak{T}J(t)$, may safely be much larger, if it is mostly due to the flow term $\mathfrak{T}t/\eta$.

3. The Normal Stress Effect

Another consequence of finite elastic strains in polymeric systems is the appearance of stresses perpendicular to those imposed in a given simple deformation, which must be balanced by additional forces from the outside to prevent distortion of the sample. Specifically, in steady flow of a viscoelastic liquid between coaxial cylinders, normal stresses appear parallel to the cylinder axes, and these cause the liquid to rise near the inner cylinder (Fig. 5–2). This phenomenon [18] is of considerable interest for its own sake, and is related to the storage of elastic energy and thus indirectly to the results of viscoelastic measurements at small strains.[9,10,12] But to achieve a simple calculation of $J(t)$ it must be avoided, again by keeping the stresses small. To make sure of its absence by visual inspection, a transparent coaxial cylinder apparatus is desirable.[1] When the ubiquitous requirement of small stresses is combined with a high viscosity, it becomes necessary to measure very small angles of deformation.

4. Analysis of Creep to Obtain η and J_e

If a polymeric system has a low enough viscosity to be classified as a viscoelastic liquid, there will ordinarily be no difficulty in achieving steady-state flow within a finite time, so the creep curve can be analyzed to obtain η and J_e as in equation 25 of Chapter 1 and Fig. 1–12. However, it is easy to be misled into believing prematurely that the linear portion has been reached; in general, the curve cannot be expected to become linear until the flow term t/η is at least as large as the intercept J_e. It is always desirable to perform the recovery experiment shown in Fig. 1–12 to confirm the calculation.

Another order-of-magnitude rule is that J_e is often of the order of $10^{-5}/c$ in cm²/dyne, and the time required to achieve steady-state flow is greater than $10^{-5}\eta/c$. This sets both upper and lower limits on the practicality of creep measurements depending on the magnitude of the steady-flow viscosity. In particular, for low viscosities (dilute

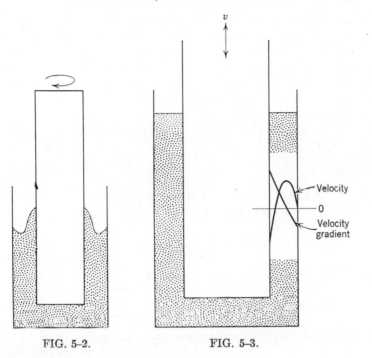

FIG. 5-2.   FIG. 5-3.

FIG. 5-2. Illustration of normal stress effect in the shear of a viscoelastic liquid between coaxial cylinders.
FIG. 5-3. Annular pumping geometry for measurements on viscoelastic liquids; profile of velocity and velocity gradient.

polymer solutions), the time scale is so short that the viscoelastic behavior is obscured by inertial effects. In such cases dynamic experiments are essential.

B. STRESS RELAXATION

For viscoelastic liquids it is usually not convenient to measure stress relaxation after sudden imposition of strain, because the stresses developed are so small. However, stress relaxation after cessation of steady-state flow can be followed, with subsequent analysis by equations 61 of Chapter 3 and 52 of Chapter 4. The geometry may be again either coaxial cylinders,[19] cone and plate, or two cones with different apex angles.[20, 21] After cessation of flow, the member which was originally rotating is held fixed and the torque exerted at rest is measured by a suitable sensing device such as a strain gauge, differential transformer, or simply the untwisting of a very stiff torque element between the system and a rigid clamp. Actually, any of these devices must admit a very small motion within the sample, since the measurement actually determines a strain to which the torque is proportional; but it is sufficient to keep the motion of the measuring element much smaller than the angle corresponding to γ_e, the elastic strain during steady-state flow $(= J_e\mathfrak{T}_{ss})$.

C. DIRECT MEASUREMENTS OF SINUSOIDALLY VARYING STRESS AND STRAIN

The remaining sections treat periodic or dynamic measurements. The simplest method for following the response of a viscoelastic system to sinusoidally varying stresses is to trace out the stress and the resulting strain as functions of time, corresponding to Fig. 1–8. The ratio of peak stress to peak strain is $|G^*|$; and the distance between them on the time scale, multiplied by the frequency ω, is the phase angle δ in radians. Then G' and G'' can be obtained by equations 9 and 10 of Chapter 1. With viscoelastic liquids, the loss component is more often calculated as η' $(= G''/\omega)$, because of the connection between η' and the steady-flow viscosity η which it approaches at vanishing frequency.

For viscoelastic liquids with suitable characteristics, this experiment can be made with the usual coaxial cylinder geometry and periodic rotation through a very small angle.[22, 23] The principal requirement is that the gap between the cylinders be small compared with the wavelength of a shear wave propagated in the medium; as will be seen in a later section, the latter is approximately $(G'/\rho)^{1/2}/\nu$, where ρ is the density of the liquid, so the upper limit of the frequency range is set by the magnitude of G'. In principle, there are no limits to the value of tan δ which can be measured, but in practice it is difficult to determine δ with sufficient precision both near 0° and near 90°. In the former case G'' and η' are uncertain, and $G' \cong |G^*|$; and in the latter, G' is correspondingly uncertain. In an apparatus of De Witt and associates,[22] the torque is traced by light from the mirror of a galvanometer in series with an electrical drive, and the angular motion is traced by light from a mirror mounted on the cylinder itself. To calculate G' and η' from these periodic functions, it is necessary to take into account not only the cylinder dimensions as with equation 1 but also the moment of inertia of the inner cylinder and the torsional stiffness of the wire by which it is suspended.

A somewhat different method of performing the experiment with periodic rotation is to suspend the inner cylinder from a wire of known torsional stiffness and rotate the outer cylinder periodically with a known angular amplitude.[24] The ratio of the angular amplitudes of the two cylinders, then, and the phase angle between them, ϕ, are related to the desired quantities $|G^*|$ and tan δ (or G' and G'', or G' and η', etc.). The relations involve again not only the dimensions of the cylinders but also the torsional stiffness of the suspension wire and the moment of inertia of the inner cylinder. The equations are somewhat complicated,[24] and may be further elaborated [25] to include the inertia of the liquid when the gap between the cylinders is an appreciable fraction of the shear wavelength $(G'/\rho)^{1/2}/\nu$. A variety of moments of inertia and suspension wires can expand the range of frequencies and consistencies over which measurements of reasonable precision can be made. The frequency range is from 5 to 100 cycles/sec. in this apparatus, also described by De Witt and associates.[24]

An alternative type of motion with coaxial cylinders which may be described as annular pumping is illustrated in Fig. 5–3. Downward motion of the inner cylinder forces the liquid up and through the annulus, with the profiles of velocity and velocity gradient shown. The amplitude of the periodic vertical motion is too small to alter the depth of immersion perceptibly. At low frequencies where the inertia of the moving system has a negligible effect, the stress and strain are simply proportional to the force $\mathbf{f}$ and displacement $\mathbf{x}$; from equations 9 and 10 of Chapter 1 it follows that

$$G' = (|\mathbf{f}|/b|\mathbf{x}|) \cos \delta \tag{2}$$

$$\eta' = (|\mathbf{f}|/\omega b|\mathbf{x}|) \sin \delta \tag{3}$$

where the absolute values are the peak magnitudes of $\mathbf{f}$ and $\mathbf{x}$, and the form factor b (units cm) is given by [26, 27]

$$b = \frac{2\pi L(R_2{}^2 + R_1{}^2)/(R_2{}^2 + R_1{}^2)}{(R_2{}^2 + R_1{}^2) \ln (R_2/R_1)/(R_2{}^2 - R_1{}^2) - 1} \tag{4}$$

R_1 and R_2 being as usual the radii of the cylinders and L the depth of immersion. If the gap between the cylinders is an appreciable fraction of the shear wavelength, an elaboration of equations 2 to 4 which takes into account the inertia of the liquid may be employed.[25]

None of these treatments considers in detail end effects at the bottom of the cylinders; for the best absolute results, it may be desirable to calibrate such apparatus with an oil of known viscosity, for which there is no elastic component. For the annular pumping, for example, then $\eta = |f|/\omega b|x|$.

Thus from the peak values of force and displacement and the phase angle between them the desired viscoelastic properties can be calculated. In the elegant apparatus of Philippoff,[28] electrical potentials proportional to f and x are delivered by differential transformers, and are applied to the horizontal and vertical plates of an oscilloscope, thus tracing an ellipse which can be photographed and from whose geometry G' and η' can be obtained. The frequency range is from 3×10^{-5} to 10 cycles/sec., this apparatus being especially suitable for extremely low frequencies.

D. TRANSDUCER MEASUREMENTS OF STRESS/STRAIN RATIOS

If a periodic stressing device such as those described in the preceding section is driven electrically by an electromechanical converter (transducer), for example a coil carrying alternating current in a magnetic field, the system reacts back on the driver in such a way that electrical measurements on the latter serve to determine the desired mechanical properties. The electrical measurements, usually of resistance and capacity, can be made with ease and precision even when the amplitude of motion is extremely small.

The viscoelastic functions are again related to the force and displacement of the moving system, but at the higher frequencies involved here the inertia of the apparatus is important and the relations are more complicated than equations 2 and 3. For linear motion, such as in the annular pumping geometry, it is convenient to define a complex ratio of the force acting on the sample (f) to its velocity ($v = dx/dt$), called the mechanical impedance:

$$Z_M = f/v \tag{5}$$

Here v is not written as a complex quantity, because it is taken in phase with the real part of f. The impedance has a real (in phase with v) component R_M and an imaginary component X_M, the mechanical resistance and reactance respectively.

The mechanical resistance depends on η' and whatever viscous effect $R_M{}^0$ may be associated with moving parts of the apparatus:

$$R_M = b\eta' + R_M{}^0 \tag{6}$$

whereas the reactance depends on G', the mass M of the moving system, and the mechanical elastance $S_M{}^0$ (force per unit displacement in the direction of motion) of the mountings of the moving unit:

$$X_M = \omega M - bG'/\omega - S_M{}^0/\omega \tag{7}$$

Here b is the form factor in cm which depends on the geometry of the sample.

We have now to show how R_M and X_M can be obtained from electrical measurements. For example, the annular pumping device illustrated in Fig. 5–3 can be driven [27] by a coil in a magnetic field of flux density B carrying a current $\mathbf{i}$. The force exerted on the mechanical system is $\mathbf{f} = Bl\mathbf{i}$, where l is the length of wire in the coil. The system will respond with a velocity $v = \mathbf{f}/\mathbf{Z_M}$, in accordance with equation 5. The motion of the coil will generate a back emf given by $e = Blv$. The applied emf is $\mathbf{Z_0i}$ where $\mathbf{Z_0}$ is the electrical impedance of the coil at rest; the total emf is $\mathbf{Z_0i} + e = \mathbf{Zi}$, where $\mathbf{Z}$ is the electrical impedance of the coil measured while in motion. Thus [29]

$$(\mathbf{Z} - \mathbf{Z_0})\mathbf{i} = Blv = (Bl)^2\mathbf{i}/\mathbf{Z_M} \tag{8}$$

The impedances $\mathbf{Z}$ and $\mathbf{Z_0}$ (i.e., their real and imaginary components, the resistances R and R_0 and the reactances X and X_0) can be measured electrically by placing the driving coil in one arm of an impedance bridge (Fig. 5–4), and the components of the mechanical impedance are calculated by difference. Separation into real and imaginary parts yields:

$$R_M = \frac{(Bl)^2(R - R_0)}{(R - R_0)^2 + (X - X_0)^2} \tag{9}$$

$$X_M = \frac{-(Bl)^2(X - X_0)}{(R - R_0)^2 + (X - X_0)^2} \tag{10}$$

Thus, once the apparatus is calibrated, only electrical measurements are necessary. The key to the calibration is M, the mass of the moving unit—the coil and inner cylinder. The constant $(Bl)^2$ can be determined from the frequency dependence of $(X - X_0)/[(R - R_0)^2 + (X - X_0)^2]$ with no sample present; in this case $G' = 0$ in equation 7 and the above quantity times ω plotted against ω^2 gives a straight line whose slope is $M/(Bl)^2$ and intercept $S_M{}^0/(Bl)^2$. The impedance components at rest, R_0 and X_0, can in principle be determined by electrical measurements with the coil clamped, but this can only be accomplished with very strong clamping.[30] Otherwise, R_0 and X_0 can be eliminated from simultaneous equations corresponding to two or more successive sets of measurements in which some parameter is varied at constant frequency.

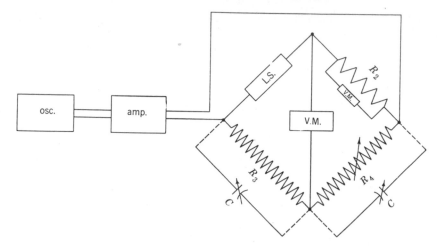

FIG. 5–4. Impedance bridge for electromagnetic transducer. The capacity C can be connected in either of two positions depending on whether the reactance of the coil (L.S.) is capacitive (parallel with R_3) or inductive (parallel with R_4). V.M. = voltmeter.

If M is varied (by attaching additional masses to the moving system), the locus of X vs. R is a circle; R_M and X_M can be obtained from the circle geometry without knowledge of the magnitudes of the masses. Finally, G' and η' are calculated by equations 6 and 7.

This transducer method has been utilized up to frequencies of several hundred cycles/sec. For a given mass and polymer consistency, there is a resonance frequency at which $X_M = 0$ because of cancellation of terms in equation 7; near this, the impedance bridge balance is sensitive and difficult. On the other hand, at frequencies too far from the resonance on either side, the differences in R and X become too small to measure accurately.

It is characteristic of the method that neither forces nor displacements are measured directly, but rather complex force/displacement (or force/velocity) ratios, in terms of complex voltage/current ratios (*i.e.*, impedances). Thus the stresses and amplitudes of motion can be kept exceedingly small, with two advantages: deviations from linear viscoelastic behavior can be avoided, and there is no concern about temperature changes from heat dissipation at high frequencies. The magnitude of the maximum force can be obtained from the driving current, but is not needed for calculations. On the other hand, variation of the driving current provides a sensitive test of whether the viscoelastic behavior is truly linear; if the impedance bridge is balanced at one current level, it should remain balanced when the current is increased say tenfold.   In making transducer measurements, this test is used routinely.

A warning should be added that because of the small amplitudes of motion in the sample there is a risk of falsification by small vibrations or lack of complete rigidity in the apparatus itself.   Careful design and tests with materials of known properties can eliminate this danger.

E. WAVE PROPAGATION

The methods described in Sections C and D are appropriate only to cases where the distance between the surfaces confining the sample is small compared with $(G'/\rho)^{1/2}/\nu$.   At the other extreme, at lower rigidities or higher frequencies, the thickness of the sample is large compared with the wavelength of a shear wave, and transverse waves are propagated from the moving surface.   The dynamic viscoelastic functions can then be obtained by observing the effects of the waves.

In viscoelastic liquids, shear waves are always substantially damped.   If the damping is not too severe, so that a train of several maxima and minima is perceptible, the wavelength and attenuation can be measured directly, as described in this section.   On the other hand, the characteristic impedance methods to be described in Section F are applicable when the damping is too high or the wavelength too short for direct perception.

For a shear wave traveling under conditions where it approximates a one-dimensional disturbance in the x direction, the damping is exponential and the amplitude (shear displacement, u) can be represented as

$$u = u_0 e^{i(\omega t - 2\pi x/\lambda) - x/x_0} \tag{11}$$

where λ is the wavelength and x_0 is the distance within which the amplitude falls off by a factor $1/e$ (Fig. 5–5).   The attenuation α in nepers/cm is $1/x_0$; the velocity v in cm/sec. is $\omega\lambda/2\pi = \nu\lambda$.   The complex propagation constant used in discussions of acoustics [31] is

$$\Gamma = A + iB = 1/x_0 + 2\pi i/\lambda = \rho\omega^2/(G' + i\omega\eta')^{1/2} \tag{12}$$

where ρ is again the density of the medium.   The acoustic attenuation in decibels/cm is 8.686α.

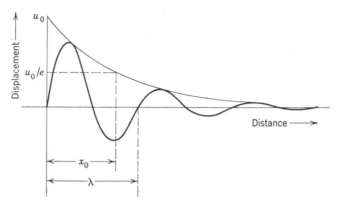

FIG. 5–5. Exponentially damped shear wave with definitions of characteristic parameters (from Ref. 34).

From measurements of the wavelength and attenuation the components of the complex shear modulus can be calculated by the following equations [32]

$$G' = \frac{\omega^2 \lambda^2 \rho [4\pi^2 - (\lambda/x_0)^2]}{[4\pi^2 + (\lambda/x_0)^2]^2} \tag{13}$$

$$\eta' = \frac{4\pi\omega\lambda^2\rho(\lambda/x_0)}{[4\pi^2 + (\lambda/x_0)^2]^2} \tag{14}$$

or in different form,[33]

$$G' = \rho v^2 (1 - r^2)/(1 + r^2)^2 \tag{15}$$

$$G'' = 2\rho v^2 r/(1 + r^2)^2 \tag{16}$$

where $r = \lambda/2\pi x_0 = \alpha\lambda/2\pi$. It is clear from equations 13 and 15 that if the damping per wavelength is small, the attenuation enters the calculation of G' only as a minor correction; hence the approximate relation stated previously that $\lambda \cong (G'/\rho)^{1/2}/\nu$, i.e., $v \cong (G'/\rho)^{1/2}$. For convenience, an auxiliary parameter $\tilde{G} = \rho v^2$ (the "wave rigidity modulus") is sometimes calculated and then subsequently converted to G' by the correction factor shown plotted in Fig. 5–6, for which only a rough estimate of the damping is needed. The frequency dependence of $\tilde{G}$ corresponding to certain mechanical models has been calculated,[34] and has been useful for analyzing measurements in which only the wavelength and not the damping was provided.[35] On the other hand, η' and G'' are directly proportional to the attenuation and require a precise determination of the latter.

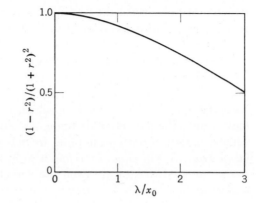

FIG. 5-6. Plot of the correction factor $(1 - r^2)/(1 + r^2)^2$ in equation 13 against λ/x_0 (*i.e.*, $2\pi r$).

Experimentally, a disturbance approximating a plane shear wave can be set up by vibrating a plate in a rectangular vessel [36,37] (Fig. 5-7); and, provided the viscoelastic liquid is transparent and becomes birefringent with straining, the wave can be observed and photographed stroboscopically using a suitable optical system (Figs. 5-8 and 5-9). (The displacements seen in the optical pattern are not directly proportional to the shear strain, but are proportional to the arctangents of the relative retardation (phase difference) in the com-

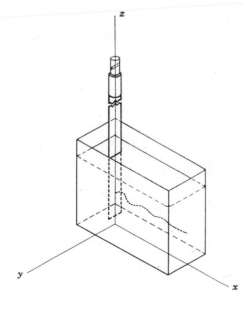

FIG. 5-7. Shear wave propagation in a rectangular vessel (from Ref. 32).

ponents of polarized light passing through the strained medium. The relative retardation is assumed to be proportional in turn to the shear strain.)

The effects of the container walls in the arrangement of Fig. 5–7 have been investigated theoretically.[32] The deviations from the one-dimensional wave assumed in equations 11–16 are not serious unless the damping λ/x_0 is rather small, in which case reflections from the walls may cause the observed damping to appear erroneously magnified. This situation is not encountered in polymeric liquids, though it may be in gels. At the other extreme, if λ/x_0 is too large, the wave will be too attenuated to measure even the wavelength; an upper limit would ordinarily be $\lambda/x_0 = 3$. It may be noted from equations 13 and 14 that, when the damping is small, $\lambda/x_0 \cong \pi G''/G'$, so this limit corresponds roughly to a loss tangent of unity.

The shear wave method described here has been used at frequencies from 4 to 5000 cycles/sec. Its most important advantage is that no dimensions of the sample need be known; there is no form factor b such as enters into the calculations of all the methods previously described. At much higher frequencies, bulk longitudinal waves can be

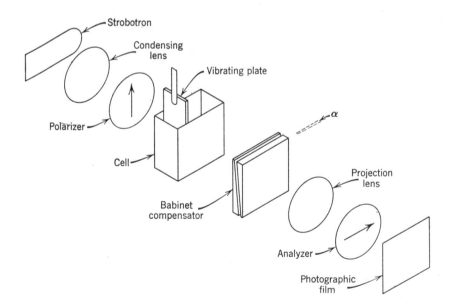

FIG. 5–8. Apparatus for following shear wave propagation by stroboscopic photoelastic observation.

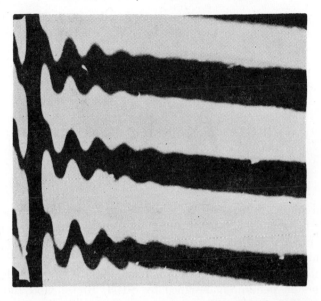

FIG. 5–9. Photograph of a wave of shear strain double refraction in a 1.0% solution of sodium deoxyribonucleate at 25°C., frequency 125 cycles/sec. The driving plate is oscillated vertically; shear waves propagated to the right horizontally produce patterns of strain double refraction. Each boundary between black and white provides the same information; the inclination of the base lines is given by the angle α in Fig. 5–8.

propagated in polymeric liquids, and these yield indirectly some information about shear properties. Since their behavior is dominated by the bulk compressional viscoelasticity, however, discussion of them will be postponed to a later chapter.

F. CHARACTERISTIC IMPEDANCE MEASUREMENTS

When a shear wave is generated in a viscoelastic liquid by a surface oscillating in its own plane, and the damping is very high and/or the wavelength is very short, the disturbance is oblivious of the confines of the vessel and is effectively being propagated in a medium of infinite extent. The complex force/velocity ratio at the driving surface, or characteristic impedance (mechanical impedance per unit area) is nevertheless related to the viscoelastic properties of the medium, though not by a simple factor of proportionality; the density of the medium plays an important role. The in-phase ($\mathfrak{R}_M$) and out-of-phase ($\mathfrak{X}_M$) components of the characteristic impedance are related to G' and G'' by the equations [38]

$$\mathfrak{R}_M = (\rho/2)^{\frac{1}{2}}(\sqrt{G'^2 + G''^2} + G')^{\frac{1}{2}} \tag{17}$$

$$\mathfrak{X}_M = (\rho/2)^{\frac{1}{2}}(\sqrt{G'^2 + G''^2} - G')^{\frac{1}{2}} \tag{18}$$

and so G' and η' can be obtained by rearrangement in the form

$$G' = (\mathfrak{R}_M{}^2 - \mathfrak{X}_M{}^2)/\rho \tag{19}$$

$$\eta' = 2\mathfrak{R}_M \mathfrak{X}_M/\omega\rho \tag{20}$$

Measurement of $\mathfrak{R}_M$ and $\mathfrak{X}_M$ is not so easy, and the means thus far available have a disadvantage not possessed by any of the preceding methods in this chapter: the frequency cannot be varied continuously, but is limited to a few discrete values.

For moderately low frequencies, from 200 to 2500 cycles/sec., a hollow torsion pendulum designed by Sittel, Rouse, and Bailey [39] has been used (Fig. 5–10). The viscoelastic liquid fills the sample holder

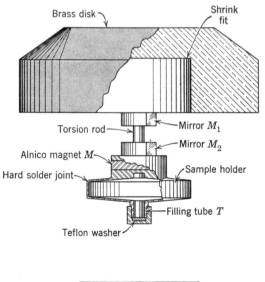

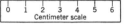

FIG. 5–10. Hollow torsion pendulum of Sittel, Rouse, and Bailey.

and is subjected to periodic motion near the inside surface when the holder is excited in free torsional oscillations with a very small amplitude. The wavelength is so small that the geometry is negligibly different from that of plane surfaces. The torsional oscillations of the pendulum are characterized by a frequency and a logarithmic decrement in amplitude which can be measured by reflection of a light beam from the mirrors shown. These quantities are influenced by the mechanical loading at the liquid surface, and from them $\Re_M$ and $\Re_M$ can be derived. There are two apparatus constants which could in principle be calculated from geometry and other measurable quantities, but in practice are determined by calibration with liquids of known viscosity. (It will be noted from equations 19 and 20 that for a purely viscous liquid $\Re_M = \Re_M$ and $\eta = 2\Re_M{}^2/\omega\rho$.) It is necessary to use a separate torsion rod for each frequency desired.

At higher frequencies, of the order of 20,000 to 100,000 cycles/sec., cylindrical piezoelectric crystals of quartz have been used by Mason [38] and others [40] to execute torsional oscillations while immersed in the liquid to be studied. The geometry of the disturbance at the surface can usually again be approximated by plane waves, though the cylindrical features can be taken into account by more complicated calculations.[41] In this case we have a piezoelectric transducer and the experimental measurements are electrical: the resonant frequency and electrical resistance of the crystal at resonance are measured first in a vacuum and then while immersed in the liquid, and $\Re_M$ and $\Re_M$ are calculated from the differences.[31, 38] Then G' and η' are obtained in turn from equations 19 and 20. A separate crystal is usually employed for each frequency desired, though one higher frequency harmonic has also been utilized. This method is ideal for very dilute polymer solutions, but becomes inapplicable when the viscosity exceeds about 10 poises.

For liquids of somewhat higher viscosity, a rod of metal or glass may be partly immersed and torsional pulses sent down it from a piezoelectric crystal attached to the top.[41] Then $\Re_M$ and $\Re_M$ are obtained from measurements of phase shift and attenuation of the reflected pulses as they return from the bottom of the rod to the crystal driver.

An alternative crystal geometry is the quartz piezoelectric tuning fork of Mason,[31] whose wide, thin arms oscillate in their own planes and set up primarily plane shear waves in the liquid surrounding them. The components $\Re_M$ and $\Re_M$ are again obtained from measurements of the change in resonant frequency and electrical resistance produced by the presence of the liquid. The frequency range is from 500 to 10,000 cycles/sec.

There are some other characteristic impedance methods in the medium

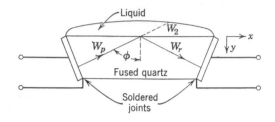

FIG. 5–11. Apparatus for characteristic impedance measurements at extremely high frequencies by reflection of a shear wave in fused quartz (Mason and Mc-Skimin).

frequency range which measure only the resistive component $\mathcal{R}_M$. That of Zimm [42] employs longitudinal vibrations of the walls of a glass container, which set up shear waves in the liquid. The driver is electromagnetic and the amplitude detector is piezoelectric; $\mathcal{R}_M$ is obtained from the decay in amplitude after the driver is shut off. There is a rather wide choice of frequencies by utilizing various overtones. A commercial instrument, the Ultraviscoson,[43] employs a magnetostrictive rod immersed in the liquid, whose longitudinal vibrations again excite shear waves; it operates at a fixed frequency. A similar device has been described by Yamamoto.[44] Although it is much easier to measure $\mathcal{R}_M$ than $\mathcal{X}_M$, the basic viscoelastic functions cannot be obtained from $\mathcal{R}_M$ alone. Nevertheless, $\mathcal{R}_M$ can be used for comparisons with theory (for example) by expressing the predictions of the latter in the form of the right side of equation 17.

Finally, for extremely high frequencies, from 3 to 100 megacycles/sec., a film of the liquid is spread on a surface of fused quartz [45, 46] (Fig. 5–11) and a shear wave sent from a piezoelectric transmitter is reflected and detected by a second piezoelectric crystal. From the differences in amplitude and phase between the incident and reflected waves, the components $\mathcal{R}_M$ and $\mathcal{X}_M$ of the characteristic impedance at the liquid surface can be calculated. The range of liquid consistencies which can be measured is very broad.

Despite their lack of a continuous frequency range, the characteristic impedance methods are of great value for measurements on systems where both G' and η' are small, as in dilute polymer solutions; indeed, they are the only methods applicable to such systems. Some additional recent references may be cited.[47, 48]

In Appendix B at the end of the book, the experimental methods described in this and the following chapters are summarized with a tabulation of their ranges of applicability.

G. ISOTHERMAL AND ADIABATIC MEASUREMENTS

The viscoelastic functions as defined refer to isothermal changes of state, and indeed the control of constant temperature is an important feature of all the experimental methods described in this chapter. It is evident, however, that the dynamic measurements described in some of the preceding sections must in fact be adiabatic rather than isothermal, because of failure to reach thermal equilibrium within the period of deformation. This distinction has usually been ignored, and reasonably so since the difference between the adiabatic and isothermal quantities is in most cases negligible. For the sake of completeness, however, some general features of the problem are mentioned here.

1. Difference between Adiabatic and Isothermal Moduli for Perfect Elastic Materials

The magnitude of the difference for viscoelastic materials can be gauged by making the calculation without considering time-dependent effects. Although the experimental methods in this chapter deal solely with shear deformations, it is useful for orientation to refer here first to deformation in bulk compression, for which the result is well known from thermodynamics [49, 50] and applicable to solids, liquids, and gases alike:

$$K_{ad} = K_{is}(1 + \alpha^2 T K_{is}/\rho C_v) \tag{21}$$

where K_{ad} and K_{is} are the adiabatic and isothermal bulk moduli, α the (volume) thermal expansion coefficient, ρ the density, and C_v the heat capacity per gram at constant volume. By substituting representative values, it is found that K_{ad} and K_{is} rarely differ by more than a few per cent.

For shear, it is usually stated that at small strains the moduli G_{ad} and G_{is} are identical in isotropic solids.[50, 51] For a solid in which G is directly proportional to T, as is closely approximated by soft rubbers, a thermodynamic calculation [52] gives

$$G_{ad} = G_{is} + [(\partial G/\partial T)^2 T/C_\gamma \rho]\gamma^2 \tag{22}$$

where γ is the strain and C_γ the heat capacity per gram at constant strain. The correction term does vanish at small strains, and is entirely negligible for the strain magnitudes limited by the conditions of linear viscoelastic behavior; for a soft rubber, the coefficient of γ^2 is of the order of 10^2 to 10^3 dynes/cm^2.

2. Critical Frequencies for Isothermal-Adiabatic Transitions

An elementary calculation shows that failure to attain thermal equilibrium with the surrounding medium will set in when the frequency (or reciprocal time in a transient experiment) exceeds the order of $\kappa/C_p\rho x^2$, where κ is the thermal conductivity (of the order of 4×10^{-4} cal cm^{-1} deg^{-1} sec^{-1} for polymeric liquids and solids), C_p the heat capacity per gram at constant pressure (of the order of 0.4 cal deg^{-1} g^{-1}), and x the thickness of the sample. For $x = 0.1$ cm, the critical frequency is of the order of 0.1 cycle/sec., so the majority of dynamic measurements are indeed adiabatic. At very high frequencies, however, where the experiment involves wave propagation or else characteristic impedance measurements at a wave-propagating surface, the wavelength becomes so short that thermal conduction prevents development of temperature gradients within a cycle, and the deformation is again isothermal. For shear, the critical frequency for this second transition is [50, 52]

$$\nu = G'C_p/2\pi\kappa \tag{23}$$

For a viscoelastic liquid with $G' = 10^4$, the corresponding frequency is about 10^6 cycles/sec.; for a soft polymeric solid with $G' = 10^7$, 10^9 cycles/sec.; for a hard solid with $G' = 10^{10}$, 10^{12} cycles/sec. Only in rare cases—possibly for dilute polymer solutions in the megacycle range—would this transition be crossed, since G' always increases with frequency.

3. Time-Dependent Effects Associated with Heat Flow

Although the change in the real part of the modulus, G' or K', accompanying the change from isothermal to adiabatic conditions may be expected to be negligibly small on the basis of the above estimates, it is accompanied by a contribution to G'' or K'' associated with the dissipation of energy by heat flow. In the viscoelastic liquids discussed in the present chapter, the effect on G'' will certainly also be negligibly small compared with contributions from ordinary viscous losses. The phenomenon may appear, however, in E'' and K'' for hard solids whose losses due to coordinated molecular motions are very small (Chapters 7 and 8).

An analysis of viscoelasticity by the methods of irreversible thermo-dynamics [53,54] shows that under adiabatic conditions the relaxation spectrum lies at slightly shorter times than under isothermal conditions.

REFERENCES

1. H. Leaderman, R. G. Smith, and R. W. Jones, *J. Polymer Sci.*, **14**, 47 (1954).
2. L. J. Hastewell and F. J. U. Ritson, *J. Sci. Instr.*, **29**, 20 (1952).
3. H. Markovitz, L. J. Elyash, F. J. Padden, Jr., and T. W. De Witt, *J. Colloid Sci.*, **10**, 165 (1955).
4. H. Goldberg and O. Sandvik, *Anal. Chem.*, **19**, 123 (1947).
5. W. Tillmann, *Kolloid-Z.*, **131**, 66 (1953).
6. D. J. Plazek, M. N. Vrancken, and J. W. Berge, *Trans. Soc. Rheology*, **2**, 39 (1958).
7. W. Philippoff et. al., *Trans. Soc. Rheology*, **2**, 263, 285 (1958).
8. J. D. Ferry and G. S. Parks, *Physics*, **6**, 356 (1935).
9. W. Philippoff, *Trans. Soc. Rheology*, **1**, 95 (1957).
10. T. W. De Witt, H. Markovitz, F. J. Padden, Jr., and L. J. Zapas, *J. Colloid Sci.*, **10**, 174 (1955).
11. J. D. Ferry, M. L. Williams, and D. M. Stern, *J. Phys Chem.*, **58**, 987 (1954).
12. J. G. Brodnyan, F. H. Gaskins, and W. Philippoff, *Trans. Soc. Rheology*, **1**, 109 (1957).
13. Y. H. Pao, *J. Applied Phys.*, **22**, 1570 (1954).
14. W. P. Cox and E. H. Merz, *J. Polymer Sci.*, **28**, 619 (1958).
15. F. Bueche, *J. Chem. Phys.*, **22**, 1570 (1954).
16. M. Yamamoto, *J. Phys. Soc. Japan*, **12**, 1148 (1957).
17. R. Cerf, *Fortschr. Hochpolymeren Forschung*, **1**, 382 (1959).
18. H. Markovitz, *Trans. Soc. Rheology*, **1**, 25, 37 (1957).
19. F. W. Schremp, J. D. Ferry, and W. W. Evans, *J. Applied Phys.*, **22**, 711 (1951).
20. J. M. Watkins, *J. Applied Phys.*, **27**, 419 (1956).
21. J. M. Watkins, R. D. Spangler, and E. C. McKannan, *J. Applied Phys.*, **27**, 685 (1956).
22. T. E. Morrison, L. J. Zapas, and T. W. DeWitt, *Rev. Sci. Instr.*, **26**, 357 (1955).
23. R. H. Shoulberg, F. H. Zimmerli, and O. C. Kohler, *Trans. Soc. Rheology*, **3**, 27 (1959).
24. H. Markovitz, P. M. Yavorsky, R. C. Harper, Jr., L. J. Zapas, and T. W De Witt, *Rev. Sci. Instr.*, **23**, 430 (1952).
25. H. Markovitz, *J. Applied Phys.*, **23**, 1070 (1952).
26. R. Seeder, *Physica*, **6**, 45 (1940).
27. T. L. Smith, J. D. Ferry, and F. W. Schremp, *J. Applied Phys.*, **20**, 144 (1949).

28. W. Philippoff, *J. Applied Phys.*, **25**, 1102 (1954).
29. W. P. Mason, *Electromechanical Transducers and Wave Filters*, Van Nostrand, New York, 1942.
30. M. H. Birnboim, unpublished experiments.
31. W. P. Mason, *Physical Acoustics and the Properties of Solids*, Van Nostrand, New York, 1958.
32. F. T. Adler, W. M. Sawyer, and J. D. Ferry, *J. Applied Phys.*, **20**, 1036 (1949).
33. A. W. Nolle and P. W. Sieck, *J. Applied Phys.*, **23**, 888 (1952).
34. J. D. Ferry, W. M. Sawyer, and J. N. Ashworth, *J. Polymer Sci.*, **2**, 593 (1947).
35. J. D. Ferry and F. E. Helders, *Biochim. Biophys. Acta*, **23**, 569 (1957).
36. J. D. Ferry, *Rev. Sci. Instr.*, **12**, 79 (1941).
37. D. J. Plazek, Ph.D. Thesis, University of Wisconsin, 1956.
38. W. P. Mason, *Trans. Am. Soc. Mech. Engrs.*, **69**, 359 (1947).
39. K. Sittel, P. E. Rouse, Jr., and E. D. Bailey, *J. Applied Phys.*, **25**, 1312 (1954).
40. P. E. Rouse, Jr., and K. Sittel, *J. Applied Phys.*, **24**, 690 (1953).
41. H. J. McSkimin, *J. Acoust. Soc. Amer.*, **24**, 355 (1952).
42. B. H. Zimm, *J. Polymer Sci.*, **26**, 101 (1957).
43. W. Roth and S. R. Rich, *J. Applied Phys.*, **24**, 940 (1953).
44. K. Yamamoto, Y. Yamada, and Y. Wada, *Ôyô Butsuri*, **27**, 98 (1958); *Chem. Abstr.*, **52**, 12495 (1958).
45. W. P. Mason, W. O. Baker, H. J. McSkimin, and J. H. Heiss, *Phys. Rev.*, **75**, 936 (1949).
46. A. J. Barlow and J. Lamb, *Proc. Roy. Soc.* **A253**, 52 (1959).
47. M. Kaneko, *Ôyô Butsuri*, **27**, 285 (1958); *Chem. Abstr.*, **52**, 16010 (1958).
48. H. Fuwa, *Ôyô Butsuri*, **25**, 149 (1956); *Chem. Abstr.*, **50**, 16187 (1956).
49. M. Zemansky, *Heat and Thermodynamics*, McGraw-Hill, New York, 1951.
50. W. P. Mason, *Piezoelectric Crystals and their Application to Ultrasonics*, Van Nostrand, New York, 1950.
51. K. Okano, *Reports on Progress in Polymer Physics in Japan*, Kobayasi Institute of Physical Research, Tokyo, 1958, p. 64.
52. J. D. Ferry, unpublished calculations.
53. J. Meixner, *Z. Naturf.*, **4a**, 594 (1949).
54. J. Meixner, *Z. Naturf.*, **9a**, 654 (1954).

Additional References

55. F. D. Dexter, *J. Applied Phys.*, **25**, 1124 (1954).
56. W. P. Cox, L. E. Nielsen, and R. Keeney, *J. Polymer Sci.*, **26**, 365 (1957).

CHAPTER 6

Experimental Methods for Soft Viscoelastic Solids

The boundary between this chapter and the preceding one is only vaguely and arbitrarily drawn; we now describe methods for materials with high enough viscosity, or if cross-linked with high enough equilibrium modulus, to support their own weight under gravitational forces. For such materials, there is considerably more freedom of choice in sample geometry and types of deformation. By specifying that the materials are "soft," *i.e.*, with a shear modulus less than something like 10^9 dynes/cm^2, the problems of measurement are further facilitated. There is no difficulty in making the structural parts of the apparatus much more rigid than the sample, so that their compliance can be neglected. Moreover, deformations in shear and in simple extension can be used interchangeably to yield the same information. This follows because with $\mu \cong \frac{1}{2}$, in accordance with equation 2 of Chapter 1, $E = 3G$; and any extensional viscoelastic function is related to the corresponding shear function by a factor of 3.

There is one type of soft solid for which recourse must be had to the apparatus described in Chapter 5—very weak gels which, though their viscosity may be infinite, have insufficient rigidity to prevent gross distortion under gravitational forces unless supported in containers. For example, stress relaxation in shear between coaxial cylinders can be followed after initial twist through a small angle; [1] and by placing a small differential pressure on a plug of gel in a cylindrical tube, shear experiments can be performed with the same deformation geometry as for liquid flow in a capillary.[2] Gels with shear moduli as low as 10^2 dynes/cm^2 can be studied.[3]

Whether or not a given polymeric system is "soft" or "hard" depends of course on the frequency range as well as the temperature. At high frequencies and low temperatures the methods described in this chapter must be replaced by those of Chapter 7.

A. CREEP

For a solid, the geometry for shear creep can correspond to the elementary definition depicted in Fig. 1–4, more conveniently with a sandwich arrangement [4,5] (Fig. 6–1) in which a moving plate shears two discs or slabs. A horizontal orientation is preferred over the vertical, since a clear-cut creep recovery experiment is impossible in the latter case; after removal of the load, the weight of the plate itself produces a small continuing stress in the original direction. Moreover, the polymer itself may in time sag perceptibly in the direction of motion.[6] In the horizontal orientation, however, a pulley is needed if the force is produced by dead weight, and its friction must be negligible. The distance moved, x, may be followed directly with a traveling microscope or sensed electrically with a differential transformer or other means.

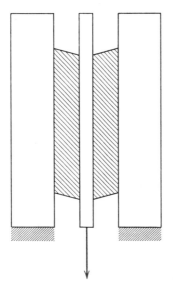

FIG. 6–1. Parallel plate sandwich arrangement for measuring shear creep.

The creep compliance is given by

$$J(t) = bx(t)/f \tag{1}$$

where f is the force in dynes and the form factor b (units cm) is given nominally by $A_1/h_1 + A_2/h_2$, the A's and h's being the areas and thicknesses of the two samples. Since the areas cannot be readily measured *in situ*, but the samples can be weighed before insertion, b is commonly calculated as $(m_1/h_1{}^2 + m_2/h_2{}^2)/\rho$, where the m's are the masses and ρ is the density of the material. The nominal value of b thus calculated assumes that the deformation is simple shear and the sides of the samples are parallel. (The shape of the cross-section area is irrelevant.) However, unless the samples are extremely thin, the actual deformation will be more complicated because of lack of restraints on the edges; the apparent compliance will then be too large, requiring a moderate correction, whose magnitude has been calculated by Read[7] for a slab of rectangular cross-section. Any bulging of the sides of the samples will also cause the apparent compliance to be too large if calculated by the simple formula.[8]

An alternative geometry for shear is that of the Pochettino viscosimeter,[9, 10, 6] in which the sample occupies an annular space between two coaxial cylinders, the space being open at both ends. One cylinder is forced along the axis with respect to the other; equation 1 applies with $b = 2\pi L/\ln (R_2/R_1)$, where R_1 and R_2 are the radii of the cylinders and L the length of the sample. This type of apparatus is very difficult to fill.[10]

Shear deformation is also produced by torsion of a right circular cylinder, as in the apparatus of Plazek, Vrancken, and Berge[11] (see also Section F and Fig. 6–7 below). The measurements here are of constant torque S and angular rotation α; equation 1 of Chapter 5 applies with the form factor b (units cm³) given by $\pi R^4/2h$, R and h being respectively the radius and height of the cylinder. In terms of mass and height (the latter, unlike the radius, can be readily measured *in situ*), $b = m^2/2\pi h^3 \rho^2$. It is clearly important that the height be measured precisely and that the sides of the cylinder be vertical.

The form factors b corresponding to these geometries are also summarized in Appendix C, together with formulas for maximum strain and stress within the sample.

If the sample is not too soft to attach clamps of some sort, it can be formed in strips, rods, or dumbbells and the creep can be measured in simple extension. If the tensile strain is very small, the tensile compliance is given by

$$D(t) = bx(t)/f \qquad (2)$$

where x is the increase in length, and the form factor b is the ratio of the area A to the length L. With somewhat larger strains, even though the stress may be small enough to fulfill the requirements of linear viscoelastic behavior, a difficulty is encountered because A and L change continuously throughout the experiment (in inverse proportion, since we are dealing in this chapter with materials whose Poisson's ratio is near $\frac{1}{2}$ and whose volume change in simple extension is very small). The tensile stress can be maintained constant, as demanded by the definition of the creep compliance, by decreasing the force f in proportion to A; this can be accomplished by automatic devices or a buoyancy correction.[12-14] However, $D(t)$ cannot be obtained from $x(t)$ by equation 2.

For a purely viscous material, with high η and no elasticity, if the cross-section area remains uniform and decreases in inverse proportion to L, the length and time are related by the equation $\ln (L/L_0) = \sigma t/\eta_l$, where σ is the tensile stress (maintained constant), and η_l is the so-called tensile viscosity or Trouton's coefficient of viscous traction;[15] by analogy with the relation $J(t) = 3D(t)$ which holds for soft solids at small strains, it can be seen that $\eta_l = 3\eta$. For a rubberlike elastic material, on the other hand, the length and stress are related by the equation $(L/L_0)^2 - (L_0/L) = 3\sigma/E$, as shown by the discussion of stress relaxation in the next section. Because of the different forms for the viscous and elastic components, it is not in general possible to relate the deformation to $D(t)$ in any simple manner.

Nevertheless, if $D(t)$ is obtained from creep in extension at *small* strains, the corresponding shear creep compliance can be calculated from it simply as $J(t) = 3D(t)$, since for soft solids μ is negligibly different from $\frac{1}{2}$.

Any uncross-linked polymer system with a viscosity high enough to be studied by the methods described in this section will be very slow in coming to steady-state flow; attempts to obtain η and J_e from linear plots such as Fig. 1–12 should be approached with caution and skepticism, and if possible tested by creep recovery experiments. From the methods described in Chapter 4, it is possible to calculate the retardation spectrum L from $J(t)$ even if one is not sure whether steady-state flow has been achieved.

B. STRESS RELAXATION

Any of the arrangements described in the preceding section can in principle be used for studying stress relaxation if the force can be measured as a function of time $f(t)$, while the deformation is maintained constant. There are in general three ways of keeping constant strain: by continuous adjustment of the force as the stress in the sample relaxes, which can be done by an automatic servomechanism; [16] by applying more than enough force, with a stop to limit the deformation, and making measurements at intervals by accurately balancing of the force so that the deformation just clears the stop; [17] and by straining a stiff spring element in series with the sample. In the latter case, the strain of the sample is not strictly constant, since it increases slightly as the spring element contracts in response to the relaxing stress. However, if the force per unit deformation is far larger for the spring than for the sample, the relaxation will approximate conditions of constant strain, and if the spring element carries a strain gauge or a differential transformer a continuous recording of the stress relaxation can be made.[18] An example is shown in Fig. 6–2, where a differential transformer records the stress in the form of changes in the deformation of a spring. The latter, strictly, affect the strain of the sample but are always less than 1% of it.

In practice, the majority of stress relaxation measurements on soft solids are made in simple extension; [19] here the tensile relaxation modulus is given by

$$E(t) = f(t)/bx \tag{3}$$

where x is the initial instantaneous displacement and b has the same meaning as in equation 2 provided $x \ll L$, i.e., the strain is quite small. If, as is not uncommon, the elongation is 50% or more, there is some question as to how the absolute magnitude of $E(t)$ should be calculated.

The theory of rubberlike elasticity [20] specifies that the equilibrium elasticity of soft cross-linked polymeric solids is Hookean in shear up to substantial strains but that the relationship between force and displacement in extension is non-linear, as follows:

$$f = (EA_0/3)[(L/L_0) - (L_0/L)^2] \tag{4}$$

where A_0 and L_0 are the undeformed (initial) area and length, and E is Young's modulus defined for small strains. If the factor in brackets

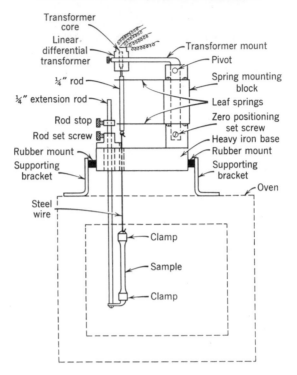

FIG. 6-2. Apparatus of McLoughlin for measuring stress relaxation in extension by the changes in position of a spring whose stiffness is much greater than that of the sample.

can be assumed to apply to the time-dependent elastic force as well, the analog of equation 3 is

$$E(t) = f(t)(3/A_0)/[(L/L_0) - (L_0/L)^2] \qquad (5)$$

Noting that $L = L_0 + x$ and that for a soft solid with negligible volume increase the actual cross-section area A is A_0L_0/L, equation 5 may be expanded in series to give

$$E(t) = [f(t)/A]/[x/L_0 + (\tfrac{1}{3})(x/L_0)^3 + \cdots] \qquad (6)$$

so that the simple form of equation 3 holds to the extent that terms in $(x/L_0)^3$ and higher powers can be neglected. For an extension of 50%, the second term in the denominator in equation 6 represents an 8% correction.

Experimentally, it is often found that the ratio $f_1(t)/f_2(t)$ for two different relaxation experiments at lengths L_1 and L_2 is constant throughout the whole course of the relaxation, even for extensions of 100% ($L/L_0 =$ 2). Then the ratio $E(t)/f(t)$ may be treated as an empirical parameter, dependent on L/L_0 alone, whose value approximates that given by equation 5 and can be determined [21] by extrapolating data at different elongations to small strains, guided by equation 6.

It has been suggested [22] that $E(t)$ in stress relaxation and the corresponding quantity for stress-strain curves at constant rate of loading can be calculated by analogy with an empirical equation of Martin, Roth, and Stiehler [23] for equilibrium stress-strain curves at elongations beyond the validity of equation 4, as

$$E(t) = [f(t)/A_0]/[(L_0/L) - (L_0/L)^2] \exp K[(L/L_0) - (L_0/L)]$$

where K is an empirical constant. In certain cases $E(t)$ thus calculated is independent of the degree of elongation over wide ranges.

C. DIRECT MEASUREMENTS OF SINUSOIDALLY VARYING STRESS AND STRAIN

The methods described in Chapter 5 for tracing out directly the periodic stresses and strains in sinusoidal deformations of polymeric liquids can be applied to soft solids with very little change. The apparatus of Philippoff [24] is used by substituting the simple shear sandwich mounting of Fig. 6–1 for the annular pumping geometry of Fig. 5–3. A force-displacement ellipse is traced out as before, and the calculations are made by equations 2 and 3 of Chapter 5 with $b = A_1/h_1 + A_2/h_2$ (cf. equation 1). Similar devices, with other means for following force and displacement, have been employed by other investigators for both shear and longitudinal deformations.[25–27] Instead of tracing an ellipse, both force and displacement can be automatically recorded against time; a versatile arrangement of Koppelmann [29] permits deformation in simple shear, simple extension, torsion, or flexure by interchange of mountings.

The two devices of De Witt and associates [30, 31] are used after replacing the coaxial cylinders for liquids by a cylindrical solid sample which is deformed in torsion through a small angle. The sample form factor is then the same as for torsional creep, but the calculations involve the moment of inertia and the stiffness of the supporting wire as before. The upper limit of the frequency range in this method is set by the requirement that the thickness of a sandwich sample must be small compared with the wavelength of a transverse wave; alternatively, the length of a twisted cylinder must be small compared with the wavelength of a torsional wave. Both wavelengths are approximately $(G'/\rho)^{1/2}/\nu$. If the frequency is too high, inertial effects will introduce errors; a first-order correction for simple shear is given in the following section. The results of dynamic measurements on solids are usually expressed as G' and G'' rather than G' and η', since η' is of less interest.

D. TRANSDUCER MEASUREMENTS OF STRAIN/STRESS RATIOS

The above-described direct measurements of sinusoidally varying force and velocity, or of amplitudes and phases of periodic rotations, again cover a frequency range from extremely low values up to a maximum of the order of 10 to 100 cycles/sec. for soft solids. At higher frequencies, the transducer method of measuring complex strain/stress ratios can be applied, and for soft solids the simple shear sandwich mounting permits design of an apparatus with considerable versatility and precision.

In the apparatus of Fitzgerald,[8, 32] shown in Fig. 6–3, two disc-shaped samples are periodically sheared between flat surfaces inside a thin cylindrical driving tube and a heavy, freely suspended floating mass. Both tube and mass are supported by fine wires which center them radially but permit longitudinal motion. Two coils around the driving tube, each in a radial magnetic field, carry an alternating current which produces a longitudinal oscillation with small amplitude. The floating mass moves with a much smaller amplitude, whose magnitude and phase are determined by its inertia and the elastance of its supports. The electrical impedance of one of the driving coils is measured with a bridge while in motion. From this, the mechanical impedance of the oscillating system can be calculated; the basic transducer equation is the same as equation 8 of Chapter 5, but the rest impedance $\mathbf{Z_0}$ is eliminated by making two measurements of $\mathbf{Z}$ with different ratios, r, of the driving currents in the two coils.

The electrical circuit of the Fitzgerald transducer is shown in Fig. 6–4, where coils 1A and 2A are the driving coils. There are several procedures for varying the ratio of the two driving currents, by changing R_3 or R_A or by reversing the direction in coil 2A. An important feature of the method is the elimination of the emf in coil 2A, whose impedance is being measured, due to mutual inductance from the current in coil 1A. This is accomplished by a current in the reverse

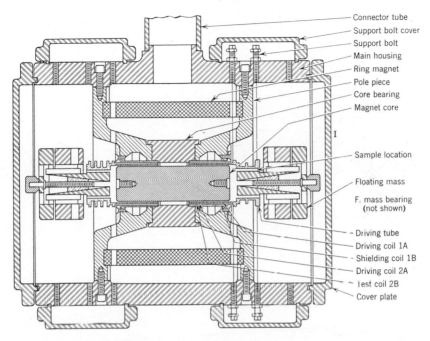

FIG. 6–3. Electromagnetic transducer apparatus of Fitzgerald [32] for dynamic measurements on soft solids, comprising two complete electromechanical units in one housing.

direction in coil 1B, which is stationary and very close to 1A on the outside. The magnitude and phase of the current in 1B are adjusted by varying R_B, C_B, and L_B until the e.m.f. in coil 2B (measured in the "test" position) vanishes. Coil 2B is stationary outside and very close to 2A. This mutual inductance balance must be made before each bridge measurement of the impedance, $\mathbf{Z}_2$, of coil 2A; without it, the useful frequency range would not go much above 100 cycles/ sec.

The mechanical impedance of the moving system is calculated as

$$\mathbf{Z_M} = -K^2 \Delta r / \Delta \mathbf{Z}_2 \tag{7}$$

where Δ refers to the difference between two sets of readings, and K^2 corresponds to $(Bl)^2$ in equation 8 of Chapter 5 except that it is the product of the magnetic field intensities and wire lengths for the two coils 1A and 2A.

From measurements on the driving tube alone, its mechanical impedance $\mathbf{Z}_{Mt}$ can be determined, as well as the constant K^2, making use of the known mass of the tube M, and the fact that at high frequencies X_{Mt} approaches ωM (cf. equation 7 of Chapter 5). The difference $\mathbf{Z_M} - \mathbf{Z}_{Mt} - i\omega m/3$ gives the mechanical

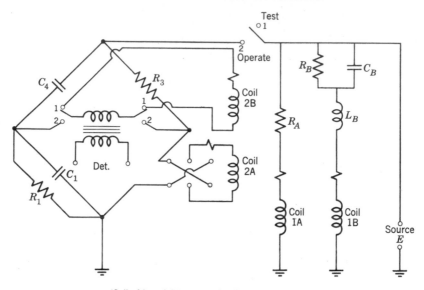

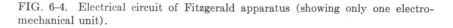

(Coils 1A and 2A are mechanically coupled)

FIG. 6-4. Electrical circuit of Fitzgerald apparatus (showing only one electro-mechanical unit).

impedance $\mathbf{Z_{AB}}$ due to motion of the samples and the floating mass. The term in m (the combined masses of the samples $m_1 + m_2$) represents a first-order correction for incipient wave propagation in cases where the sample thickness is an appreciable fraction of the wavelength.[33] The correction is valid only when it is small compared with the imaginary part of $\mathbf{Z_M}$. In practice, it is often quite negligible. The motions of the samples and the floating mass add as reciprocal impedances or admittances ($\mathbf{Y}$) since their displacements are in series; thus

$$1/\mathbf{Z_{AB}} = \mathbf{Y_{AB}} = \mathbf{Y_{Ms}} + \mathbf{Y_{Mm}} \qquad (8)$$

so if $\mathbf{Y_{Mm}}$, the reciprocal impedance of the floating mass, is known from a separate calibration with the driving tube and mass coupled rigidly together, the reciprocal impedance $\mathbf{Y_{Ms}}$ of the samples can be obtained by a second subtraction.

In making the two subtractions to obtain $\mathbf{Y_{Ms}}$ (each of which is a complex operation with a real and an imaginary part), it is necessary to keep $\mathbf{Z_{Mt}}$ and $\mathbf{Y_{Mm}}$ relatively small, or at least not overwhelmingly large, compared with the respective remainders. To cover a wide range of frequencies, samples of different sizes and shapes may be necessary.

Finally, the real and imaginary parts of the complex compliance of the material are calculated as

$$J' - iJ'' = -ib\mathbf{Y_{Ms}}/\omega \qquad (9)$$

The form factor b is the same as that for sandwich creep measurements (*cf.* equation 1), and is subject to the same corrections for stress distribution and bulging. The components J' and J'' can of course be converted to G' and G'' by equations 14 and 15 of Chapter 1.

The Fitzgerald apparatus has been used at frequencies from 10 to 6000 cycles/sec. It can be operated over an unusually wide temperature range, from $-60°$ to $155°C$. The temperature control is very good because the entire apparatus is immersed in a liquid bath. Like the transducers described in Chapter 5, it is operated with exceedingly small stresses and deformations because neither needs to be measured directly; and stability of the bridge balance with changing driving current provides a sensitive test of linearity of the viscoelastic behavior of the sample.

E. COMPOUND RESONANCE DEVICES (FORCED OSCILLATIONS)

If one is willing to sacrifice a continuously variable frequency range and make dynamic measurements at a few discrete frequencies, considerable simplification can be achieved through profiting by an apparatus resonance. This principle has already been alluded to in the characteristic impedance measurements, Section F of Chapter 5, without a detailed explanation. It may be illustrated now for simple shear sandwich geometry [34] by the apparatus of Fig. 6-5. Here an electromagnetic drive causes periodic shearing of two discs. The complex ratio of driving force to velocity is the same as that given in equations 5 to 7 of Chapter 5:

$$f/v = \mathbf{Z_M} = bG''/\omega + i(\omega M - S_M{}^0/\omega - bG'/\omega) \qquad (10)$$

where the symbols have their usual significance (*cf.* Appendix F); M is of course the mass of the entire moving system, not just the principal inertial member illustrated, and the elastance $S_M{}^0$ is ordinarily kept small compared with bG' by using supports which yield freely in the direction of motion. The form factor b is the same as that associated with equation 1.

At the resonance frequency, ω_0, the imaginary term vanishes and the force and velocity are in phase; the response is determined only by G'', and passes through a maximum as a function of frequency. In transducers such as those of Figs. 5-4 and 6-4, the immediate vicinity of the resonance is to be avoided because of extreme sensitivity. But

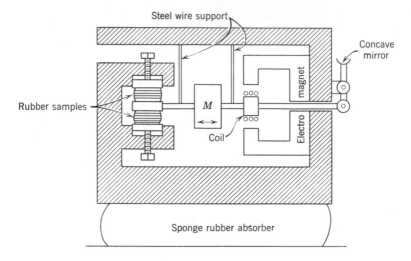

FIG. 6–5. Resonance apparatus for dynamic measurements on soft solids (Dillon, Prettyman, and Hall [34]).

advantage of the resonance may now be taken by solving for G' in terms of ω_0:

$$G' = \omega_0{}^2 M/b - S_M{}^0/b \tag{11}$$

whereas G'' can be obtained by either of two procedures: measurement of the absolute values of peak displacement $|\mathbf{x}|$ and peak force $|\mathbf{f}|$ at resonance, in which case

$$G'' = |\mathbf{f}|/b|\mathbf{x}| \tag{12}$$

or else measurement of the relative values of $|\mathbf{x}|$ at a series of frequencies near ω_0 and construction of a response curve from which the half-width, $\Delta\omega$, corresponding to the difference between the frequencies at which $|\mathbf{x}|$ is half its maximum value, is read. Then

$$G'' = G'\Delta\omega/\omega_0\sqrt{3} \tag{13}$$

(Alternatively, if $(\Delta\omega)'$ is the difference between frequencies at which $|\mathbf{x}|$ is $1/\sqrt{2}$ of its maximum value, $G'' = G'(\Delta\omega)'/\omega_0$.) The above formulas assume that the sample itself makes a negligible contribution to M, in contrast to the situation to be described in Chapter 7 where the resonance is determined by the inertia of the sample itself. Moreover, it is assumed that $R_M \ll \omega M$, or $\tan\delta \ll 1$; only under these conditions is a sharply defined resonance obtained. When these conditions are fulfilled, the resonance corresponds to both maximum $|\mathbf{x}|$ and maximum velocity $|\mathbf{v}|$.

The measurement can of course be made only at the frequency ω_0, which can be adjusted by varying the mass M and/or the form factor of the sample. There are various modifications of this principle, employing deformation in shear,[35] extension-compression,[36-38] and shear between coaxial cylinders [39-40] (for very soft gels). In the latter case, the resonance frequency corresponds to torsional oscillations of a suspended system.

If G' is small (and it will generally not be over 10^7 dynes/cm² for the low-loss soft solids handled by these methods), the upper limit of the frequency range is rather restricted by limitations of convenience and design on the smallness of M and the largeness of b. Higher frequencies can be used by increasing the magnitude of the term $S_M{}^0/b$ in equation 11; but then the calculation of G' loses precision by becoming a small remainder of a subtraction, and the result may be that only the component G'' can be determined.[41]

If $S_M{}^0$ is made large and provision is made for an accurate subtraction, the equations can be formulated somewhat differently in terms of resonant frequencies with and without presence of the sample. With this modification, it is no longer necessary to have $\tan \delta \ll 1$ for the material of the sample; a sharp resonance is obtained so long as $R_M \ll S_M{}^0/\omega$ (i.e., $G'' \ll bS_M{}^0$), and high-loss as well as low-loss materials can be studied. For example, in the method of Rorden and Grieco,[42] the resonant frequency and the response width $\Delta\omega$ of an electrically driven tuning fork are modified by deforming two soft samples in simple shear between the fork and an inertia bar (Fig. 6–6). The storage modulus G' is obtained from the difference between the two resonant frequencies with and without samples, and the loss modulus G'' from the difference between the two $\Delta\omega$ values. Because of the complex vibration modes of a tuning fork, the relations involve some rather complicated calibration parameters which will not be described here. (This method has been modified by Hopkins [43, 44] for high-viscosity polymeric liquids.)

The frequency range of the forced-oscillation resonance devices described in this section is generally from ten to a few thousand cycles/sec. It should be emphasized that we are still dealing with situations where the dimensions of the sample (thickness in the case of shear, length for torsion or extension, etc.) are small compared with the wavelength of an elastic wave corresponding to the type of deformation used. Thus,

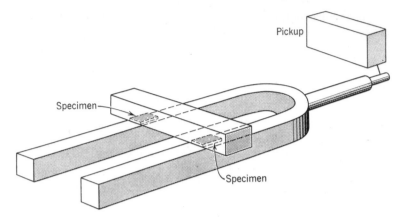

FIG. 6–6. Tuning fork compound resonator for dynamic measurements on soft solids (Rorden and Grieco,[42] Hopkins [43]).

the inertia of the sample itself does not enter into the calculations. The same is true for the following section.

F. COMPOUND RESONANCE DEVICES (FREE OSCILLATIONS)

Any one of the forced-oscillation arrangements described above can in principle be operated in free vibrations; the system is set into oscillation and it continues freely with a constant frequency ω_c and a gradually decreasing amplitude. The viscoelastic properties are calculated from the characteristic frequency ω_c and the decrement. It is again important that (for linear oscillations) $G'' \ll G' + S_M^0/b$, so that either tan δ must be small (material of low loss) or (rarely) S_M^0 must be made deliberately large. Otherwise, the relations between the measured quantities and the viscoelastic functions are very complicated,[45] and if $G'' \cong G'$ the amplitude will decay too rapidly to establish a characteristic frequency. For linear oscillations, if S_M^0 makes a negligible contribution and $G'' \ll G'$,

$$G' = (\omega_c^2 M/b)(1 + \Delta^2/4\pi^2) \tag{14}$$

$$G'' = (\omega_c^2 M/b)\Delta/\pi \tag{15}$$

where Δ is the logarithmic decrement (natural logarithm of the ratio between two successive displacements), and b is the form factor with dimensions of cm (for shear of 2 discs, $A_2/h_2 + A_1/h_1$; for extension of a rod, A/L, etc.).   The corresponding equations for torsional oscillations of a cylindrical or prismatic sample are identical except that I, the moment of inertia of the oscillating system, must be substituted for M; and b, in units of cm^3, is now defined as the polar second moment of the cross-section area divided by the height h.   For a circular cylinder of radius R, $b = \pi R^4/2h$; for a prism of rectangular cross-section, with

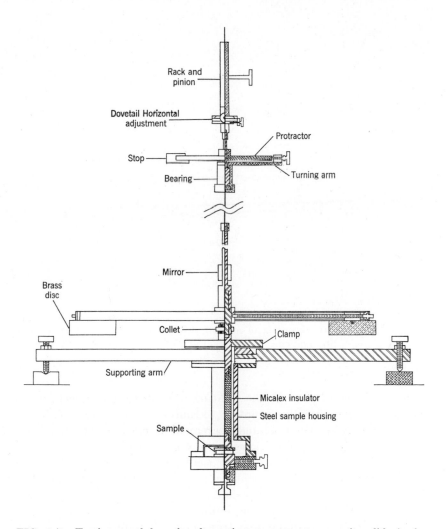

FIG. 6–7. Torsion pendulum for dynamic measurements on soft solids in free oscillating deformation (Plazek, Vrancken, and Berge [11]).

width c and thickness d, $b = cd^3\mu/16h$. Here μ is a shape factor which depends [46] on the ratio c/d and lies between 2.249 and 5.333.

An example of a free oscillation device whose deformation geometry is torsion of a circular cylinder is shown in Fig. 6–7. The apparatus of Plazek, Vrancken, and Berge [11] mentioned above under creep is equipped here with a moment arm to provide an adjustable moment of inertia. The oscillations are followed by reflection of a light beam

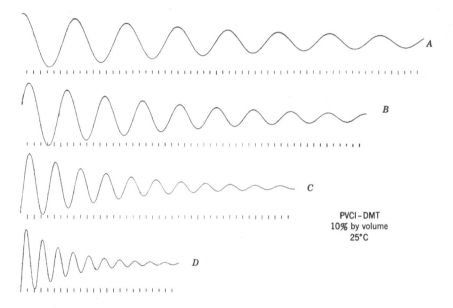

FIG. 6–8. Automatic recording of angular deflection *vs.* time in free torsional oscillations for a 10% polyvinyl chloride gel at 25°C with four different moments of inertia (Plazek, Vrancken, and Berge [11]).

from a mirror attached to the rotating unit on to a photocell, whose output is automatically recorded. From the trace (Fig. 6–8), the characteristic frequency ω_c and decrement Δ can be obtained. The latter is proportional to the slope of a plot of the logarithm of the maximum amplitude against number of oscillations (Fig. 6–9). This particular design is especially suited for very soft solids with low loss. In other modifications with torsional geometry, the sample is held in place with clamps,[47–49] and the oscillations are followed by the tangential motion of a differential transformer,[47] induction of an e.m.f. in a coil attached to the rotating system (from a stationary coil at right

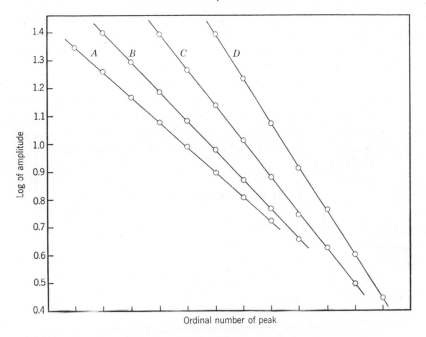

FIG. 6–9. Logarithmic plots of the maximum amplitude obtained from Fig. 6–8 *vs.* oscillation number, to determine logarithmic decrement.

angles energized with a carrier frequency [48]), or even by a trace of light on a photographic film. It is possible to use an electrical recorder whose trace amplitude is proportional to the logarithm of the signal,[29, 48] so that Δ can be obtained directly from the slope of the envelope of the maxima (Fig. 6–10), eliminating the need for constructing a second ¹ogarithmic graph like Fig. 6–9. Free oscillations in simple extension

FIG. 6–10. Automatic recording of free torsional oscillations with logarithmic amplitudes (Koppelmann [48]).

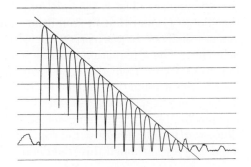

can also be used;[50] in this case the real and imaginary components of Young's modulus, E' and E'', are given by equations 11 and 12 with $b = A/L$ (*cf.* equation 2). For soft solids, then, $G' = E'/3$ and $G'' = E''/3$.

The free oscillation devices cover in general a frequency range of 0.01 to 25 cycles/sec. The precise temperature control needed for all viscoelastic measurements can be achieved by suitable design; any mechanical connections with parts of the apparatus outside the thermostat must be made through members of low heat conductivity.

G. WAVE PROPAGATION

At higher frequencies, the wavelength of shear or extensional waves becomes too short to satisfy the requirement in Sections C to F that the critical dimension of the sample must be small compared with a wavelength. At the other extreme, as in Chapter 5, when the sample is large compared with the wavelength, the propagation of traveling waves may be observed. For soft solids, the usual geometry is simple extension, requiring the propagation of longitudinal waves along thin strips[50] whose lateral dimensions are *small* compared with a wavelength. The velocity and attenuation here provide the components of the complex Young's modulus; equations 15 and 16 of Chapter 5 give E' and E'' without any modification. A nomograph for the calculation has been drawn by Nolle.[50] The strip is placed under slight constant tension to keep it taut, and longitudinal vibrations are excited in the long direction by an electromechanical driver such as a phonograph cutting head. An electromechanical pickup is then moved along the strip with constant velocity, and its output is compared in amplitude and phase with the driving signal. An automatic plot of the phase difference gives the wavelength, and the amplitude of the pickup gives the attenuation (Fig. 6–11). It may be noted[51] that the linearity of the plots of logarithm of amplitude and of number of wavelengths against distance is a sensitive test of the linearity of the viscoelastic behavior. The attenuation must be high enough so that no appreciable reflection occurs from the far end of the strip. At the same time, of course, the attenuation cannot be too high, or an insufficient number of wavelengths will be detectable. The coupling with the pickup must be light to prevent reflection back from its point of contact; it is sometimes worthwhile to adjust the contact pressure at each point of measurement,[51] even though this practically eliminates automatic recording.

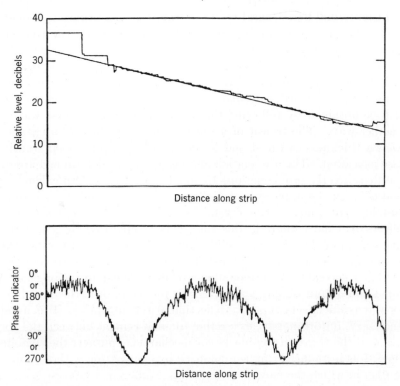

FIG. 6–11. Automatic recording of longitudinal waves in thin strips (Nolle [50]).

An alternative is to use flexural waves, excited by transverse motions of an electromechanical driver.[52] A flexural (bending) deformation of a rod or strip measures Young's modulus because one side of the sample is stretched and the other compressed at a bend. For traveling flexural waves, the analogs of equations 15 and 16 of Chapter 5 are (for small damping, $r \ll 1$): [52]

$$E' = (3/\pi^2)\rho v^2 (\lambda/d)^2 \tag{16}$$

$$E'' = (12/\pi^2)\rho v^2 r(\lambda/d)^2 \tag{17}$$

where d is the thickness of the strip in the direction of the bending displacement. In this case, one dimension of the sample must be known with considerable accuracy, in contrast to the extensional waves described above and the shear waves described in Chapter 5 where no dimensions are needed at all.

Longitudinal and flexural waves in thin strips can cover a frequency range from the order of 100 to 40,000 cycles/sec., and the frequency can be continuously varied. At much higher frequencies, where the wavelengths are too small to measure conveniently and the requirement that the lateral dimensions are small compared with the wavelength is no longer satisfied, information about dynamic shear behavior can still be obtained by following the propagation of transverse waves in another way. The transit of a shear wave pulse through a sample of known thickness is timed and its decrease in amplitude in transit is also measured. The attenuation and velocity thus determined are substituted directly into equations 15 and 16 of Chapter 5 to calculate G' and G''. In the apparatus of Nolle and Sieck,[53] a shear wave from a suitably cut piezoelectric crystal is sent through two transmission blocks of a hard solid (in this case, glass) separated by a soft polymeric solid of the order of a millimeter thick to a second crystal which serves as a detector. The transit time for wave pulses (several hundred per second) and attenuation are determined by comparing the input and output signals, and correcting for the path in the glass blocks as well as the effects of partial reflection at the interfaces. It is usually necessary, unfortunately, to use thin films of cement between the polymer and the transmitting blocks for mechanical contact; the complications thus introduced can be minimized by comparison with a duplicate system in which the polymer sample has a different thickness, as in the apparatus of Cunningham and Ivey [54] (Fig. 6–12). (Here the transmitting blocks are aluminum.) The method has been used in the range from 0.2 to 10 megacycles/sec.

If the piezoelectric crystals are cut differently to produce longitudinal rather than transverse vibrations, this pulse method measures the dynamic modulus for bulk longitudinal deformation, which will be discussed in Chapter 8.

The characteristic impedance method with reflection of a shear wave from a quartz surface [55] as described for liquids in Chapter 5 may also be used for soft solids in the megacycle range. In this case, where reflection occurs at an angle, there should be direct contact between the quartz and the sample.

The discussion of transitions between adiabatic and isothermal conditions in dynamic measurements as given in Chapter 5 is of course relevant to measurements on soft solids as well as on viscoelastic liquids.

At intermediate frequencies where the sample is neither small in one dimension compared with (as demanded by the methods of Sections C to F)

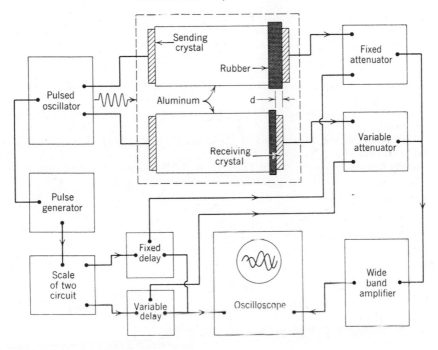

FIG. 6–12. Shear wave pulse apparatus for measuring the components of the dynamic shear modulus in the megacycle range (Cunningham and Ivey [54]).

nor large in one dimension compared with λ (as demanded for wave propagation measurements as described in the present section) resonance vibrations of the sample itself can be used to determine dynamic viscoelastic properties. Although this method is occasionally applied to soft solids and even viscoelastic liquids, it is much more commonly used for hard solids, and is therefore discussed in the following chapter.

REFERENCES

1. M. Miller, J. D. Ferry, F. W. Schremp, and J. E. Eldridge, *J. Phys. Colloid Chem.*, **55**, 1387 (1951).
2. P. R. Saunders and A. G. Ward, *Proc. 2nd Intern. Congr. Rheol.*, Oxford, p. 284 (1953).
3. G. Stainsby, private communication.
4. K. E. Van Holde and J. W. Williams, *J. Polymer Sci.*, **11**, 243 (1953).
5. J. W. Berge, Ph.D. Thesis, University of Wisconsin, 1958.
6. D. M. Stern, Ph.D. Thesis, University of Wisconsin, 1957.
7. W. T. Read, *J. Applied Mech.*, **17**, 349 (1950).

8. E. R. Fitzgerald and J. D. Ferry, *J. Colloid Sci.*, **8**, 1 (1953).

9. A. Pochettino, *Nuovo cimento*, **8**, 77 (1914).

10. T. G. Fox and P. J. Flory, *J. Amer. Chem. Soc.*, **70**, 2384 (1948).

11. D. J. Plazek, M. N. Vrancken, and J. W. Berge, *Trans. Soc. Rheology*, **2**, 39 (1958).

12. W. L. Holt, E. O. Knox, and J. L. Roth, *J. Res. Nat. Bur. Standards*, **41**, 95 (1948).

13. E. N. da C. Andrade, *Proc. Roy. Soc. (London)*, **A84**, 1 (1910); **A90**, 339 (1914).

14. C. A. Dahlquist, J. O. Hendricks, and N. W. Taylor, *Ind. Eng. Chem.*, **43**, 1404 (1951).

15. M. Reiner, *Deformation and Flow*, H. K. Lewis and Co., London, 1949.

16. R. S. Stern and H. Schaevitz, *Rev. Sci. Instr.*, **19**, 835 (1948).

17. R. D. Andrews, N. Homfan-Bang, and A. V. Tobolsky, *J. Polymer Sci.*, **3**, 669 (1948).

18. J. R. McLoughlin, *Rev. Sci. Instr.*, **23**, 459 (1952).

19. A. V. Tobolsky, *J. Applied Phys.*, **27**, 673 (1956).

20. L. R. G. Treloar, in H. A. Stuart, *Die Physik der Hochpolymeren*, Vol. IV, Chapter V, Springer-Verlag, Berlin, 1956.

21. R. D. Andrews and A. V. Tobolsky, *J. Polymer Sci.*, **7**, 221 (1951).

22. R. F. Landel, P. Stedry, and T. L. Smith, private communication.

23. G. M. Martin, F. L. Roth, and R. D. Stiehler, *Trans. Inst. Rubber Ind.*, **32**, 189 (1956).

24. W. Philippoff, *J. Applied Phys.*, **24**, 685 (1953).

25. H. Roelig, *Proc. Rubber Technol. Conf.*, pp. 821–829 (1938).

26. L. Mullins, *Trans. Inst. Rubber Ind.*, **26**, 27 (1950).

27. W. P. Fletcher and A. N. Gent, *J. Sci. Instr.*, **29**, 186 (1952).

28. A. Betticher, V. Hardung, and J. Maillard, *Kolloid-Z.*, **148**, 66 (1956).

29. J. Koppelmann, *Rheol. Acta*, **1**, 20 (1958).

30. T. E. Morrison, L. J. Zapas, and T. W. DeWitt, *Rev. Sci. Instr.*, **26**, 357 (1955).

31. H. Markovitz, P. M. Yavorsky, R. C. Harper, Jr., L. J. Zapas, and T. W. DeWitt, *Rev. Sci. Instr.*, **23**, 430 (1952).

32. E. R. Fitzgerald, *Phys. Rev.*, **108**, 690 (1957).

33. R. S. Marvin, Ph.D. Thesis, University of Wisconsin, 1949.

34. J. H. Dillon, I. B. Prettyman, and G. L. Hall, *J. Applied Phys.*, **15**, 309 (1944).

35. R. S. Enabnit and S. D. Gehman, *Ind. Eng. Chem.*, **43**, 346 (1951).

36. C. W. Kosten and C. Zwikker, *Physica*, **4**, 221 (1937).

37. W. J. S. Naunton and J. R. S. Waring, *Trans. Inst. Rubber Ind.*, **14**, 340 (1939).

38. S. D. Gehman, D. E. Woodford, and R. B. Stambaugh, *Ind. Eng. Chem.*, **33**, 1032 (1941).

39. H. Goldberg and O. Sandvik, *Ind. Eng. Chem., Anal. Ed.*, **19**, 123 (1947).

40. J. R. Van Wazer and H. Goldberg, *J. Applied Phys.*, **18**, 207 (1947).

41. W. Philippoff, *Physik Z.*, **35**, 884 (1934).

42. H. C. Rorden and A. Grieco, *J. Applied Phys.*, **22**, 842 (1951)

43. I. L. Hopkins, *Trans. Am. Soc. Mech. Engrs.*, **73**, 195 (1951).

44. I. L. Hopkins, *J. Appl. Phys.*, **24**, 1300 (1953).

45. H. C. Brinkman, unpublished calculations.

46. L. R. Nielsen, *Am. Soc. Testing Matls. Bull.* No. 165, p. 48 (1950).

47. L. R. Nielsen, *Rev. Sci. Instr.*, **22**, 690 (1951).
48. J. Koppelmann, *Kolloid-Z.*, **144**, 12 (1955).
49. W. Kuhn and O. Künzle, *Helv. Chim. Acta,* **30**, 839 (1947).
50. A. W. Nolle, *J. Applied Phys.*, **19**, 753 (1948).
51. P. Mason, private communication.
52. G. W. Becker, *Kolloid-Z.*, **140**, 1 (1955).
53. A. W. Nolle and P. W. Sieck, *J. Applied Phys.*, **23**, 888 (1952).
54. J. R. Cunningham and D. G. Ivey, *J. Applied Phys.*, **27**, 967 (1956).
55. W. P. Mason, W. O. Baker, H. J. McSkimin, and J. H. Heiss, *Phys. Rev.*, **75**, 936 (1949).

CHAPTER 7

Experimental Methods for Hard Viscoelastic Solids

The devices of the preceding chapter are designed for viscoelastic solids with moduli in the general range from 10^6 to 10^8 dynes/cm^2; some are appropriate for low values of tan δ, others for intermediate to high tan δ. For harder solids with moduli in the range of 10^9 to 10^{11} dynes/cm^2, there is no difference in principle in the application of the same experimental methods, and indeed some of them can be used without modification, but some new features appear with the increase in stiffness of several orders of magnitude.

Since $J(t)$ and $\mathbf{J}^*(\omega)$ are no longer much greater than $B(t)$ and $\mathbf{B}^*(\omega)$—i.e., μ is perceptibly less than $\frac{1}{2}$—shear and elongation do not yield equivalent information. Experiments with simple shear or torsion give time-dependent shear moduli and compliances, whereas experiments with simple extension or flexure give time-dependent Young's moduli. The ratio between the respective moduli is itself time-dependent, corresponding to a variable μ in equation 2 of Chapter 1. The shear moduli, $G(t)$ and $\mathbf{G}^*(\omega)$, representing the resistance to change in shape alone, are the more readily interpretable in terms of molecular properties; nevertheless, Young's modulus, $E(t)$ or $\mathbf{E}^*(\omega)$, is often the experimenter's choice, since its measurement is somewhat simpler for hard materials. When $E(t)$ is measured, $G(t)$ can be obtained from it only if $B(t)$ or $K(t)$ or $\mu(t)$ is also known.

When $G > 10^9$ dynes/cm^2, the stiffness of the sample approaches that of structural parts of the apparatus, and the sample shape must be chosen to keep the form factor b as small as possible. Simple shear sandwich geometry is practically eliminated; torsion is applied to long thin rods instead of squat discs; extension is applied to long thin strips, and flexural geometry is especially favored because it can give relatively large displacements.

A. CREEP AND STRESS RELAXATION

For transient experiments the applied stresses must be large, requiring massive construction, and small displacements must be measured accurately. It will suffice to quote a few representative references for specific details: for creep in torsion; [1-3] creep in extension; [4,5] stress relaxation in torsion; [6] and stress relaxation in tension.[7,8] The calculations have already been given in previous chapters. Since the strains are always small, there is no trouble with non-linear problems arising from large extensions as in the preceding chapter. Care must be taken, however, that the stresses do not exceed the limits of linear viscoelastic behavior; it is desirable to make plots of stress against strain interpolated at equal time intervals (from several relaxation experiments at different strains, or several creep experiments at different stresses) to insure linearity.[9] A versatile commercial instrument for transient experiments is the Instron tester,[10] in which the stress is determined by a strain gauge and can be continuously recorded.

B. DIRECT MEASUREMENTS OF SINUSOIDALLY VARYING STRESS AND STRAIN

A stress-strain ellipse can be traced for sinusoidal deformations of a hard solid with the methods described previously after suitable modifications in the sample mounting.[11] The most common geometry is flexure; several examples are shown in Fig. 7–1. The necessary equations are analogous to 2 and 3 of Chapter 5, except that now the components of Young's modulus are determined:

$$E' = (|\mathbf{f}|/b|\mathbf{x}|) \cos \delta \tag{1}$$

$$E'' = (|\mathbf{f}|/b|\mathbf{x}|) \sin \delta \tag{2}$$

The form factor b (units cm) depends on the details of the arrangement. When a bar clamped at both ends is bent in the middle (Fig. 7–1a),

$$b = 16cd^3/L^3 \tag{3}$$

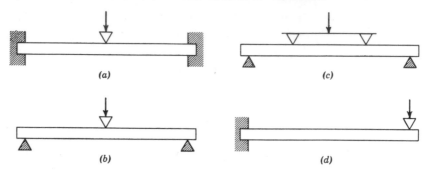

FIG. 7–1. Examples of flexure geometry for measurements of mechanical properties of hard solids. (a) Clamped ends; (b) Knife-edge supports; (c) Two-point load application;[14] (d) Cantilever.[13]

where c, d, and L are the width, thickness, and length of the bar between the clamps, respectively. It is characteristic of such flexural measurements that the thickness and length of the sample, which enter to the third power, must be known with great accuracy; moreover, the manner in which the sample is clamped must be definitely specified. For example, if the bar is supported on knife edges at the ends and bent by a knife edge in the center (Fig. 7–1b), the form factor is [12]

$$b = 2cd^3/L^3 \qquad (4)$$

For flexure of a bar clamped at one end only, as used by Koppelmann [13] (Fig. 7–1d), the form factor corresponds to the engineer's cantilever formula:

$$b = cd^3/4L^3 \qquad (5)$$

Another device for sinusoidally varying deformation in flexure has been described by Högberg.[14] The form factors and maximum stresses and strains are summarized in Appendix C.

An ingenious method for steady-state dynamic measurements [15, 16] has been applied to hard polymeric solids by Maxwell.[17] A rod of circular cross-section is rotated at a given frequency and simultaneously flexed by a yoke with negligible friction (Fig. 7–2). Each element of the rod undergoes a sinusoidally varying strain in extension; if $\tan \delta \neq 0$, the rod will have a steady-state deflection with components both in the direction of the flexing force (A) and perpendicular to it (B), and the two components are inversely proportional to E' and E'' respectively, thus:

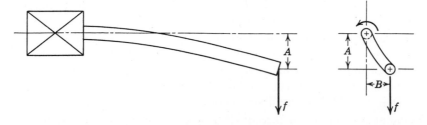

FIG. 7-2. Apparatus for dynamic measurements by a rotating rod strained in flexure (Maxwell).

$$E' = f/bA \tag{6}$$

$$E'' = f/bB \tag{7}$$

where the form factor b (*cf.* equation 5) is given by

$$b = 3\pi R^4/4L^3 \tag{8}$$

R and L being the radius and length of the rod respectively. This method has been used over a frequency range from somewhat less than 0.001 to somewhat over 100 cycles/sec.

For measuring G' and G'', the usual geometry is torsion, with the end of a long rod, bar,[13] or tube [18] oscillated through a small angular rotation. The torque and angular displacement can be measured by any of the methods previously described; the form factors for rods and bars are those given in Section F of Chapter 6. That for tubes is $b = \pi(R_2^4 - R_1^4)/2L$, where R_1 and R_2 are the inner and outer radii, and L the length.[12]

C. RESONANCE VIBRATIONS

The methods of the previous section are of course subject to the usual restriction for direct sinusoidal measurements that the critical dimension of the sample must be small compared with the wavelength of the corresponding elastic wave (flexural or torsional, respectively). The opposite extreme is attainable for hard solids only at very high frequencies, since the wavelength is proportional to the square root of the modulus, other things being equal, and we are dealing here with moduli of the order of 10^{10} dynes/cm^2. However, an intermediate situation is readily achieved, where the wavelength is the same order of magnitude as the sample dimensions. Then, at specified frequencies, standing waves can be set up within the sample; i.e., it vibrates in various characteristic modes. It is necessary that tan δ be quite small, but for hard viscoelastic solids this is usually the case.

The available frequencies are limited to discrete values corresponding to different vibrational modes, though several sets can be obtained by using samples of different shapes and sizes. Determination of a resonant frequency (in forced vibrations) or characteristic frequency (in free vibrations) permits calculation of the storage modulus; and the corresponding loss tangent is obtained just as in the compound resonance devices discussed in Chapter 6—for forced vibrations, by measurement of the absolute value of the amplitude at resonance, or by constructing a response curve around the resonance frequency and measuring its width, $\Delta\omega$ or $(\Delta\omega)'$; for free vibrations, by measuring the logarithmic decrement Δ.

Since the resonance is determined by the inertia of the sample, and there is no added mass associated with the apparatus, the density ρ enters all the calculations of the storage modulus. The details depend on the sample geometry. Thus, for forced vibrations of a bar or reed in flexure (sample mounted as in Fig. 7–1d but with nothing attached to the free end), the components of the dynamic Young's modulus are given by [19-21]

$$E' = \rho B_n (L^4/d^2)[\omega_0{}^2 + (\Delta\omega)'^2/2] \tag{9}$$

$$E'' = E' \tan \delta = \rho B_n (L^4/d^2)\omega_0(\Delta\omega)' \tag{10}$$

where L and d are the length and thickness of the reed, and ω_0 and $(\Delta\omega)'$ are defined as in Section E of Chapter 6. The numerical coefficients B_n are equal to 0.974, 0.0247, and 0.00315 for the fundamental and first and second harmonic modes of vibration respectively. In the corresponding equations for free vibration, ω_0 is replaced by ω_c and $(\Delta\omega)'/\omega_0$ by Δ/π. Obviously the dimensions of the sample must be known with high precision. Uniformity of the sample shape is sometimes a troublesome problem. If it is molded, it must be free from anistropy (cf. Chapter 9), and if it is machined, alteration of the surface must be avoided. Equations 9 and 10 hold only for quite small tan δ. Further corrections for somewhat higher damping have been discussed by Becker,[20] and a general analysis, leading to some rather complicated relations, has been given by Bland and Lee.[22]

Flexural vibrations can also be excited in a rod of circular cross-section which is not clamped at all but suspended by fine threads

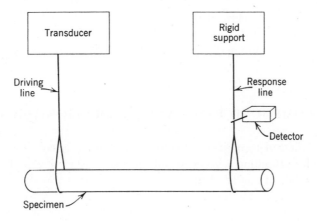

FIG. 7–3. Apparatus for measuring flexural vibrations in a freely suspended rod (Kline).

looped around it and subjected to slight oscillating tension at the chosen frequency [23, 24] (Fig. 7–3). For vibration in the first transverse mode, the components of Young's modulus are obtained by the equations:

$$E' = 12.54 \, \rho(L^4/R^2)\omega_0{}^2 \tag{11}$$

$$E'' = 12.54 \, \rho(L^4/R^2)\omega_0(\Delta\omega)' \tag{12}$$

where the symbols have their usual significance.

Longitudinal resonance vibrations in reeds [25] have also been used to determine E' and E'', and torsional vibrations in rods [26–29] to determine G' and G'' of hard polymeric solids. In longitudinal vibrations, only the length of the sample enters the calculation, and only to the first power, in contrast to the high powers of L, d, and R in equations 9 to 12.

The frequency range of devices of this sort is of the order of 10 to 5000 cycles/sec. Since neither the frequency response curve nor the logarithmic decrement requires an absolute measurement of amplitude, the relative amplitudes are rather easily measured by optical or electrical elements or even by observation with a microscope.[18] The limited choice of frequencies is a serious drawback, however. Usually only a few harmonics can be applied, and, in contrast to the flexibility of the compound resonance devices in Chapter 6, whose frequencies can be adjusted by changing the mass or moment of inertia of the apparatus, a new set of values can be obtained only by shaping a new sample. Temperature control can be satisfactorily arranged, since the mechanical system can easily be isolated in a thermostat, and in fact measurements have been made [30] at temperatures down to 4.2°K.

D. COMPOUND RESONANCE VIBRATION DEVICES

The method of resonance vibrations can be made considerably more versatile by attaching a layer of polymer to a layer of a high-modulus, low-loss solid. Usually long, narrow metal strips are employed, covered with a uniform thickness of polymer on one or both sides, and suspended from threads or supported on knife edges at nodal points. Flexural vibrations are excited; the resonance frequencies ω_0 and response half-widths $\Delta\omega$ or $(\Delta\omega)'$ depend on the properties of both materials. Knowing the properties of the metal, the corresponding quantities for the polymer alone can be calculated by solving some rather complicated expressions. The theory has been given by van Oort [31] and Oberst.[32]

This method can be used for materials which are too soft or too lossy to support resonance vibrations alone. By making measurements at various vibration modes (up to 20 nodes along the sample length), a considerable frequency range can be obtained with a single sample. The choice of the thickness ratio for the two layers depends on their modulus and loss tangent ratios. Interest in such measurements stems not only from the opportunity of deriving viscoelastic data but also from the importance of polymeric coatings in reducing vibrational noise of metal plates (Chapter 19).

E. PULSE PROPAGATION

When a single compressive pulse is sent into a rod, such as by detonation of an explosive at one end,[33] the deformation is equivalent to a group of Fourier components with a wide range of frequencies, and in a polymeric material these of course travel with different velocities, so the pulse is distorted and broadened in transit.[34] If the length of the pulse well exceeds the thickness of the rod, the form of E' should in principle be obtainable from studies of the change in shape as determined by recording the deformation-time patterns at the opposite ends of rods of different lengths. The reverse calculation has been successfully made.[35] For thicker rods, however, there is additional distortion from other causes which are mentioned in the following chapter.

A variety of experimental devices similar to those described in this chapter have been devised for study of metals and other non-polymeric solids, and a supplementary list of references covering some of them is included below. In principle, the distinction between isothermal and adiabatic measurements should again be drawn, but in practice the difference between the two will be small. For a classification of all experimental methods, the reader is again referred to Appendix B.

REFERENCES

1. W. Lethersich, *J. Sci. Instr.*, **24**, 66 (1947).
2. K. Sato, H. Nakane, T. Hideshima, and S. Iwayanagi, *J. Phys. Soc. Japan*, **9**, 413 (1954).
3. J. J. Benbow, in P. Mason and N. Wookey, *Rheology of Elastomers*, Pergamon Press, London, 1958.
4. K. Van Holde, *J. Polymer Sci.*, **24**, 417 (1957).
5. J. A. Sauer, J. Marin, and C. C. Hsiao, *J. Applied Phys.*, **20**, 507 (1949).
6. S. Iwayanagi, *J. Sci. Research Inst. Japan*, **49**, 4 (1955).
7. J. R. McLoughlin, *Rev. Sci. Instr.*, **23**, 459 (1952).
8. K. Nagamatsu, T. Yoshitomi, and T. Takemoto, *J. Colloid Sci.*, **13**, 257 (1958).
9. H. Sommer, Ph.D. Thesis, University of Braunschweig, 1958.
10. H. Hindman and G. S. Burr, *Trans. Amer. Soc. Mech. Engrs.*, **71**, 789 (1949).
11. W. Philippoff, *J. Applied Phys.*, **25**, 1102 (1954).
12. L. S. Marks, *Mechanical Engineers' Handbook*, 5th Ed., McGraw-Hill, New York, 1951.
13. J. Koppelmann, *Rheol. Acta*, **1**, 20 (1958).
14. H. Högberg, *Symposium on Plastics Testing and Standardization*, American Society for Testing Materials, Special Technical Publication No. 247, 1958, p. 95.
15. W. Mason, *Engineering*, **115**, 698 (1923).
16. A. L. Kimball and D. E. Lovell, *Trans. Amer. Soc. Mech. Engrs.*, **48**, 479 (1926).
17. B. Maxwell, *J. Polymer Sci.*, **20**, 551 (1956).
18. W. Lethersich, *J. Sci. Instr.*, **27**, 303 (1950).
19. A. W. Nolle, *J. Applied Phys.*, **19**, 753 (1948).
20. G. W. Becker, *Kolloid-Z.*, **140**, 1 (1955).
21. D. W. Robinson, *J. Sci. Instr.*, **32**, 2 (1955).
22. D. R. Bland and E. H. Lee, *J. Applied Phys.*, **26**, 1497 (1955).
23. F. Förster, *Z. Metallkunde*, **29**, 109 (1937).
24. D. E. Kline, *J. Polymer Sci.*, **22**, 449 (1956).
25. H. S. Sack, J. Motz, H. L. Raub, and R. N. Work, *J. Applied Phys.*, **18**, 450 (1947).
26. K. Schmieder and K. Wolf, *Kolloid-Z.*, **127**, 65 (1952).

27. J. J. Benbow, *J. Sci. Instr.*, **30**, 412 (1953).
28. I. Heyboer, P. Dekking, and A. J. Staverman, *Proc. 2nd Intern. Congress Rheology*, Butterworths, London, 1954, p. 123.
29. E. Jenckel, *Kolloid-Z.*, **136**, 142 (1954).
30. K. M. Sinnott, *Bull. Amer. Phys. Soc.*, **3**, 109 (1958).
31. W. P. Van Oort, *Microtecnic*, **7**, 246 (1952).
32. H. Oberst, *Akust. Beih.*, 1952, p. AB181.
33. H. Kolsky, *Stress Waves in Solids*, Clarendon Press, Oxford, 1953.
34. H. Kolsky, *Proc. 2nd Intern. Congress Rheology*, Butterworths, London, 1954, p. 79.
35. H. Kolsky, *Phil. Mag.* [8], **1**, 693 (1956).

Additional References

36. C. Zener, *Elasticity and Anelasticity of Metals*, University of Chicago Press, 1948.
37. R. L. Wegel and H. Walther, *Physics*, **6**, 141 (1935).
38. F. Birch, *J. Applied Phys.*, **8**, 129 (1937).
39. F. Birch and D. Bancroft, *J. Geol.*, **46**, 59, 113 (1938).
40. A. Gemant, *J. Applied Phys.*, **14**, 204 (1943).
41. T. S. Kê, *Phys. Rev.*, **71**, 533 (1947); **72**, 41 (1947).
42. W. N. Findley and W. J. Worley, *Proc. Soc. Exp. Stress Analysis*, **17**, 15 (1959)

CHAPTER 8

Experimental Methods
for Bulk Measurements

The two basic types of mechanical deformation, from a physical and molecular standpoint, are shear and bulk compression. The experimental methods described in the preceding three chapters yield information primarily about shear; only in extension measurements on hard solids does a perceptible volume change influence the results. By combining shear and extension measurements, the bulk properties can be calculated by difference, as for example in creep by equation 3 of Chapter 2, but the subtraction is unfavorable for achieving a precise result. Alternatively, bulk properties can be measured directly, or they can be obtained by combining data on shear and bulk longitudinal deformations (corresponding to the modulus M discussed in Chapter 1), where the subtraction does not involve such a loss of precision. Methods for such measurements are described in the present chapter.

An unfortunate usage of the term "bulk viscosity" has developed among polymer chemists, in the sense of the ordinary shear viscosity of a polymer "in bulk," as contrasted with its viscosity in dilute solution. In acoustics, "bulk viscosity" means the viscosity associated with a compression in all directions, and this definition fits in best with the nomenclature of viscoelasticity. In this book, the complex dynamic bulk viscosity refers to $\eta_v^* = K^*/i\omega$.

137

A. BULK TRANSIENT MEASUREMENTS

In the bulk analog of a stress relaxation experiment, the sample is suddenly compressed to a smaller volume and the pressure required to hold it compressed is recorded as a function of time. Apparatus for this purpose has been described by Matsuoka and Maxwell [1] (Fig. 8–1). In practice, it is more often used to obtain pressure-volume curves at a constant rate of volume decrease, from which the bulk relaxation modulus can be obtained by differentiation; equation 57 of Chapter 3 would be applied, with $\Delta V/V$ (volume strain), P, and $K(t)$ replacing γ, $\mathfrak{T}$, and $G(t)$. Measurements of this sort require the techniques of high-pressure physics; [2] in particular, freedom from voids and gas bubbles is naturally very important. Alternatively, in the bulk analog of a creep experiment, the pressure is maintained constant and the decrease in volume is followed with time. [3] Accurate measurements are achieved by following the motion of a piston with a linear differential transformer. [3]

A simple experiment which yields qualitatively similar information is an abrupt temperature change followed by precise measurements of volume, as performed by Jenckel and associates, [4,5] Davies and Jones, [6] and Kovacs. [7] The sample is contained in a dilatometer surrounded by a confining liquid. If it is suddenly cooled from T_1 to T_2, it can exist at equilibrium with no volume change only under a (negative) pressure given by

$$\Delta P = \int_{T_1}^{T_2} (\alpha/\beta) \, dT \tag{1}$$

where α and β are the thermal expansion coefficient and (equilibrium) coefficient of compressibility respectively. Consequently, it begins to contract as though an external (fictive) pressure ΔP had been applied. In the neighborhood of the glass transition temperature and just below it, the contraction is time-dependent with a time scale which can be followed over a period up to many hours. The experiment does not really correspond to either creep or stress relaxation, but it can yield useful information as shown in Chapter 18.

B. BULK DYNAMIC MEASUREMENTS

Two methods for measuring bulk viscoelastic properties in sinusoidally oscillating deformations have recently been described. The

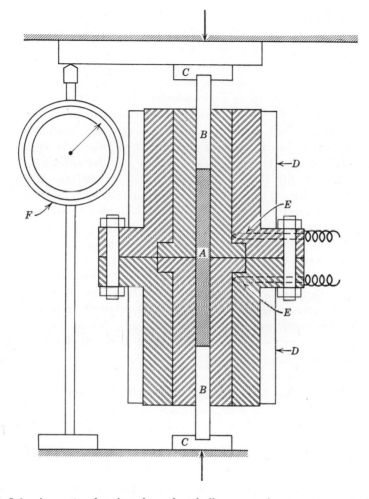

FIG. 8–1. Apparatus for time-dependent bulk compression measurements (Maxwell and Matsuoka [1]). *A* denotes the sample.

first involves direct measurements of stress and strain by the versatile apparatus of Philippoff.[8] This has already been quoted in connection with shear measurements on viscoelastic liquids and soft solids (Chapters 5 and 6), and flexure of hard solids (Chapter 7), but can be provided with still another attachment for bulk compression:[9] the sample is confined under mercury and compressed by an oil-sealed plunger. From the stress-strain ellipse geometry, the components K' and K'' of the complex bulk modulus are obtained after correcting for the compression of the mercury and slight compliances of the apparatus itself. The frequency range is from 3×10^{-4} to 6 cycles/sec.

At the other end of the frequency scale, the apparatus of McKinney, Edelman, and Marvin [10] provides measurements from 50 to 5000 cycles/sec. The sample is confined in a cavity under oil. Periodic volume changes are imposed by a piezoelectric transducer; a second transducer detects the periodic pressure changes specified by the volume changes and the bulk compliance of the cavity and contents. From the (complex) ratio of the input and output voltages, the components K' and K'' of the dynamic bulk modulus can be calculated, again after correction for the compliances of the oil and the block containing the cavity. The cavity is small compared with the wavelength of a compressional wave at the frequencies employed, so the method is analogous to the shear transducer methods described in Chapter 5, Section D and Chapter 6, Section D; the inertia of the sample plays no role. A static pressure of the order of 100 kg/cm² is imposed initially to force any residual air into solution. Afterwards, measurements may be made at any pressure from 1 to 1000 atm.

The frequency ranges of the two devices described here are such that they measure primarily isothermal and adiabatic moduli respectively (Chapter 5); and the difference between the two will be larger for bulk compression than for any other type of deformation. For a soft polymeric solid with $\alpha = 6 \times 10^{-4}$ deg⁻¹ and $K_{is} = 3 \times 10^{10}$ dynes/cm², K_{ad} would be higher than K_{is} by about 20% (Chapter 5, equation 21).

C. LONGITUDINAL BULK WAVE PROPAGATION

When longitudinal waves are propagated in thin strips, as described for soft solids in Chapter 6, the deformation corresponds to simple extension because the wavelength is large compared to the sample thickness (though small compared with its length), and the components of Young's modulus are measured. When the thickness is an appreciable fraction of the wavelength, complications ensue because the lateral contraction characteristic of simple extension is opposed by the elasticity and inertia of the material. The resulting effects, predicted for cylindrical rods by the so-called Pochhammer-Cree equations, have been discussed by various authors; [11–13] the phase and group velocities differ, and both depend on the ratio of radius to wavelength. The effects are particularly noticeable in the distortion of pulses over and above the distortion due to dispersion such as discussed in Section E of the preceding chapter.

When, at the other extreme, the thickness of the sample is large compared with the wavelength, the situation becomes relatively simple again and the wave propagation is governed by the complex modulus $\mathbf{M}^* = \mathbf{K}^* + (4/3)\mathbf{G}^*$, as pointed out in Chapter 1 (equation 4). The components of $\mathbf{M}^*$ can be calculated from the velocity and attenuation by the analogs of equations 15 and 16 of Chapter 5, with M' and M'' replacing G' and G''.

If the components of $\mathbf{G}^*$ have been determined in a separate experiment, those of $\mathbf{K}^*$ can be obtained from $\mathbf{M}^*$ by difference.[14] For a soft solid, in a frequency range where $G' \ll K'$, M' is practically equal to K' and no subtraction is necessary; but in this case K'' is usually much smaller than G'' and cannot be measured. Alternatively, if both $\mathbf{M}^*$ and $\mathbf{E}^*$ have been determined from longitudinal waves in wide fronts and in thin strips respectively, $\mathbf{K}^*$ and $\mathbf{G}^*$ can in principle be obtained by rearranging the complex analogs of equations 1 and 4 of Chapter 1.

Direct measurements of velocity and attenuation are usually made by passage of pulses which are sufficiently long to approximate steady-state oscillating deformation at the chosen frequency—from 0.1 to 30 megacycles/sec. The shear wave pulse system of Nolle and Sieck as described in Chapter 6 can be modified by substituting piezoelectric crystals cut to produce longitudinal vibrations, in this case with transmission blocks of aluminum.[15] Alternatively, a liquid can be used as a transmission medium between the crystal and the polymer; [16-18] measurements are made first with, then without, a sample of polymer inserted in the wave path through the liquid, determining the changes in amplitude and phase of a signal echoed back from a reflector (Fig. 8-2) or of a signal sent from a transmitter to a receiver.[18] Since the measurement gives the difference between the bulk longitudinal properties of the polymer and the liquid, the latter must of course be known; generally the attenuation for the liquid can be neglected in comparison with that for the polymer. The liquid medium has the advantage that no cement is required to establish mechanical coupling, but there is always the danger that it will diffuse into the polymer to a slight extent (even if its chemical properties are so chosen that the polymer does not swell in it to any substantial degree) and thereby modify the mechanical properties (cf. Chapter 16).

At somewhat lower frequencies, from 30 to 300 kilocycles/sec., standing waves may be employed in a method devised by Koppelmann,[18] which really belongs in the classification of resonance vibrations rather than wave propagation. Longitudinal "thickness" vibrations are excited across a plate of known thickness d, which is lightly supported at only a few points, by an electrostatically vibrated metal membrane; a second membrane serves as a detector. A series of resonances ω_{0n} is observed, whence the velocity is $v = d\omega_{0n}/n\pi$; the loss tangent is determined from the width of a frequency response curve or from the logarithmic decrement of free vibrations after the driving potential has been switched off. By using periodic on–off pulses, the decrement can be portrayed on an oscilloscope.

In a polymeric liquid with low enough viscosity to permit a receiving element to be moved through it, the liquid itself can be the sole transmitting medium for a bulk longitudinal wave and the attenuation and phase shift can be measured as a function of the distance between the sending and receiving piezoelectric crystals [19] (Fig. 8–3). The calculations are analogous to those for longitudinal wave transmission in thin strips as described in Section G of Chapter 6.

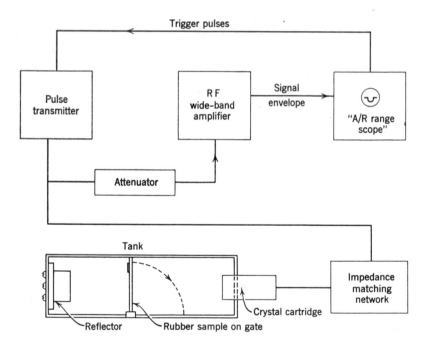

FIG. 8–2. Apparatus for longitudinal bulk wave propagation measurements, by echoing longitudinal pulses through a liquid with and without a polymeric sample in the path (Nolle and Mowry [16]).

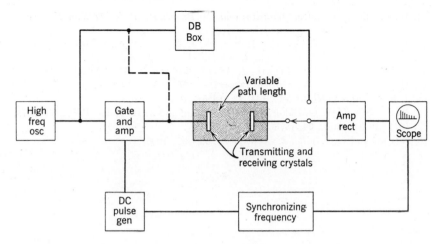

FIG. 8–3. Apparatus for longitudinal bulk wave propagation measurements in a viscoelastic liquid, with variable path length (Mason, Baker, McSkimin, and Heiss [19]).

Alternatively, the positions of nodes in standing waves can be determined,[20] with transducer measurements of attenuation in terms of the electrical resistance of the propagating crystal.

REFERENCES

1. S. Matsuoka and B. Maxwell, *J. Polymer Sci.*, **32**, 131 (1958).
2. P. W. Bridgman, *The Physics of High Pressure*, G. Bell and Sons Ltd., London, 1952.
3. E. Jenckel and P. Gehrke, unpublished work; P. Gehrke, Dissertation, Aachen, 1960.
4. E. Jenckel, in H. A. Stuart, *Die Physik der Hochpolymeren*, Vol. III, pp. 621–629, Springer-Verlag, Berlin, 1957.
5. E. Jenckel and G. Rehage, unpublished work.
6. R. O. Davies and G. O. Jones, *Proc. Roy. Soc.*, **A217**, 26 (1953).
7. A. Kovacs, Sc.D. Thesis, University of Paris, 1955.
8. W. Philippoff, *J. Applied Phys.*, **24**, 685 (1953).
9. W. Philippoff and J. Brodnyan, *J. Applied Phys.*, **26**, 846 (1955).
10. J. E. McKinney, S. Edelman, and R. S. Marvin, *J. Applied Phys.*, **27**, 425 (1956).
11. H. Kolsky, *Stress Waves in Solids*, Clarendon Press, Oxford, 1953.
12. W. P. Mason, *Piezoelectric Crystals and Their Applications in Ultrasonics*, Van Nostrand, 1950.

13. W. P. Mason, *Physical Acoustics and the Properties of Solids,* Van Nostrand, 1958.
14. R. S. Marvin, R. Aldrich, and H. S. Sack, *J. Applied Phys.,* **25,** 1213 (1954).
15. A. W. Nolle and P. W. Sieck, *J. Applied Phys.,* **23,** 888 (1952).
16. A. W. Nolle and S. C. Mowry, *J. Acoust. Soc. Amer.,* **20,** 432 (1948).
17. H. S. Sack and R. W. Aldrich, *Phys. Rev.,* **75,** 1285 (1949).
18. J. Koppelmann, *Kolloid-Z.,* **144,** 12 (1955).
19. W. P. Mason, W. O. Baker, H. J. McSkimin, and J. H. Heiss, *Phys. Rev.,* **73,** 1074 (1948); *ibid.,* **74,** 1873 (1949).
20. R. Cerf and G. Laville, *J. chim. phys.,* **53,** 292 (1956).

CHAPTER 9

Experimental Methods for Fibers

Considerable effort has been devoted to measuring viscoelastic properties of polymers in the form of fibers, because of their technological importance. Such materials are usually hard viscoelastic solids, and the methods of Chapter 7 are therefore applicable in principle, but the restrictions imposed by sample size and shape require some modifications. In particular, the sample shape cannot be chosen to suit the experimenter's convenience; often the only dimension which can be adjusted is the length.

Frequently, a fiber is anisotropic, with different properties in different directions. For practical purposes, the only types of deformation which can be readily measured are simple extension, torsion, and flexure. Extension and flexure should both measure Young's modulus E for elongation in the fiber direction, and should therefore yield the same result. Torsion measures the shear modulus G for a direction of slide *perpendicular* to the fiber direction, and in case of anisotropy these moduli E and G are not connected in any simple manner. Some examples of such behavior will be given in Chapter 15.

The fiber cross-section frequently has a shape other than circular, such as the "racetrack" or "dogbone" contours. Although this causes no particular complication for measurements in extension, where the sample coefficient is determined directly by the cross-section area, it makes difficult the calculation of absolute values of viscoelastic properties from measurements in torsion or flexure, which involve higher moments of the area.[1] Moreover, the lateral dimensions are usually far from uniform.[2]

145

Another special problem which enters into measurements on a fiber is the necessity of maintaining its content of moisture (or other diluent) constant by equilibrium with a liquid or a vapor of known composition. Although fibers are no more sensitive to traces of diluent than are other hard polymers (glassy or crystalline), their small diameter enables them to absorb or lose diluent rapidly if the composition of the environment fluctuates.

A. CREEP AND STRESS RELAXATION

Transient viscoelastic measurements are almost invariably made in simple extension,[3-7] but occasionally in torsion.[8,9] The principal problem is the measurement of rather small deforming forces, since the cross-section area is very small though the modulus is high. Beam balances and electrical (resistance) strain gauges have been successfully employed for extension. In torsion, the concomitant twist of a torsion member in series with the sample (the angle of twist of the torsion member being comparatively small, for stress relaxation, or comparatively large, for creep), can be measured. Even for small forces, the stresses are high, and frequently the smallest experimentally practicable stresses exceed the limits of linear viscoelastic behavior, as illustrated for polycrystalline fibers in Chapter 15.

Stress-strain curves at constant rate of loading or of elongation are also measured by various devices, often with cycling of the loading pattern, and often with automatic recording.[10,11]

B. DYNAMIC MEASUREMENTS

Most of the various types of dynamic methods described in preceding chapters have been applied to fibers. The simplest principle, that of direct measurement of sinusoidally varying stress and strain, has been employed below 0.5 cycle/sec. by mechanical deformation and optical recording of both stress and strain with rotating mirrors,[12] somewhat in the manner of the corresponding device of Roelig[13] for soft rubberlike polymers (Chapter 6).

Compound resonance devices in free oscillations, where the measurements are a characteristic frequency and a logarithmic decrement of amplitude (Section F of Chapter 6) have been widely used. In its simplest form, a mass serves to keep the fiber taut under static stress

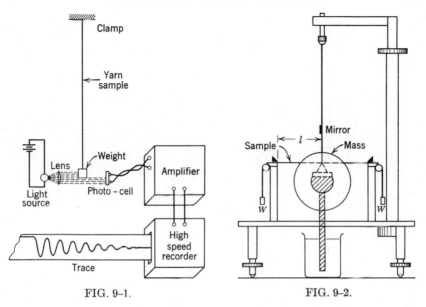

FIG. 9–1.   FIG. 9–2.

FIG. 9–1. Apparatus of Ballou and Smith[14] for measurement of dynamic Young's modulus of fibers by free vibrations.
FIG. 9–2. Torsion pendulum of Tokita[15] for measurement of dynamic Young's modulus of fibers by free vibrations.

and also functions as the inertia in longitudinal oscillation[14] (Fig. 9–1). This device is operated in the range from 2 to 20 cycles/sec. At lower frequencies, down to 0.04 cycles/sec., a torsion pendulum has been used by Tokita[15] in which the samples (two fibers) are actually deformed in extension although the oscillation of the apparatus is torsional (Fig. 9–2). In other frequency ranges, a rocking beam balance can be used to deform fibers in extension, either freely rocking or attached to a torsion wire at right angles to increase the characteristic frequency.[15] Forced oscillation (Section E of Chapter 6) can also be employed,[16,17] extending the frequency to 5000 cycles/sec.

Propagation of longitudinal waves along the fiber direction provides measurements of the components of the complex Young's modulus, in accordance with Section G of Chapter 6, in the range from 4 to 100 kilocycles/sec.[18,19,15] Figure 9–3 shows an example of such an apparatus, in which piezoelectric Rochelle salt crystals are used as driver and pickup. The fiber is doubled back at the pickup, which slides up and down to vary the path length; a more positive contact than

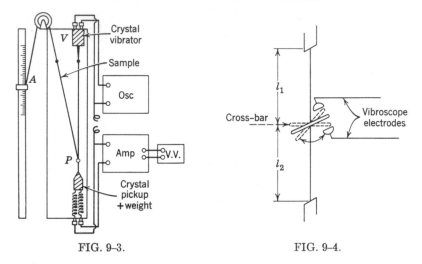

FIG. 9–3.   FIG. 9–4.

FIG. 9–3. Apparatus for measurement of longitudinal wave propagation in fibers (Tokita [15]).

FIG. 9–4. Measurement of dynamic shear modulus of a fiber by forced torsional vibrations (Wakelin *et al.*[2]).

the slight sideways pressure used for rubber strips is desirable. The equations for calculation are, as before, the same as 15 and 16 of Chapter 5, which in extension give E' and E''. In the case of high damping, the pickup amplifier can be lightly coupled to the oscillator so that it records a vector sum of pickup and (attenuated) driving voltages; this permits observing a sufficient number of wavelengths to determine the velocity of propagation.[15] The method has been adapted to measurements of high precision by Dick and Müller.[20] In another modification,[21] longitudinal wave pulses are sent down the fiber (*cf.* Section C of Chapter 8).

The method of resonance vibrations (Section C of Chapter 7) has also been used, in the form of standing longitudinal wave measurements[18] and flexural vibrations of short fiber segments.[2, 14, 22, 23] In the latter case, the fiber cross-section shape and dimensions must be known with high accuracy; the equations for calculating E' and E'' are similar to equations 12 and 13 of Chapter 7 (for circular cross-section) but with different numerical coefficients for one end clamped and one free. Despite the small flexural stiffness of thin fibers, this method has been employed on filaments as thin as 0.03 mm.[2]

All the dynamic measurements thus far mentioned furnish the complex Young's modulus in the fiber direction. The shear modulus at right angles can be measured by torsional vibrations of the fiber itself, using a light crossbar or disc to provide the moment of inertia for a compound oscillating system in forced [2] or free [24] vibration. An example [2] is shown in Fig. 9–4, where the forced vibrations are driven by an electrostatic device.[25] Here the analog of equation 11 of Chapter 6 is [2]

$$G' = \rho' A' L'^3 \omega_0^2 / 6\pi R^4 [1/L_1 + 1/L_2] \tag{1}$$

where ρ', A', and L' are the density, cross-section area, and length of the crossbar, R is the fiber radius, and L_1 and L_2 are the lengths of the fiber above and below the crossbar attachment.

Apparatus has also been devised for continuous measurement of dynamic mechanical properties during drawing or processing.[26,27]

REFERENCES

1. R. Meredith, *J. Textile Inst.*, **45**, T489 (1954).
2. J. H. Wakelin, E. T. L. Voong, D. J. Montgomery, and J. H. Dusenbury, *J. Applied Phys.*, **26**, 786 (1955).
3. H. Leaderman, *Elastic and Creep Properties of Filamentous Materials and Other High Polymers*, The Textile Foundation, Washington, 1943.
4. J. J. Press, *J. Applied Phys.*, **14**, 224 (1943).
5. R. Meredith, *J. Textile Inst.*, **45**, T138 (1954).
6. W. J. Thorsen, *Textile Res. J.*, **24**, 407, 899 (1954).
7. E. T. Kubu, *Textile Res. J.*, **22**, 765 (1952).
8. W. G. Hammerle and D. J. Montgomery, *Textile Res. J.*, **23**, 595 (1953).
9. T. Yoshitomi, K. Nagamatsu, and K. Kosiyama, *J. Polymer Sci.*, **27**, 335 (1958).
10. W. Meskat and O. Rosenberg, in H. A. Stuart, *Die Physik der Hochpolymeren*, Vol. IV, p. 235, Springer-Verlag, Berlin, 1956.
11. R. Meredith, editor, *Mechanical Properties of Textile Fibers*, North Holland Publishing Co., Amsterdam, 1956.
12. W. Wegener, in E. Wagner, *Mechanische technologische Textilprüfungen*, Wuppertal, 1953, p. 206.
13. H. Roelig, *Proc. Rubber Technol. Conf.*, pp. 821–829 (1938).
14. J. W. Ballou and J. C. Smith, *J. Applied Phys.*, **20**, 493 (1949).
15. N. Tokita, *J. Polymer Sci.*, **20**, 515 (1956).
16. H. Kawai and N. Tokita, *J. Phys. Soc. Japan*, **5**, 17 (1950).
17. B. A. Dunell and J. H. Dillon, *Textile Res. J.*, **21**, 393 (1951).
18. J. W. Ballou and S. Silverman, *J. Acoust. Soc. Amer.*, **16**, 113 (1944).
19. K. W. Hillier and H. Kolsky, *Proc. Phys. Soc.*, **62B**, 701 (1949).
20. W. Dick and F. H. Müller, *Kolloid-Z.*, **166**, 113 (1959).

21. M. Chaikin and N. H. Chamberlain, *J. Textile Inst.*, **46**, T25 (1955).
22. J. P. A. Lochner, *J. Textile Inst.*, **40**, T220 (1949).
23. J. C. Guthrie, D. H. Morton, and P. H. Oliver, *J. Textile Inst.*, **45**, T912 (1954).
24. R. Meredith, *J. Textile Inst.*, **45**, T489 (1954).
25. D. J. Montgomery and W. T. Milloway, *Textile Research J.*, **22**, 729 (1952).
26. F. Breazeale and J. Whisnant, *J. Applied Phys.*, **20**, 621 (1949).
27. W. Meskat and O. Rosenberg, Reference 10, p. 286.

CHAPTER 10

Molecular Theory

Although the phenomenological theory of linear viscoelasticity, whose results were summarized in Chapters 3 and 4, is of great value for interrelating different kinds of experimental measurements, and for formulating certain limits on the behavior of polymeric systems which conform to the Boltzmann superposition principle, it provides no insight into the molecular origin of viscoelastic behavior. Qualitatively, we have seen in Chapter 1 that the prominence of viscoelastic phenomena in polymers is associated with the versatility of movement of flexible threadlike macromolecules. In Chapters 2 and 3, scrutiny of the shapes of the viscoelastic functions revealed certain characteristic zones which were roughly correlated with different types of molecular motions. The transition zone between rubberlike and glasslike consistency involves configurational rearrangements of the chain backbone with different degrees of intramolecular cooperation; the plateau zone (where the spectrum H is relatively flat, and the spectrum L goes through a maximum) involves similar configurational rearrangements of groups of molecules coupled tightly by entanglement points; the pseudo-equilibrium zone, in cross-linked polymers, presumably involves coordinated motions coupled over considerable distances through permanent junction points; the terminal zone, in uncross-linked polymers, involves motions of molecules or groups of molecules in which the coordination of individual segments is almost complete; the glassy zone involves much more limited local motions, with no gross changes in backbone contour. We must now examine these processes in more detail, to see what quantitative predictions can be made at the present stage of development, and what guidance

151

these can provide in interpreting the effects of chemical structure in the chapters to follow.

The theories to be described here deal only with deformation in shear, or for soft polymeric systems the closely related deformation in simple extension with negligible change in volume. The subject of bulk viscoelastic behavior has not yet reached a stage ripe for theoretical development.

A. THEORY BASED ON BROWNIAN MOTION OF ISOLATED FLEXIBLE CHAINS

By far the most spectacular feature of polymer viscoelasticity is the transition from glasslike to rubberlike consistency, where the viscoelastic functions change by several orders of magnitude, and theoretical efforts have primarily been devoted to understanding the behavior in this zone.[1-5] The most comprehensive recent treatments have dealt with very dilute solutions in which the polymer molecules are supposed to be isolated.

1. General Features

Such a molecule, surrounded and pervaded by solvent, is continually rearranging its configuration by random motions. The driving force for these Brownian motions is the thermal energy; they are opposed by viscous forces involving the hydrodynamic resistance of the solvent and intramolecular steric effects which are usually referred to as internal viscosity. The assortment of configurations and the rates of configurational change are only slightly disturbed by the application of an external shear stress if the latter is small enough to correspond to the usual restrictions of linear viscoelastic behavior; the Brownian motion goes on just the same.

The discussion could be pursued in terms of any of the viscoelastic functions surveyed in Chapter 2. It is convenient for the moment to choose the components of the dynamic compliance, J' and J''. For a periodic stress, the relative amounts of energy storage and dissipation per cycle—i.e., the relative contributions of the solute to J' and J'' of the solution—depend on to what extent the random Brownian motions are correlated with the varying external forces. Displacement in phase with force corresponds to energy storage, but velocity in phase with force corresponds to energy dissipation.

On a scale of atomic dimensions (*cf.* Fig. 1–3), the configurational motions must be accounted for by rotations around all the bonds in the chain backbone. For complete specification of a configuration, with all the positions of jZ backbone atoms relative to each other (Z being the degree of polymerization, and j the number of chain atoms per monomer unit—often 2), a point in phase space with $3jZ$ dimensions would be required.[6-8] It can be seen qualitatively that for very high frequencies there will be no time for any rotations within a period of alternation and the response to stress will be limited to bending and stretching chemical bonds; such deformations correspond to a high elastic stiffness, and J' is small. At lower frequencies, regions of the chain not too far removed from each other have time to change their relative positions within a period; there will be components of both displacement and velocity in phase with the changing stress, and substantial contributions to both J' and J''. At very low frequencies, J'' increases without limit; J' approaches a limiting value which is a measure of the stored energy in a freely flexible chain due to the entropy decrease accompanying a certain average distortion (see below). The limiting low-frequency value of J' is proportional to molecular weight and for polymeric molecules is greater by orders of magnitude than the high-frequency limiting value. This sort of behavior of J' and J'' in an undiluted polymer of moderately low molecular weight can be seen in Curves I, Figs. 2–6 and 2–7.

The complete specification of configuration requires a more detailed knowledge of the dimensions and shapes of the monomeric units, local packing effects, and interactions with the solvent molecules than can in practice be available—as well as being mathematically intractable. A valuable simplification can be made if one is willing to sacrifice consideration of short-range relationships and attendant behavior at the very highest frequencies. It utilizes the prediction from polymer chain statistics that any two points on the chain backbone separated by 50 or more chain atoms will be related to each other in space in accordance with a Gaussian distribution of vectors.[9,10] In the absence of external forces, the form of this distribution holds regardless of the bond distances and angles, local packing effects, interaction with solvents, and other hindrances to free rotation, all of which enter only into a proportionality constant with dimensions of length.[11,12] Thus the root-mean-square distance between two points separated by q monomer units ($qj \gtrsim 50$) is $\sigma = a\sqrt{q}$, where a depends on local geometric parameters and is generally of the order of several times the length of a single chain bond.[9]

The statistical theory of rubberlike elasticity shows that the fluctuations in length of such a chain segment cause it to act like a Hooke's law spring under tension, storing energy because of the entropy decrease associated with restrictions on the assortment of configurations it can assume.[13] The force constant (force per unit displacement) of the spring is $3kT/qa^2$, and one may regard the elastic part of the viscoelastic behavior of polymers (liquids and soft solids) as arising from Brownian motion in this manner. In some of the theoretical treatments, molecular chain segments are represented by "entropy springs."

When a dilute solution of polymer molecules is subjected to shearing stress, the flowing solvent distorts it so that the assortment of vectors between two chain atoms q units apart is slightly perturbed from a Gaussian distribution. The Brownian motion will result in a diffusion back to approach this distribution, however, and the viscoelastic behavior is determined by the interaction between these two effects. In the theories of Rouse [14] and Zimm,[15] the molecule is considered as subdivided into N submolecules each with q monomer units, and the hydrodynamic forces exerted by the flowing solvent are concentrated at the junctions between the submolecules. The root-mean-square end-to-end length of the entire molecule is $(\overline{r_0^2})^{1/2} = \sigma\sqrt{N} = a\sqrt{Z}$; the magnitudes of q, σ, and N do not have to be definitely specified, but it is understood that $qj \gtrsim 50$, and the high-frequency limits of applicability of the theories depend on the value of q.

Some of the gross features of polymer viscoelastic behavior can also be predicted on the basis of far simpler molecular models, such as an elastic dumbbell [16] or a viscoelastic sphere.[17]

2. Theory of Rouse: Relaxation and Retardation Spectra

In Rouse's treatment,[14, 19] the above model is combined with the assumption of no hydrodynamic interaction between the motions of the submolecule junctions, corresponding to the "free-draining" chain in calculations of steady-flow viscosity of dilute solutions.[18] The resistance encountered by a submolecule junction moving through its surroundings is characterized by a friction coefficient f_0, and it is assumed that an average value can be used for all such junctions; f_0 is proportional to q. (Specifically, $f_0 = q\zeta_0$, where ζ_0 is the monomeric friction coefficient.) No intramolecular friction (internal viscosity) is taken into account.

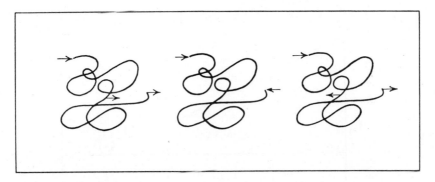

FIG. 10–1. Schematic illustration of characteristic modes of coordinated motion of a flexible chain molecule.

The simultaneous motions of all the segment junctions can be described through a transformation of coordinates as the sum of a series of cooperative modes. Each mode represents motion away from a given instantaneous configuration in which the segments are coordinated along the molecular contour somewhat similarly to the segments of a vibrating string (Fig. 10–1). Each mode, moreover, corresponds to a discrete contribution to the relaxation spectrum. It is convenient to express the results in terms of the spectrum H, from which any of the experimental viscoelastic functions can be derived by the relations in Chapter 3:

$$H = nkT \sum_{p=1}^{N} \tau_p \delta(\tau - \tau_p) \tag{1}$$

$$\tau_p = \sigma^2 f_0 / 24 kT \sin^2 \left[p\pi / 2(N+1) \right] \tag{2}$$

where δ is the Dirac delta and n the number of polymer molecules per cc.; i.e., a line spectrum is predicted, in which each contribution to the shear modulus G_p has the magnitude nkT and the relaxation times become progressively more closely spaced at shorter times (Fig. 10–2). When equation 1 is substituted into equations 19, 23, and 25 of Chapter 3, the following summations are obtained:

$$G(t) = nkT \sum^{N} e^{-t/\tau_p} \tag{3}$$

$$G'(\omega) = nkT \sum^{N} \omega^2 \tau_p^2 / (1 + \omega^2 \tau_p^2) \tag{4}$$

$$\eta'(\omega) = nkT \sum^{N} \tau_p / (1 + \omega^2 \tau_p^2) \tag{5}$$

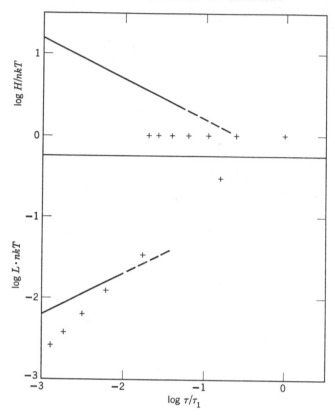

FIG. 10-2. Line spectra (crosses) for relaxation and retardation as predicted by the Rouse theory, with equivalent continuous spectra at short times (solid lines). τ_1 is longest relaxation time.

The finite limit of the sum at $p = N$ is an artificial consequence of the submolecular model, and the treatment must break down as $p \to N$, because configurational changes within the segments are ignored. It can be applied only where the series converges for $p < N$; specifically, if it is limited to $p < N/5$, equation 2 can be replaced by the much more convenient approximation

$$\tau_p = \sigma^2 N^2 f_0 / 6\pi^2 p^2 kT = a^2 Z^2 \zeta_0 / 6\pi^2 p^2 kT \tag{6}$$

The convergence requirements restrict the applicability to times or reciprocal frequencies greater than $5\tau_N \cong 0.1a^2 q^2 \zeta_0 / kT$. However, the values of τ_p fortunately depend only on ζ_0 and a, not on any properties of the artificial submolecule.

Following calculations similar to those of Gross,[19] it can be shown that the retardation spectrum corresponding to equations 1 and 6 is also discrete:

$$L = (16/5\pi^2 nkT) \sum_{\lambda=1}^{N} [\tau_\lambda/(2\lambda - 1)^2]\delta(\tau - \tau_\lambda) \tag{7}$$

$$\tau_\lambda = 2a^2 Z^2 \zeta_0/75(2\lambda - 1)^2 \pi^2 kT \tag{8}$$

Here, the contributions to the shear compliance J_λ decrease rapidly with decreasing τ (Fig. 10–2). From equation 7, calculations of $J(t)$, J', and J'' can be made as summations analogous to equations 3 to 5.

3. Evaluation in Terms of Steady-Flow Viscosity

The magnitude of ζ_0, to which all relaxation and retardation times are proportional, depends on the solvent viscosity and for dilute solutions is found experimentally to be roughly proportional to it.[20] For comparison of the theory with experimental results, it is frequently convenient to eliminate ζ_0 in terms of the contribution of the polymer to the steady-flow viscosity, $\eta - \eta_s$ (where η_s is the viscosity of the solvent). By substituting equation 1 into equation 28 of Chapter 3, or alternatively by setting $\omega = 0$ in equation 5, it is found that

$$\eta - \eta_s = na^2 Z^2 \zeta_0/36 \tag{9}$$

in agreement with the corresponding treatment of steady-flow viscosity of dilute solutions by Debye.[18] It follows that equation 6 can be written

$$\tau_p = 6(\eta - \eta_s)/\pi^2 p^2 nkT \tag{10}$$

and the time-dependent properties can be completely predicted from easily measured macroscopic quantities. (Knowledge of n implies a known molecular weight, and of course the polymer is supposed to be homogeneous with respect to molecular weight.) The results of the theory can be expressed by certain dimensionless reduced functions which are tabulated in Appendix E at the end of this book.

4. Limiting Forms at Moderately Short Times or High Frequencies

Except for the two or three longest relaxation (or retardation) times, the contributions in Fig. 10–2 are closely enough spaced to be well approximated by continuous spectra. The appropriate equations are: [21]

$$H = (aZn/2\pi)(\zeta_0 kT/6)^{\frac{1}{2}}\tau^{-\frac{1}{2}} \tag{11}$$

$$L = (2/\pi aZn)(6/\zeta_0 kT)^{\frac{1}{2}}\tau^{\frac{1}{2}} \tag{12}$$

or, in terms of the steady-flow viscosity,

$$H = (\sqrt{6}/2\pi)[nkT(\eta - \eta_s)]^{\frac{1}{2}}\tau^{-\frac{1}{2}} \tag{13}$$

$$L = (2/\pi\sqrt{6})[nkT(\eta - \eta_s)]^{-\frac{1}{2}}\tau^{\frac{1}{2}} \tag{14}$$

Thus these functions plotted with logarithmic scales are linear with slopes of $-\frac{1}{2}$ and $\frac{1}{2}$ respectively.

The limit of applicability of equations 11 and 12 is set at long times roughly by $\tau < \tau_3$, corresponding to $H > (\frac{3}{2})nkT$, or $L < 2/3\pi^2 nkT$; at short times, it is set by the requirement that $\tau > 0.1a^2 q^2 \zeta_0/kT$, corresponding to $H < 0.1(Z/q)nkT$, or $L > 1/(Z/q)nkT$. If $q = 25$ and $Z = 10^4$ (e.g., molecular weight of 10^6 and monomer molecular weight of 10^2), the linear logarithmic plot would be expected over about one and a half decades of H or L, or three decades of time scale.

5. Effect of Hydrodynamic Interaction: Theory of Zimm

In Zimm's treatment,[15, 10] hydrodynamic interaction between the moving submolecules is introduced in the same manner as by Kirkwood and Riseman [22] for calculating the steady-flow viscosity of dilute solutions. There is still no account taken of internal viscosity. Analysis of the motion of the submolecules and transformation of the coordinates leads to another discrete spectrum

$$H = nkT \sum_{k=1}^{N} \tau_k \delta(\tau - \tau_k) \tag{15}$$

$$\tau_k = 0.806\eta_s a^3 Z^{\frac{3}{2}}/\lambda'_k kT \tag{16}$$

where η_s is the solvent viscosity and the λ'_k are numerical coefficients [23] whose first few values ($k = 1, 2, 3, 4$) are 4.04, 12.79, 24.2, and 37.9. The frictional resistance is now characterized not by a friction coefficient but by the solvent viscosity η_s. This parameter can be eliminated as a factor, to obtain a more direct comparison of the Rouse and Zimm results, by calculating the solute contribution to steady-flow viscosity to give a relation analogous to equation 9:

$$\eta - \eta_s = 0.47n\eta_s a^3 Z^{\frac{3}{2}} \tag{17}$$

whence equation 16 can be written in terms of the solute contribution to steady-flow viscosity, analogous to equation 10:

$$\tau_k = 1.71(\eta - \eta_s)/\lambda'_k nkT \tag{18}$$

These values are somewhat smaller than those predicted by equation 10, for equal values of n and $\eta - \eta_s$. The dispersion of η' as predicted by the Zimm theory thus lies at somewhat higher frequencies than that predicted by Rouse,[10] as well as being somewhat different in shape.

At moderately short times, but not so short that k must approach N for convergence of the series, the line spectrum of Zimm can also be closely approximated by a continuous spectrum:

$$H = [(4/6\pi)^{1/3}/3]a^2 Zn(kT)^{1/3}\eta_s^{2/3}\tau^{-2/3} \tag{19}$$

so this has a slope of $-\frac{2}{3}$ on logarithmic scales. The corresponding region of L should have a slope of $\frac{2}{3}$.

6. Comparison with Experimental Data for Dilute Solutions

Although detailed presentation of experimental results and their relation to molecular structure is being reserved for later chapters, a few examples will be given in the present chapter for evaluating the predictions of theory.

Data of Rouse and Sittel [20] on solutions of polystyrene (molecular weight 6.2×10^6) in toluene, at concentrations from 0.1 to 0.2 g./dl., are shown in Figs. 10–3 and 10–4. The experimental points for G' (plotted logarithmically) and η' are compared with predictions from equations 4, 5, and 10, which involve measurements of the steady-flow viscosity and require no arbitrary parameters. The agreement is excellent, despite the neglect of hydrodynamic interaction and internal viscosity. Since for calculating the ordinary intrinsic viscosity (at high molecular weights) the treatment with hydrodynamic interaction [22] is far more satisfactory than the free-draining hypothesis,[18] it is not clear at present why the viscoelastic data should agree better with the theory based on the latter simplification; [24, 10] the question needs further clarification.

However, in a semi-quantitative manner, these and other data of Rouse and Sittel, and dynamic data of Mason [25] which are presented in a form difficult to compare directly with theory, as well as recent data of Zimm,[24] are all in general agreement with the Rouse and Zimm treatments. Experimentally, G' increases with frequency over several powers of ten; whereas with increasing frequency η' falls progressively

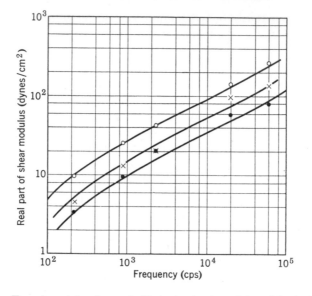

FIG. 10–3. Experimental values of G' (points) plotted logarithmically against frequency for solutions of polystyrene, molecular weight 6.2×10^6, in toluene at 30.3°C., compared with values calculated from equations 4 and 10 (curves). Concentrations, left to right: 0.222, 0.144, and 0.101 g./100 cc.

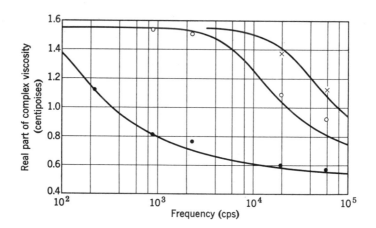

FIG. 10–4. Experimental values of η' (points) plotted against log frequency for solutions of different polystyrene fractions in toluene, compared with values calculated from equations 5 and 10 (curves). Molecular weights, left to right: 6.20, 0.52, and 0.25×10^6; concentrations chosen so that $\eta - \eta_s$ is approximately the same for each solution.

from its low-frequency limit of η and at very high frequencies approaches η_s. There can be little doubt that these changes are associated with cooperative motions of the flexible molecules as pictured by the theories.

In some discussions of the viscoelastic properties of dilute solutions, "intrinsic" quantities analogous to the intrinsic viscosity are used for the viscoelastic functions.[10, 25] Thus the intrinsic dynamic viscosity, $[\eta']$, is the limit as $c \to 0$ of $(\eta' - \eta_s)/\eta_s c$, whereas the intrinsic rigidity, $[G']$, is the corresponding limit of $G'/\eta_s c$. Here c is the concentration of polymer, usually in g. per cc. An intrinsic rigidity has alternatively been defined [2, 26] as the limit of G'/c as $c \to 0$. Equations 4 and 5 can be written in terms of these variables. Experimental extrapolations to infinite dilution cannot be made to determine $[\eta']$ and $[G']$ as they conventionally are for $[\eta]$, however, since with changing c all the relaxation times change, proportional to $\eta - \eta_s$ (equation 10), and the frequency scale of the dispersion region shifts accordingly.

7. Extension of the Dilute Solution Theory to Undiluted Polymers

In an undiluted polymer above its glass transition temperature, each molecule executes much the same kind of motions that it does in dilute solution, except that they are far slower because of higher frictional resistance.[27] In one respect the situation is simpler, since in the undiluted polymer each segment of the chain is in much the same kind of environment—surrounded by other polymer segments— whereas in dilute solution the central segments in each molecule have a higher average proportion of polymer neighbors than those on the periphery. Although the motion of a segment through its surroundings involves very complicated readjustments of its own chain as well as those of its neighbors, the resistance can still be expressed by an average monomeric friction coefficient ζ_0 as in the Rouse theory, and under certain circumstances the same friction coefficient may be considered to govern all types of coordinated motions. (This will not be true if entanglement coupling is present, but even here there appears to be a limited group of modes with the same average friction coefficient, as discussed below.)

In the condensed polymer there is certainly no need to introduce the intramolecular friction or internal viscosity explicitly, since the resistance to motion of a chain unit is determined primarily by its neighbors and very little by the intramolecular steric effects which would be observed in an isolated chain. (This statement is borne out by comparisons between the friction encountered by polymer chain units and by small foreign molecules, as discussed in Chapter 12.) Even in dilute solution, the role of internal viscosity is subdued as the solvent viscosity is increased,[10] and in an undiluted polymer the effective local viscosity is very high.

In extending the theory for dilute solutions to undiluted polymers, it is not clear *a priori* whether the Rouse or the Zimm results should be employed. Experimental determinations of H and L in the transition region between glasslike and rubberlike consistency are approximately linear on a logarithmic plot (*cf.* Figs. 3–1 and 3–2), but the slopes vary from $\frac{1}{2}$ to slightly over $\frac{2}{3}$ (+ for L, − for H), so the characteristic exponents in equations 11, 12, and 19 cannot be used as the basis for choice. The Rouse treatment is somewhat arbitrarily selected here, partly because the observed slope for H is usually close to $-\frac{1}{2}$ in the region of time scale where the theory should be most closely applicable; partly because the mathematics corresponds to certain mechanical and electrical models which are more easily manipulated to obtain extensions of the theory (Section B below); and partly because the parameter ζ_0 which describes the local friction appears to have a more direct physical significance in an undiluted polymer than the corresponding parameter η_s in the Zimm theory. In dilute solutions, η_s is the solvent viscosity, but in an undiluted polymer it would presumably represent an effective local viscosity far smaller than the macroscopic viscosity.

Under circumstances where the same ζ_0 governs all modes of motion, we have after replacing n by its equivalent $\rho N_0/M$ (where ρ is the polymer density, N_0 Avogadro's number, and M the molecular weight):

$$H = (\rho RT/M)\Sigma \tau_p \delta(\tau - \tau_p) \tag{20}$$

The values of τ_p in terms of the friction coefficient as given by equation 6 are unchanged; in terms of the steady-flow viscosity, equation 10 becomes, after dropping η_s since there is no solvent

$$\tau_p = 6\eta M/\pi^2 p^2 \rho RT \tag{21}$$

while the limiting values of the spectra at moderately high frequencies are, from equations 13 and 14:

$$H = (\sqrt{6}/2\pi)(\rho RT\eta/M)^{\frac{1}{2}}\tau^{-\frac{1}{2}} \tag{22}$$

$$L = (2/\pi\sqrt{6})(\rho RT\eta/M)^{-\frac{1}{2}}\tau^{\frac{1}{2}} \tag{23}$$

For polymers of low molecular weight, where entanglement coupling is absent, the magnitude of H in the transition zone should be proportional to $(\eta/M)^{1/2}$; since η increases with something [28] like M^2, the level of H should increase and that of L decrease with increasing M. At the same time, the terminal zones of the spectra extend rapidly to longer times with increasing M, since according to equation 21 the terminal relaxation time τ_1 is proportional to the product ηM.

The well-known fact that, experimentally, η/M is not constant implies that the average friction coefficient ζ_0 changes with molecular weight; it increases with M, presumably because the loosening effect of free molecular ends is gradually eliminated. Eventually, with increasing M, the effect of free ends disappears asymptotically, being proportional to $1/M$. Qualitatively, when the molecular ends are far enough apart, the average polymer segment is oblivious of their existence. Then ζ_0 should become independent of molecular weight, and there is good experimental evidence that it does (Chapter 12). Meanwhile, entanglement coupling has set in, so η/M is still not constant, but for a different reason: the frictional resistance to long-range motions, which primarily determine η as well as the viscoelastic behavior at long times, is strongly influenced by the entanglements. But the shorter range modes of motion are oblivious of the entanglements and are governed by a ζ_0 which is independent of M. Thus, when M is high, H and L can be represented by the following relations analogous to equations 11 and 12:

$$H = (a\rho N_0/2\pi M_0)(\zeta_0 kT/6)^{1/2}\tau^{-1/2} \tag{24}$$

$$L = (2M_0/\pi a\rho N_0)(6/\zeta_0 kT)^{1/2}\tau^{1/2} \tag{25}$$

where M_0 is the monomeric molecular weight, M/Z. Equation 24 has been extensively used to calculate friction coefficients from experimental data, and its application will be discussed in Chapter 12. Its limit of applicability at long times depends on the distance between entanglement points, as mentioned in a subsequent section; at short times, it is the same as that of equation 11, corresponding in the present notation to $H < 0.1\rho RT/qM_0$. For $M_0 = 100$, $q = 25$, $\rho = 1$, and $T = 300$, this corresponds to $H < 10^6$ dynes/cm^2, thus restricting the range to the long-time end of the transition zone as seen in the plots of Figs. 3–1 and 3–2. (Actually, as pointed out by Ham,[29] these limits may be unnecessarily restrictive.) In the neighborhood of this region, G' and G'' should be nearly equal and proportional to $\omega^{1/2}$; J' and J'' should be nearly equal and proportional to $\omega^{-1/2}$. The upper limit of G' for strict applicability of the theory should be [30] about 10^7 dynes/cm².

It is difficult to portray equations 20 to 25 graphically, since they involve a combination of line and equivalent continuous spectra. To illustrate the dependence of viscoelastic properties on molecular weight, therefore, the functions G' and J' have been chosen. Semi-schematic logarithmic plots for polyisobutylenes of several molecular weights are shown in Figs. 10–5 and 10–6. The storage modulus has the prescribed slope of 2 in the terminal zone (*cf.* Chapter 2), the location of which is spread widely in accordance with the product ηM; it goes into the prescribed slope of ½ in the transition zone. At high molecular weights, the transition zone becomes independent of molecular weight, and the terminal zone is omitted because it requires consideration of entanglements. The storage compliance levels off at low frequencies at a value which is directly proportional to M (*cf.* Section C below); it goes into the prescribed slope of $-½$ in the transition zone. These plots are roughly similar to observed behavior

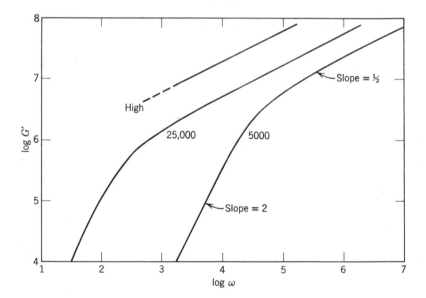

FIG. 10–5. Schematic dependence of G' on frequency and molecular weight as predicted by the modified Rouse theory for undiluted polyisobutylenes, assuming that for low molecular weights (5000 and 25,000) η is proportional to M^2, whereas for high molecular weights ζ_0 becomes independent of molecular weight and is taken from Table 12–II. Temperature 298°K.

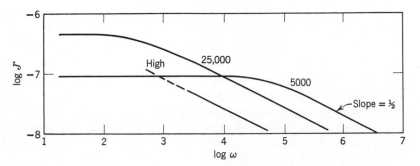

FIG. 10–6. Schematic dependence of J' on frequency and molecular weight as predicted by the modified Rouse theory as in Fig. 10–5.

as illustrated in Figs. 2–3 and 2–6, in particular for the polymer of low molecular weight (Curve 1).

The effect of temperature on viscoelastic properties, as predicted by the theory, appears primarily in the temperature dependence of ζ_0 (in equations 24 and 25) or of η (in equations 22 and 23). This subject is discussed in detail in the following chapter.

8. Application of the Theory to Concentrated Polymer Solutions

In concentrated solutions, where the molecules are substantially intertwined, the situation is qualitatively the same as for an undiluted polymer, except that the friction coefficient ζ_0 is smaller because some of the nearest neighbors of a given polymer segment are solvent molecules and much more mobile. The range of conditions over which the modes of motion are governed by a single value of ζ_0 may be somewhat different, and will certainly depend on the concentration, but within their limits all the equations of the preceding section should hold with ρ (in g./cc.) replaced by the polymer concentration c (in g./cc.). This substitution arises from the fact that the number of molecules per cc., n, is now cN_0/M instead of $\rho N_0/M$. The solvent viscosity η_s in equations such as 10 is negligible compared with η. The magnitudes of contributions to H (and G', G'', and $G(t)$) are directly proportional to c. The effect of c on the magnitudes of the relaxation times (and hence the time and frequency scales for the experimental functions) will for low molecular weights be governed by the concentration dependence of η (equation 21); for high molecular weights, it will be governed by the concentration dependence of ζ_0. Information on these relations from experimental sources is discussed in Chapter 16.

It should be emphasized that the theory for isolated flexible molecules as thus far presented does not account for viscoelastic behavior in the glassy or plateau zones, nor for the properties of cross-linked networks. Modifications for these purposes, as well as some additional consequences of the flexible chain theory in the terminal zone, will be taken up in subsequent sections. First, however, some alternative formulations of the theory in terms of other functions and models will be described.

B. EQUIVALENT FORMULATIONS OF THE FLEXIBLE CHAIN THEORY

Some of the results of the Rouse theory were actually anticipated by a calculation of Blizard [31] in which polymer molecules were represented as springs moving in a viscous medium. With a constant compliance per unit length (equivalent to the property of a Gaussian chain molecule that its "spring constant" is inversely proportional to the number of monomer units in it, $viz.$, equal to $3kT/qa^2$), and a constant viscous coupling per unit length to the surrounding medium (equivalent to the applicability of a constant friction coefficient ζ_0 to all modes of motion), the mechanical behavior was represented by a model as in Fig. 10–7, which is analogous to the so-called ladder network in electrical network theory.[32] When the finite (lumped) springs and dashpots are uniformly distributed along the length, the mechanical model becomes exactly analogous to an electrical model of an inductive transmission line, for which the frequency dependence of the impedance is well known. The corresponding frequency dependence of $\mathbf{G}^*$ is then, expressed for an undiluted polymer homogeneous with respect to molecular weight (M),

$$G' + iG'' = (C_1/M)[(iC_2M^2\omega)^{1/2} \coth (iC_2M^2\omega)^{1/2} - 1] \qquad (26)$$

where C_1 and C_2 are unspecified constants which give no information about the absolute magnitudes of the moduli or the frequency scale.

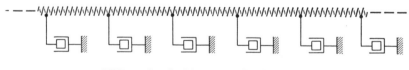

FIG. 10–7. Ladder network of Blizard.

At high frequencies, equation 26 yields for limiting values

$$G' = G'' = C_1(C_2\omega/2)^{1/2} \tag{27}$$

$$J' = J'' = 1/C_1(2C_2\omega)^{1/2} \tag{28}$$

which in their frequency dependence, and their independence of molecular weight, are identical with the predictions of the Rouse theory. At low frequencies the limiting values are

$$G' = C_1C_2{}^2M^3\omega^2/45 \tag{29}$$

$$G'' = C_1C_2M\omega/3 \tag{30}$$

$$J' = M/5C_1 \tag{31}$$

$$J'' = 3/C_1C_2M\omega \tag{32}$$

which, in their respective dependences on ω and M, also agree with the Rouse results.

In a thorough study of ladder networks with both lumped and distributed parameters, Gross and Fuoss [32,19] have shown that a continuous dynamic modulus function of the form of equation 26 corresponds to a discontinuous relaxation spectrum with discrete lines, so that the series expressions for dynamic properties given in equations 4 and 5 are in fact equivalent to equation 26 and may be replaced by the latter for convenience in calculations. The unspecified constants in Blizard's theory, evaluated by equations 28 and 31, correspond to the following molecular parameters for Rouse's theory applied to an undiluted polymer:

$$C_1 = \rho RT/2 \tag{33}$$

$$C_2 = a^2\zeta_0/6M_0{}^2kT \tag{34}$$

For the transient viscoelastic functions, however, calculation by infinite series as in equation 3 is still necessary.

In a recent treatment of the same ladder model, using a capacitative transmission line analogy, which according to the Blizard analogy corresponds to a molecular spring with one end free and one end fixed, Marvin [33] has obtained a slightly different continuous function for $\mathbf{G}^*$:

$$G' + iG'' = (C'_1/M)(iC'_2M^2\omega)^{1/2} \tanh (iC'_2M^2\omega)^{1/2} \tag{35}$$

At high frequencies, the limiting values of G' and G'' are identical with those of equation 27, but the low frequency values of G' and G'' are larger by factors of 15 and 3 respectively than those given by equations 29 and 30; and the limiting value of J' at low frequencies is $M/3C'_1$. One means of identifying C'_1 and C'_2 in terms of molecular quantities is to use this limiting low-frequency value of J' together with the high-frequency behavior as specified by equation 27 or 28. It then follows that

$$C'_1 = 5\rho RT/6 \tag{36}$$

$$C'_2 = 3a^2\zeta_0/50M_0^2kT \tag{37}$$

Although all these treatments are identical at high frequencies, there are slight divergences at the lowest frequencies. For example, the low-frequency limiting relation for G' in all of them has the form

$$G' = (1/K)\rho RT(a^2\zeta_0/6M_0^2kT)^2M^3\omega^2 \tag{38}$$

but K has the values 3500, 3240, and 1000 respectively in the original Rouse series expression and the Blizard and Marvin continuous functions.

Although the continuous functions may be scarcely more convenient than the Rouse series for direct numerical calculation, on account of the troublesome separation into real and imaginary parts of the complex expressions,[32] they are particularly valuable for analytical treatments in modifications of the original theory.

There has been some interest [34, 35] in representing dynamic viscoelastic data by the analog of the complex plane plot of Cole and Cole [36] for the complex dielectric constant, $\epsilon' - i\epsilon''$. In the latter, the locus of ϵ' and ϵ'' is often closely approximated by a semicircle whose center lies below the real axis. Its geometry corresponds to the frequency dependence

$$\epsilon^*(i\omega) = \epsilon_\infty + \frac{\epsilon_0 - \epsilon_\infty}{1 + (i\omega\tau_0)^{1-\alpha}} \tag{39}$$

where ϵ_0 and ϵ_∞ are the limiting values of ϵ' at low and high frequencies, τ_0 is a characteristic time constant, and the numerical parameter α lies between 0 and 1. Radii drawn from the center of the circle intersect the real axis at angles of $\alpha\pi/2$. In the mechanical analog, ϵ' is replaced by J' and ϵ'' by $J'' - 1/\omega\eta$; sometimes a rather good representation of experimental data is obtained, with α in the neighborhood of 0.6. However, the arc covers only the low-frequency end of the transition zone and the terminal or pseudo-equilibrium zone, everything else being crowded on a linear scale into an invisible spot at the left end. The relation between this formulation and the foregoing has been discussed by Schrama,[37] who concludes that equation 39 in general corresponds to a ladder network model of a more complicated design than Fig. 10–7.

C. BEHAVIOR OF UNCROSS-LINKED SYSTEMS IN THE TERMINAL ZONE

For an uncross-linked polymer of moderately low molecular weight, the viscoelastic behavior in the terminal zone is strongly dominated by the first few relaxation times in the series expressed by equations 20 and 21. The two viscoelastic constants which characterize this region, the steady-flow viscosity and the steady-state compliance, are given by equations 28 and 31 of Chapter 3 and according to the flexible chain theory of Rouse are:

$$\eta = (\rho RT/M)\Sigma\tau_p \tag{40}$$

and $$J_e = (M/\rho RT)\Sigma\tau_p{}^2/\eta^2 = (\tfrac{2}{5})M/\rho RT \tag{41}$$

In these summations, which hold only for a polymer of uniform molecular weight, the first term contributes 61% of the total viscosity and 92% of the total compliance. Since the first mode of motion corresponds to coordinated movement of the molecule as a whole, the properties in the terminal zone are sensitive to the long-range features of molecular topology, such as molecular weight, molecular weight distribution, and branching. (By contrast, the properties in the transition zone where equations 24 and 25 are applicable depend very little on these long-range features.)

1. Effect of Molecular Weight Distribution

To the extent that all modes of motion are governed by the same friction coefficient, the predictions of the flexible chain theory concerning a mixture heterogeneous with respect to molecular weight may be formulated as follows.[38] In a blend of two molecular weight species M_1 and M_2, the contributions of component 1 to the relaxation spectrum will have the magnitude $w_1\rho RT/M_1$, where w_1 is the weight fraction (since $n_1 = w_1\rho N_0/M_1$). Their relaxation times will be given by $\tau_{p1} = a^2Z_1{}^2\zeta_{0b}/6\pi^2p^2kT$, where ζ_{0b} is the average friction coefficient in the blend; similarly for component 2 with changed subscripts. Since in a homogeneous polymer of low molecular weight ζ_0 increases with M (attributable to the effect of free ends, as mentioned in Section A), ζ_{0b} cannot be assumed equal to either ζ_{01} or ζ_{02}, the values for the homogeneous components; it will lie somewhere between them. It is reasonable to assume that ζ_{0b} is the same for both molecular species in the blend, however, since the concept of a constant ζ_0 has already been successfully used to characterize frictional resistance to a variety of molecular motions involving coordination of segments of various lengths. Then the relaxation spectrum corresponding to equations 20 and 6 is

$$H = (w_1 \rho RT/M_1) \Sigma \tau_{p1} \delta(\tau - \tau_{p1}) + (w_2 \rho RT/M_2) \Sigma \tau_{p2} \delta(\tau - \tau_{p2}) \quad (42)$$

$$\tau_{p1} = a^2 Z_1{}^2 \zeta_{0b}/6\pi^2 p^2 kT \quad (43)$$

$$\tau_{p2} = a^2 Z_2{}^2 \zeta_{0b}/6\pi^2 p^2 kT \quad (44)$$

When the relaxation times are recalculated in terms of the steady-flow viscosity of the blend, η_b, they become

$$\tau_{p1} = 6\eta_b M_1{}^2/\pi^2 p^2 \rho \overline{M}_w RT \quad (45)$$

$$\tau_{p2} = 6\eta_b M_2{}^2/\pi^2 p^2 \rho \overline{M}_w RT \quad (46)$$

where $\overline{M}_w$ is the weight-average molecular weight; the ratio $M_i{}^2/\overline{M}_w$ replaces the factor M appearing in the corresponding expression for a homogeneous polymer (equation 21).

Equation 42 specifies that the contributions of the components to H are additive by mole fraction, on an absolute basis, since the mole fraction is proportional to w_1/M_1. However, if H is represented in terms of the spectra of the individual homogeneous components, the latter are additive by weight (or volume) fraction; i.e., if $H_1(\tau)$ and $H_2(\tau)$ are the individual spectra for the respective pure components, equations 42 to 44 can be written

$$H_b = w_1 H_1(\tau \eta_1 \overline{M}_w/\eta_b M_1) + w_2 H_2(\tau \eta_2 \overline{M}_w/\eta_b M_2) \quad (47)$$

The argument τ of the function is modified here to provide for the fact that in the blend all τ_{p1} differ from the corresponding values in pure component 1 by the factor $\zeta_{0b}/\zeta_{01} = \eta_b M_1/\eta_1 \overline{M}_w$, and similarly for component 2. It follows that the time-dependent moduli, $G(t)$, $G'(\omega)$, and $G''(\omega)$, can be similarly expressed for a blend in terms of the functions for the individual pure components: additivity on a weight fraction basis, after shifting the time scale of each by a factor which depends on the viscosity and weight-average molecular weight of the blend.

The viscosity and steady-state compliance of the blend in terms of those of the individual pure components are

$$\eta_b = w_1 \eta_1 \zeta_{0b}/\zeta_{01} + w_2 \eta_2 \zeta_{0b}/\zeta_{02} \quad (48)$$

(a tautology, if the ζ_0 ratios are expressed in terms of the viscosities as above), and

$$J_{eb} = w_1 J_{e1}(M_1/\overline{M}_w)^2 + w_2 J_{e2}(M_2/\overline{M}_w)^2 \quad (49)$$

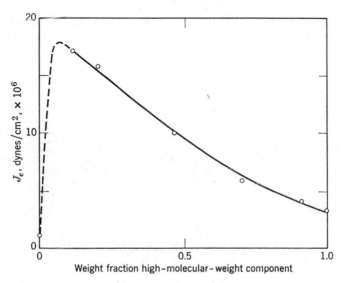

FIG. 10–8. Steady-state shear compliances of blends of two polyisobutylene fractions with weight-average molecular weights of 1.00 and 13.1 $\times$ 10⁴, plotted against the weight fraction of the component of higher molecular weight (data of Leaderman, Smith, and Williams [51]).

Although η_b always lies between η_1 and η_2, J_b can exceed both J_1 and J_2, especially if $M_2 \gg M_1$ and $w_2 < w_1$. This somewhat startling fact is illustrated in Fig. 10–8. Qualitatively, it can be anticipated from equation 41 for the extreme case of a polymer dissolved in a homologous solvent of low molecular weight. Here the density ρ would be replaced by polymer concentration c in g/cc. (since $n = cN_0/M$); J_e is then inversely proportional to c, and it is higher for the solution than for the pure polymer. Equation 49 can also be written, after substituting the values of J_{e1} and J_{e2}:

$$J_{eb} = (\tfrac{2}{5}) \overline{M}_{z+1} \overline{M}_z / \overline{M}_w \rho RT \qquad (50)$$

where $\overline{M}_z$ and $\overline{M}_{z+1}$ are the usual progressively higher moments of the molecular weight distribution. This relation emphasizes the importance of the higher averages in determining the steady-state compliance, and hence the energy stored in steady-state flow.

The above relations for blends reduce to the correct equations for concentrated solutions when component 1 is taken as a solvent of low molecular weight. In this case, $\overline{M}_w$ averaged over polymer and solvent is negligibly different from $w_2 M_2$ (unless the solution is extremely dilute), and $\overline{M}_z \cong \overline{M}_{z+1} \cong M_2$. Then equation 46 becomes $\tau_p = 6\eta M_2/\pi^2 p^2 cRT$, and equation 50 becomes $J_e = (\tfrac{2}{5})M_2/cRT$. These are the same as equations 21 and 41 respectively, with c ($=w_2\rho$) substituted for ρ.

The calculations for a blend can be readily extended to a continuous distribution of molecular weights. If $\varphi(M)\,dM$ is the number fraction of molecules lying in the molecular weight range dM (so that $\int M\varphi\,dM$ $= \overline{M}_n$, the number-average molecular weight), then the relaxation spectrum is given by

$$H = (\rho RT/\overline{M}_n)\int_0^{\infty} \Sigma\tau_p\delta(\tau - \tau_p)\varphi(M)\,dM \qquad (51)$$

$$\tau_p = a^2 Z^2 \zeta_{0b}/6\pi^2 p^2 kT \qquad (52a)$$

or $\qquad\qquad \tau_p = 6\eta M^2/\pi^2 p^2 \rho \overline{M}_w RT \qquad (52b)$

(It may be noted that ζ_{0b} again involves $\overline{M}_w$, as it does for a two-component blend.) In these circumstances, H is a continuous function, and it is entirely possible that the limiting forms of the viscoelastic functions in the terminal zone (logarithmic plot of G' with slope of 2, single exponential term for $G(t)$ in accordance with equation 3) corresponding to a line spectrum or a finite mechanical model can never be reached experimentally on account of the shapes of certain molecular weight distributions.

With an assumed form for $\varphi(M)$, such as the most probable distribution obtained in certain synthetic procedures,[39] the viscoelastic functions could be calculated from equations 51 and 52 or (in the case of G' and G'') from an equivalent hyperbolic formulation as in equation 26. Some approximate analyses have been made [40] by taking only the term in equation 51 for $p = 1$; to this rather rough approximation, the form of $\varphi(M)$ can be obtained from the shape of H.

The steady-state compliance of a polymer with a continuous distribution of molecular weights is given, [41] in accordance with the assumption used throughout this section that ζ_{0b} is the same for all components, by equation 50 regardless of the form of the distribution $\varphi(M)$.

In dealing with a concentrated solution of a polymer with a continuous molecular weight distribution, one normally does not include the solvent in the molecular weight averages, of course; the example given above was calculated in this manner merely to show the consistency of the equations for solutions and blends. If the averages are calculated over the polymer components only, equations 50 to 52 hold with c substituted for ρ. This is quite satisfactory as long as the smallest polymer component is large compared with the solvent molecule. But if there is a continuous spread of polymer components down to monomeric dimensions, the theory will have to be re-examined *ab initio*.

In earlier work,[40,41] the fact that ζ_{0b} should depend on the average molecular weight of the mixture was ignored. This omission did not affect equation 50, but it led to a factor of M instead of $M^2/\overline{M}_w$ is equation 52b and hence a different form of the relaxation spectrum. That the effect of the average molecular weight on ζ_{0b} must be considered was clearly shown by the work of Ninomiya,[42] though the latter involved polymers of high rather than low molecular weight. When the molecular weight becomes sufficiently high, the effect of free ends disappears and ζ_0 *does* become independent of M, as mentioned above; but ζ_0 governs only the motions reflected in the transition zone, which are in fact independent of molecular weight and molecular weight distribution. In the terminal zone for polymers of high molecular weight, the effective friction depends on M for another reason—entanglement coupling (*cf.* below).

2. Effect of Branching

If the polymer molecules have long branches, comparable in length to the principal chain (not short side groups of a few chain atoms, which affect short-range properties rather than the long-range motions dominating the terminal zone), the characteristic modes of motion will be different and the longest relaxation times will be given by a different set of discrete values. Calculations for various types of topology have been made by Ham,[20] using a method which is somewhat different from that of Rouse but yields identical results for unbranched chains. For a branched molecule, the terminal relaxation time τ_1, the viscosity η, and the steady-state compliance J_e are always smaller than for an unbranched molecule of the same molecular weight; the more branches and the more nearly equal their lengths, the greater the discrepancy. The appropriate ratios are listed in Table 10–I for various examples in which all the branches radiate from one point. The terminal relaxation time is the most sensitive of the three quantities.

For a complete prediction of the viscoelastic behavior, it would be necessary to substitute the individual relaxation times, which are given by Ham for a number of topologies, into equation 20. For many purposes, however, Table 10–I combined with equations 21 and 41 will provide useful information. At very short times, where the effects of branching vanish, H and L should be given by equations 22 and 23 without modification, noting however that η will not be the same as for an unbranched polymer of the same molecular weight.

The relaxation spectra for various types of branching when hydro-

Table 10-I

COMPARISONS OF τ_1, η, AND J_e FOR BRANCHED AND UNBRANCHED
POLYMERS OF THE SAME MOLECULAR WEIGHT [29]

Lengths of Branches	$\tau_{1,B}/\tau_{1,U}$	η_B/η_U	$J_{e,B}/J_{e,U}$
¼, ¼, ½	0.68	0.81	0.76
⅕, ⅕, ⅗	0.80	0.86	0.89
⅕, ⅖, ⅖	0.64	0.81	0.73
¼, ¼, ¼, ¼	0.25	0.63	0.46
⅕, ⅕, ⅕, ⅖	0.48	0.66	0.60
⅙, ⅙, ⅓, ⅓	0.60	0.67	0.58
⅕, ⅕, ⅕, ⅕, ⅕	0.16	0.52	0.36
⅙, ⅙, ⅙, ⅙, ⅓	0.48	0.56	0.49

dynamic interaction is taken into account, in dilute solution, have been calculated by Zimm and Kilb.[43]

3. The Terminal Zone in Uncross-Linked Polymers of High Molecular Weight

The discussion of the terminal zone has thus far been limited to polymers of low molecular weight where entanglement coupling is absent and all the modes of molecular motion can be described by a single average friction coefficient ζ_0, although this ζ_0 depends on the average molecular weight of the system because of the loosening effect of free molecular ends. We now consider high molecular weights, where ζ_0 has approached an asymptotic value, but the long-range co-ordinated motions which determine the longest relaxation times are much slower than would be specified by ζ_0, because of the coupling entanglements. The latter will be discussed in more detail in Section F below; here it is sufficient to say that they cause the effective friction coefficient to be enormously greater [27] than ζ_0, by a factor Q_e which depends on the average number of coupling loci per molecule— but only for those motions whose "nodes" (cf. Fig. 10-1) are much more widely spaced than the entanglement loci.

Qualitatively, Q_e is expected [41,43] to be the same for all characteristic modes whose index p is considerably less than $M/2M_e$, where M_e is the average molecular weight between entanglement points, usually [28] somewhere between 5000 and 20,000. If $M/2M_e$ is of the order of 10 or more, constancy of Q_e will hold over enough modes to comprise essentially all of the contributions to η and J_e in accordance with equations 40 and 41. It follows that the first few relaxation times, which prescribe the properties in the terminal zone, should be calculable from the steady-flow viscosity, and equations 20 and 21 are valid *in the terminal zone* for a polymer of sufficiently high molecular weight. Moreover, the effects of molecular weight distribution and branching as predicted by equations 50, 51, and 52b and Table 10–I should be valid also under these circumstances, provided $M > 2M_e$ for all, or at least a substantial majority of the molecular components. The scale of the relaxation times in the terminal zone is set by the viscosity (equation 52b), and *not* by the monomeric friction coefficient (equation 52a does not hold); whereas the time scale in the transition zone is set by the friction coefficient (equation 24) and *not* by the viscosity (equation 22 does not hold).

When $M/2M_e$ is of the order of unity, the effective factor Q_e is different for each mode, even for the lowest values of the index p; in fact, it is no longer useful to describe the problem in terms of such a factor. The viscoelastic properties in the terminal zone are then very complicated, and have not been treated theoretically in terms of the flexible chain theory. When $M/2M_e$ is less than unity, entanglement coupling does not affect any of the relaxation times, so $Q_e = 1$ throughout, corresponding to the condition of low molecular weight to which the earlier discussion was specifically limited.

4. Comparison with Experimental Data in the Terminal Zone

Unfortunately, there appear to be no data on polymers homogeneous with respect to molecular weight, except for some stress relaxation data [45] on a specially synthesized sample of polystyrene. For the others available, the molecular weight distributions have been moderately broad (rough fractions) to very broad (whole polymers), and in the absence of specific information about distribution we can only compare the experimental viscoelastic function with the prediction for a homogeneous polymer and see if the discrepancies are consistent with molecular weight heterogeneity.

A convenient function is η', whose shape can be completely predicted by equations 5 and 21 if the molecular weight and steady-flow viscosity are known. In the terminal zone, the ratio η'/η starts from unity at low frequencies and falls gradually until it enters either the transition zone with a slope of $-\frac{1}{2}$ on a logarithmic plot (when

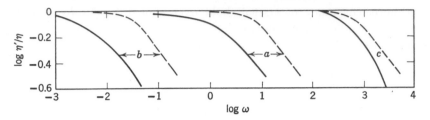

FIG. 10–9. Experimental logarithmic plots of η'/η in the terminal zone (solid curves), compared with predictions of the modified Rouse theory for uniform molecular weight (dashed curves), for three polymer systems described in the text. The curves for system (a) have been shifted to lower frequencies by 2.5 logarithmic decades.

$M/2M_e < 1$) or the plateau zone with a steeper slope approaching -1 (when $M/2M_e > 1$); cf. Fig. 2–5. Experimental curves of η'/η are compared in Fig. 10–9 with calculated curves for the following systems: (a) a low molecular weight silicone polymer;[46] (b) a 20% solution of high molecular weight polyisobutylene in decalin;[47] (c) concentrated solutions of a high-molecular-weight cellulose tributyrate fraction in 1,2,3-trichloropropane,[48] with data at several concentrations reduced to 10.0% by weight, using the method of reduced variables (Chapter 16). (In each example, data measured at different temperatures have been combined by the method of reduced variables.) Viscosity-average values of M were used in constructing the calculated curves; for the concentrated solutions, the concentration c was substituted for ρ in equation 21.

In each case, the experimental curve is similar in shape to the calculated, is somewhat more gradual in slope, and lies at lower frequencies. These are the deviations to be expected from molecular weight distribution, where components of higher than average molecular weight will give some contributions to the relaxation spectrum with much longer relaxation times in accordance with the factor $M^2/\overline{M}_w$ in equation 52b. The discrepancies are naturally greater for the unfractionated polymers of systems (a) and (b), with broad molecular weight distributions, than for the fractionated polymer of system (c).

An alternative analysis is to compare the experimentally determined continuous function $H(\tau)$ with the terminal relaxation time calculated from M and η by equation 21 with $p = 1$; for a homogeneous polymer, H should vanish for $\tau > \tau_1$. Figure 10–10 shows this comparison for the following systems: (a) a low-molecular-weight polyisobutylene;[46]

(b) a 35% solution of a high-molecular-weight polymethyl methacrylate fraction in dibutyl phthalate; [40] (c) concentrated solutions of a high-molecular-weight fraction of polyisobutylene,[49] with data at several concentrations reduced to 24.8% by weight, using the method of reduced variables. The spectrum H has reached a relatively low level at the theoretical cut-off time, but extends to longer times with contributions which can again be attributed to components of higher than average molecular weight.

A more specific test of theoretical predictions can be applied to the steady-state compliance in terms of molecular weight averages as given by equation 50. In certain cases where M_z and M_{z+1} were estimated from indirect evidence,[41, 51] moderately good agreement with measured values of J_e was obtained. In others,[51] J_e was found to be experimentally more sensitive to molecular weight distribution than predicted by theory. This difference may arise from the presence in the mixture of some components for which $M < 2M_e$ and others for

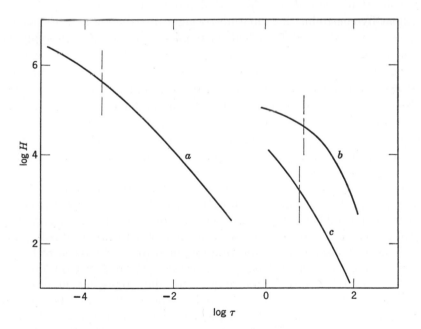

FIG. 10–10. Experimental logarithmic plots of the relaxation spectrum in the terminal zone (solid curves), compared with the terminal relaxation times predicted by the modified Rouse theory for uniform molecular weight (dashed vertical lines), for three polymer systems at 25°C. as described in the text.

which $M > 2M_e$; the derivation of the equation holds only for all $M < 2M_e$ or all $M > 2M_e$.

The results of an experimental study by Leaderman [51] on the effects of blending on J_e are shown in Fig. 10-8. The dependence on composition is qualitatively similar to that predicted by equation 49 or 50. It may be concluded that the essential features of the flexible chain theory as applied to the terminal zone are correct, and that the theory can be valuable for semi-quantitative predictions of many kinds.

5. Practical Aspects of Behavior in the Terminal Zone

The viscoelastic constants η and J_e are important in extrusion and molding processes. The former is a measure of the energy expended in flow; the latter is a measure of the energy stored, whose recovery can cause distortion of an extruded object when it emerges, or frozen-in strain if a molded object is cooled below its glass transition temperature without annealing. It is evident from the foregoing paragraphs that η and J_e can be varied independently to a considerable extent by controlling the molecular weight distribution and branching. Also, η is much more dependent on temperature than J_e. In applying the theoretical predictions to practical cases, however, it must be remembered that the theory applies only to small stresses. At high stresses, the apparent viscosity η_a will be less than η because of non-Newtonian flow (Chapter 5). On the other hand, a high confining pressure will cause the viscosity to be higher than at atmospheric pressure, because of the diminution of free volume (Chapter 11, Section C). The effects of high stress and pressure on J_e, however, should be minor.

Of considerable practical importance also are the magnitudes of the terminal relaxation time and retardation time, which according to equations 6 and 8 differ from each other only by a small numerical factor. They serve as a measure of the time required to attain steady-state flow under constant stress, the time required for elastic recoil to be accomplished after removal of stress, or the time required for internal stresses to relax during annealing; also, they represent in order of magnitude the ratio of energy stored to energy dissipated per second during steady-state flow. For a polymer homogeneous with respect to molecular weight, the relaxation time τ_1 can be readily estimated from the molecular weight and viscosity by equation 21 with $p = 1$. For a heterogeneous polymer, small amounts of components with very high molecular weights will cause small residual stresses, residual recoil, etc., at very long times (equations 51 and 52*b*); and the problem requires, strictly, specification of the minimum detectable residual effect and knowledge of the molecular weight distribution $\varphi(M)$. However, an order-of-magnitude estimate of a characteristic time can be made from equation 52*b* with $p = 1$ by substituting a rather high molecular weight average, *e.g.*, M_{z+1}, for M.

D. BEHAVIOR IN AND NEAR THE GLASSY ZONE

At high frequencies and short times, the flexible chain theory as thus far elaborated can only predict that G', G'', and $G(t)$ increase without limit and J', J'', and $J(t)$ decrease without limit. At the highest frequencies to which equations 24 and 25 are applicable, they specify that

$$G'(\omega) = G''(\omega) = 1.26G(t) = (a\rho N_0/4M_0)(\zeta_0 kT/3)^{\frac{1}{2}}\omega^{\frac{1}{2}} \tag{53}$$

$$J'(\omega) = J''(\omega) - 1/\omega\eta = 0.62[J(t) - t/\eta] =$$
$$(2M_0/a\rho N_0)(3/\zeta_0 kT)^{\frac{1}{2}}\omega^{-\frac{1}{2}} \tag{54}$$

where t is the corresponding time $1/\omega$.

The failure to predict the fact that $G'(\omega)$ and $G(t)$ level off at an approximately limiting value of G_g, and $J'(\omega)$ and $J(t)$ level off at $J_g = 1/G_g$, as seen in the figures in Chapter 2, arises of course from the inability of the theory to deal with chain motions at very short range. When chain units very close to each other rearrange their relative positions, their configurations do not have a Gaussian distribution, and the energy changes do not correspond to the stretching of an entropy spring. Moreover, the resistance to motion cannot be described by an average viscous friction. It depends on details of local geometry, and at frequencies so high that no configurational rearrangements are possible it develops an elastic rather than a viscous character; whatever slight motions are accomplished involve bending and stretching of chemical bonds.

1. Limiting Behavior at High Frequencies

An extension to the flexible chain theory taking into account the elastic reaction at high frequencies has been introduced by Marvin.[33] It replaces the viscous force by an elastic and a viscous force in series, so ζ_0 becomes $\zeta_0(1 - i\omega\zeta_0/\zeta_E)/(1 + \omega^2\zeta_0^2/\zeta_E^2)$. At low frequencies, the force per unit velocity is ζ_0 as before; at high frequencies, it is $-i\zeta_E/\omega$, where ζ_E is the force per unit displacement of a monomer unit. The value of ζ_E is chosen to give the proper limiting value of G_g at high frequencies; $\zeta_E = 24G_g{}^2v_0{}^2/a^2kT$, where v_0, the volume per monomer unit, is $M_0/N_0\rho$. Otherwise there are no additional adjustable parameters. (The coefficient ζ_0 is of course determined empirically in any case.) The calculation is made by the equivalent ladder network model illustrated in Fig. 10–11. The results predict a rather abrupt transition from the square root relations of equations 53 and 54 to the properties of a single Maxwell element (equations 1 to 8 of Chapter 3) with $G_i = G_g$ and $\eta_i = G_g\zeta_0/\zeta_E$. Correspondingly, the spectra H and L are cut off at a time of the order of ζ_0/ζ_E. The functions G', $G(t)$, J', and $J(t)$ approach their proper asymptotic values, and, in agreement with experiment (Fig. 2–4), G'' passes through a maximum. Beyond this maximum, both G'' and J'' are inversely proportional to the first power of the frequency. The theory predicts the height of the maximum to be $0.613G_g$, and its location on the frequency scale to be at $\omega_M = 0.576\zeta_E/\zeta_0$. Experimentally, the maxima in Fig. 2–4 (except for that of rubber, Curve V, which is unusually sharp) correspond to $G''_M/G_g \cong 0.2$ to 0.3, so the entrance into the glassy zone is somewhat more gradual than predicted by the theory.

The minimum relaxation time ζ_0/ζ_E in the Marvin theory can be shown to be equal to the time at which the Rouse expression for H, as given by equation 24, has the value G_g/π.

A detailed comparison of theory with experiment is given for polyisobutylene in Fig. 10–12, where the components of the complex compliance are chosen for representation. The general aspects of the onset of the glassy zone are evidently semi-quantitatively reproduced. However, there are several features which remain unexplained and will eventually require a more detailed treatment, as discussed below.

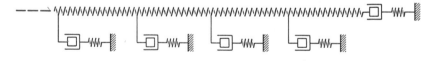

FIG. 10–11. Modification of ladder network by Marvin to account for limiting value of modulus at high frequencies and short times.

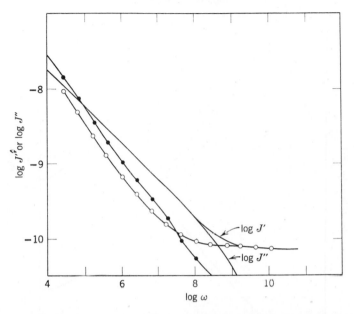

FIG. 10–12. Comparison of calculated curves for J' and J'' for polyisobutylene, by the Marvin modification of the flexible chain theory at high frequencies, with experimental results reduced to 25°C. Points, experimental; solid lines, theory.

2. Deviations from Logarithmic Slope of ½ in the Transition Zone

The theory prescribes slopes of ½ (or $-½$) for logarithmic plots of all the viscoelastic functions and spectra right up to the point where the glassy zone is entered. Actually, in most polymeric systems these functions are somewhat steeper over a substantial part of the transition zone between rubberlike to glasslike consistency, i.e., for several logarithmic decades of time or frequency scale, occasionally even exceeding the slope of ⅔ specified by the Zimm theory with hydrodynamic interaction (equation 19). As an example, the experimental spectra H and L for the polyisobutylene of Fig. 10–12 are plotted in Fig. 10–13 and compared with lines drawn with slopes of ½ and $-½$ respectively. As will be seen in Chapters 12 and 16, the deviation from the slope of ½ occurs to different extents in polymers of different chemical structure; it is less marked in concentrated solutions, for example when half the volume is occupied by solvent molecules, than in undiluted polymers. The deviation is no doubt due to gradually increasing failure of the concept of an average friction coefficient, as

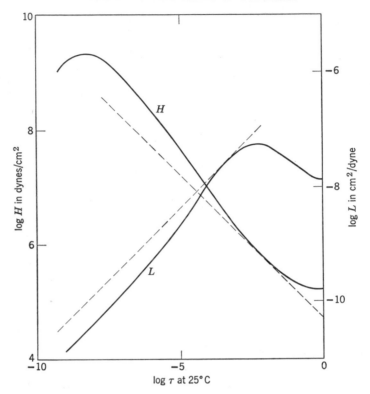

FIG. 10–13. Comparison of H and L calculated for polyisobutylene (dashed lines) with experimental results (solid curves) reduced to 25°C.

one progresses to shorter times which reflect modes of motion with shorter-range configurational changes corresponding to rearrangements within a Rouse submolecule. The concept is most nearly satisfactory at the long-time end of the transition zone; *e.g.*, in Fig. 10–13, where H has a magnitude near 10^6 dynes/cm². It is in this neighborhood that friction coefficients are commonly calculated from viscoelastic data by equation 24.

It has been shown by Onishi and Yamamoto [52] that spectral shapes such as the experimental curves in Fig. 10–13 can be semi-quantitatively reproduced by modifying the flexible chain theory, introducing elastic interactions between next-to-nearest neighbor submolecules. The effect is essentially to make the compliance per unit length larger in compact configurations than in extended configurations. To account fully for the exact shape of the viscoelastic functions at shorter times, a more detailed picture of the local motions of polymer segments is needed.

3. Persistence of Relaxation and Retardation Spectra into the Glassy Zone

In the Marvin modification of the flexible chain theory for the glassy end of the transition, the minimum retardation time ($= \zeta_0/\zeta_E$) and minimum relaxation time occur near $1/\omega_M$, and at shorter times H and L vanish. Actually, although H goes through a maximum with decreasing τ, it does not vanish but persists at a rather high level (Fig. 3-3). This corresponds to the fact that G' and $G(t)$ do not really approach an upper asymptotic value of G_g, but continue to change slightly (Figs. 2-2 and 2-3). From the behavior of polymers below their glass transition temperatures (Curves IV in the figures quoted), it may be inferred that contributions to H and L extend practically indefinitely out in the short-time direction. No clear interpretation of these relaxation mechanisms has been given. However, Miyake [53,54] has suggested that a two-dimensional distribution of characteristic modes of motion with viscous friction (in contrast to the one-dimensional distribution along the contour of an isolated chain molecule in the usual theory) should lead to flat spectra, with H and L independent of τ.

4. Secondary Maxima in the Spectra in the Glassy Zone

Although the experimentally determined spectra for polymers below their glass transition temperatures (corresponding perhaps in principle to experimentally inaccessible regions at very short times above the glass transition temperatures) are almost flat, they have perceptible maxima and minima. These features are visible in Curves IV of Figs. 3-3 and 3-4 and can be seen more readily with an enlarged scale, revealing characteristic shapes. They have usually been attributed to the motions of short side groups attached to the main polymeric backbone (Chapter 14), but only with a qualitative correlation.

E. BEHAVIOR OF CROSS-LINKED SYSTEMS

The flexible chain theory must be modified somewhat for application to lightly cross-linked polymers such as the vulcanized rubber and the gel whose properties are illustrated by Curves V and VI of the figures in Chapter 2. The short-range cooperative motions should be oblivious of the presence of cross-links, just as they are of free ends (if the molecular weight is sufficiently high) and of branch points (for long branches); therefore the relaxation and retardation spectra at short times should be given by equations 24 and 25 for cross-linked and uncross-linked polymers alike, although the value of ζ_0 may possibly depend slightly on the cross-linking density. At long times, however, the theory for a cross-linked system must diverge and predict an essentially constant finite modulus and infinite viscosity instead of a zero modulus and finite viscosity.

1. Theoretical Formulations

The ladder network theory of Blizard [31] provided the necessary modification by specifying electrical connections corresponding to anchoring points on the chains at equally spaced intervals. The resulting expression for G^* is rather complicated, but it reduces at high frequencies to the same equations 27 and 28 which hold for the uncross-linked case, whereas at low frequencies the limiting values are

$$G' = C_1/M \tag{55}$$

$$G'' = 2C_1C_2M\omega/3 \tag{56}$$

Equation 56 corresponds to a limiting low frequency value of η' given by $2C_1C_2M/3$; thus η' remains finite, even though η is infinite (*cf.* discussion following equation 28 of Chapter 3).

A result with similar limiting values, but providing identification of the coefficients with molecular parameters, was obtained by Bueche [55] through analysis of the characteristic modes of motion of the flexible chains. The approach was somewhat different from Rouse's, in that Brownian motion was not explicitly taken into account, its effect being introduced in the form of an entropy spring constant. The final equations are similar to Rouse's, however, giving a discrete line spectrum of retardation times:

$$L = (8/\pi^2 n_c kT) \sum_{\lambda=1}^{N} [\tau_\lambda/(2\lambda - 1)^2]\delta(\tau - \tau_\lambda) \tag{57}$$

$$\tau_\lambda = a^2 Z_c^2 \zeta_0/3(2\lambda - 1)^2\pi^2 kT \tag{58}$$

where n_c is the number of network strands per cc. (*i.e.*, number of chains with both ends terminating in cross-links), Z_c is the number of monomer units in such a strand, and the other symbols are the same as in equations 7 and 8. The initial factor in equation 57 can alternatively be written $8M_c/\pi^2\rho RT$, where M_c is the molecular weight of a strand between cross-linking points.

Comparison of equations 7, 8, 57, and 58 shows that the retardation spectra of cross-linked and uncross-linked polymers are identical except for small numerical factors. The relaxation spectra correspond similarly except that in the cross-linked case there is a contribution with an infinite relaxation time and a magnitude equal to the equilibrium shear modulus as predicted by the kinetic theory of rubberlike elasticity,[13] $G_e = \rho RT/M_c$. When equation 57 is substituted into equation 30 of Chapter 3, the equilibrium compliance J_e is correctly obtained as $(8/\pi^2 n_c kT)\Sigma[1/(2\lambda - 1)^2] = M_c/\rho RT$. At short times, equations 57 and 58 reduce to the continuous spectrum (expressed in terms of M_0, the monomer molecular weight),

$$L = (2M_0/\pi a\rho N_0)(3/\zeta_0 kT)^{1/2}\tau^{1/2} \tag{59}$$

and the corresponding relaxation spectrum is

$$H = (a\rho N_0/2\pi M_0)(\zeta_0 kT/3)^{1/2}\tau^{-1/2} \tag{60}$$

These differ from the Rouse equations, 24 and 25, only by a factor of $\sqrt{2}$. Since the difference must be attributable to the theories rather than to a real effect of cross-linking, we shall for the sake of consistency employ equation 24 in calculating ζ_0 from experimental data for both cross-linked and uncross-linked systems (Chapter 12).

Bueche [55] also proposed a retardation spectrum for uncross-linked polymers, whose form however does not correspond to the Rouse spectrum nor to a Blizard ladder network; its contributions are proportional to $(2\lambda - 1)^{-4}$ instead of the $(2\lambda - 1)^{-2}$ which appears in equation 7. It leads to a limiting form at short times proportional to $\tau^{3/2}$ instead of the $\tau^{1/2}$ in equations 12, 23, 25, and 59, in disagreement with experimentally observed behavior.

A similar calculation, leading to an equation for H at short times identical in form to equation 60, was made by Nakada.[56] A consideration of characteristic modes of motion in several types of lattices of linked strands, by Ham,[29] led to the same limiting form at short times. An earlier network treatment by Kirkwood,[2] in which the rotations around the individual chain bonds were considered instead of using the simplified concepts of Gaussian submolecules or entropy springs, gave a different result, in the form of a continuous retardation spectrum:

$$L = (M_c/\rho RT)(\tau/\tau_m)/(1 + \tau/\tau_m)^2 \tag{61}$$

$$\tau_m = 2jZ_c b^2 \zeta_0/kT \tag{62}$$

where j is the number of bonds per monomer unit and b is the bond length. At short times, this reduces to

$$L = (M_0/2\rho N_0 jb^2 \zeta_0)\tau \tag{63}$$

which like equation 59 is independent of M_c, being governed only by the properties of the monomer unit, but has a first-power dependence on τ instead of the usual square root. A modification of this calculation by Hammerle and Kirkwood,[57] taking into account hydrodynamic interaction, when translated from the dielectric to the mechanical case in the same manner that the earlier treatment was translated from the dielectric dispersion calculation of Kirkwood and Fuoss,[6] gives a slightly different spectrum:

$$L = (2M_c/\rho RT)(\tau/\tau_0)^2/(1 + \tau/\tau_0)^3 \tag{64}$$

$$\tau_0 = Cb^3 \eta_0 \sqrt{Z_c}/kT \tag{65}$$

where C is a numerical constant, $(45\pi/64)(\pi/6)^{1/2}$, and η_0 is the local effective viscosity (cf. η_s in the Zimm calculation, equation 16). At short times, this one reduces to

$$L = (2M_0 kT/\rho N_0 C^2 b^6 \eta_0)\tau^2 \tag{66}$$

with a *square* dependence on τ.

2. Comparison with Experiment

Since Bueche's retardation spectrum is discrete and the others are continuous, a direct comparison can be made only through one of the viscoelastic functions, and for this purpose the loss compliance has been chosen for the plots shown in Fig. 10–14. Here D'' for the lightly vulcanized rubber illustrated in Fig. 2–7 is compared with calculated curves from equations 57, 61, and 64. The data are for extension rather than in shear, but in this range the conversion is simple since $D'' = J''/3$. The required value of M_c was obtained from the experimental figure for D_e; the frequency scale was set for the Bueche curve by determining ζ_0 from the region where H_l has a slope of $\frac{1}{2}$, and for the Kirkwood curves by making the frequency of the maximum in D'' coincide with its experimentally determined location.

The general shape of the maximum is semi-quantitatively predicted

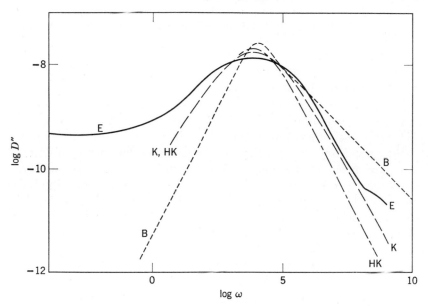

FIG. 10–14. Comparison of experimental loss compliance (E) for lightly vulcanized rubber (Curve V of Fig. 2–7) with predictions of the Bueche (B), Kirkwood (K), and Hammerle-Kirkwood (HK) theories.

by all the theories, although the experimental peak is somewhat less sharp than indicated by any of them ($D''_{max}/D_e = 0.21$, as compared with 0.42, 0.29, and 0.32 for the Bueche, Kirkwood, and Hammerle-Kirkwood theories respectively). At high frequencies, the Kirkwood curve is closest to the experimental, though this agreement is associated with an unusually sharp transition zone in natural rubber; some other cross-linked systems conform more closely to the Bueche slope of $-\frac{1}{2}$ at high frequencies (Chapter 13). The deviations appearing at low frequencies will be discussed below.

Although the shapes of the three theoretical curves are rather similar, the predictions of the dependence of the frequency location of the maximum on the density of cross-linking are quite different. The frequency corresponding to D''_{max} should be inversely proportional to Z_c^2, Z_c, and $Z_c^{1/2}$ according to the three respective theories (cf. the exponents of Z_c in equations 58, 62, and 65). Unfortunately, there appear to be no experimental studies with a systematic variation of the degree of cross-linking from which an appraisal of these differences can be made.

3. Effects of Chain Length Distribution in the Cross-Linked Network

The fact that all the theories assume a uniform spacing between cross-linking points may be a serious disadvantage in comparing with experimental results at low frequencies or long times, since all real polymer networks (with the possible exception of certain polyurethane systems [58]) undoubtedly have a wide distribution of strand lengths. The problem is therefore somewhat similar to that presented by Fig. 10–9; comparison of theory for a homogeneous polymer with data for a heterogeneous one cannot be expected to be entirely satisfactory.

It is possible that the relaxation spectrum of a cross-linked polymer with distribution of strand lengths can be adequately represented by summing, on a mole fraction basis, the contributions corresponding to individual species of strands, by analogy with equation 51. If so, the results of the Kirkwood and Hammerle-Kirkwood theories are quite insensitive to strand length heterogeneity. However, equation 51 is based on isolated flexible chains coupled together only by their viscous environment, whereas in a network all the strands are rigidly attached through their junction points. The dependence of the spectrum on strand length distribution may depend on this feature, as well as on the degree of connectivity (*e.g.*, whether 4 chains meet at a junction point, as in the usual rubber vulcanizate, or a large number of chains as in a gel cross-linked by crystallite formation).

In any case, the dependence of equilibrium compliance on the strand length distribution in a network is entirely different from that of the steady-state compliance on the molecular length distribution in an uncross-linked polymer. Each species of strand with molecular weight M_c will have a contribution to H with infinite relaxation time; substitution of equation 51 into equation 31 of Chapter 3 thus yields

$$J_e = (\rho RT/\overline{M}_{nc}) \int_0^\infty \tau_0^2 \varphi(M) \, dM / [(\rho RT/\overline{M}_{nc}) \int_0^\infty \tau_0 \varphi(M) \, dM]^2$$

with $\tau_0 \to \infty$; the result is $J_e = \overline{M}_{nc}/\rho RT$, as required by the equilibrium theory of rubberlike elasticity.[13] The equilibrium compliance thus depends on the number-average molecular weight between cross-links rather than the higher averages appearing in equation 50.

4. Behavior of Cross-Linked Systems in the Pseudo-Equilibrium Zone

It was pointed out in Chapter 2 that strictly speaking there is no equilibrium compliance in cross-linked polymers; at very long times and very low frequencies, $J(t)$ and $J'(\omega)$ keep on changing slightly. The changes are too small to affect significantly the magnitude of J_e or the validity of calculations such as those in the preceding paragraph. Nevertheless, they represent contributions to L and H extending out to very long times, far in excess of the terminal retardation time predicted by equation 58 with $\lambda = 1$.

The effects of the retardation mechanisms at long times are seen in the experimental curve in Fig. 10–14, where at low frequencies J'' levels off and even rises slightly with decreasing frequency instead of dropping steeply as prescribed by all the theories. The leveling in J'' corresponds to an increase in η' with decreasing frequency, apparently without limit, instead of the finite low-frequency limiting value implied in equation 56 by the Blizard and Bueche theories (also by the Kirkwood and Hammerle-Kirkwood theories).

These very slow mechanisms are not accounted for by any of the network or lattice theories quoted.[2, 29, 31, 55–57] They probably arise from characteristic modes of motion in which groups of strands are coordinated to different extents through coupling by the junction points. Such motions would be limited in extent only by the finite size of the sample, and the ratio of macroscopic to molecular (or even macromolecular) dimensions is sufficiently high to make the time scale extend well past practical experimental limits.

F. BEHAVIOR OF UNCROSS-LINKED SYSTEMS IN THE PLATEAU ZONE

1. Entanglement Coupling

The concept of entanglement coupling in uncross-linked polymers of high molecular weight has already been referred to several times. The qualitative view that transient networks could be formed by adherence of individual molecules at widely separated points in the absence of true chemical cross-links was advanced in several earlier investigations.[59–61] The existence of such a phenomenon was clearly indicated by the stress relaxation experiments of Tobolsky,[61] whose curves for polyisobutylenes of high molecular weights exhibited inflections like those in Curves II and III of Fig. 2–2, and by Bueche's analysis[27] of the well-known dependence of steady-flow viscosity on molecular weight.

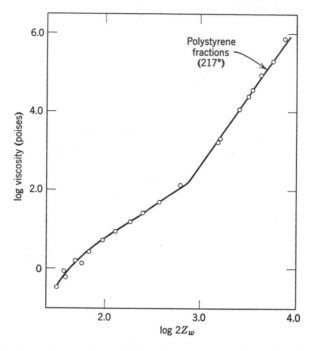

FIG. 10–15.   Dependence of steady-flow viscosity on number of chain atoms per molecule for polystyrene fractions at 217°C. (Fox, Gratch, and Loshaek [28]).

The latter is illustrated in Fig. 10–15 for polystyrene fractions.[28] For low molecular weights, η increases somewhat faster than directly proportional to M, in harmony with equation 9—rewritten for an undiluted polymer in the form $\eta = \rho N_0 a^2 M \zeta_0 / 36 M_0^2$—if ζ_0 increases somewhat with M. Such a dependence of ζ_0 is reasonable because of the loosening effect on the average structure due to free molecular ends,[28] which disappears as M increases. At high M, if this were the only anomaly, η should approach proportionality to M, and indeed the slope of the lower portion of the curve appears to be approaching unity just before it undergoes a sudden change in slope. The latter occurs at a critical molecular weight characteristic of the nature of the polymer, and beyond it η increases with the 3.4 power of M. This behavior is supposed to be due to the onset of an entanglement network beyond the point where $M > 2M_e$, M_e being the average molecular weight between entanglement coupling points; if $M > 2M_e$, there are on the average two coupling points per molecule, and by analogy with the theory of gelation by cross-links [62] this means that the coupling extends throughout the system.

The mobility of a molecule in the entanglement network is no longer determined by an average friction coefficient ζ_0 alone, but is greatly diminished by the restrictions of the coupling loci. The viscosity is higher by a factor Q_e (cf. Section C above):

$$\eta = \rho N_0 a^2 M Q_e \zeta_0 / 36 M_0^2 \tag{67}$$

which depends on the average number of coupling loci per molecule:

$$Q_e = (M/2M_e)^{2.4} \qquad \text{when } M > 2M_e \tag{68}$$

The product $Q_e \zeta_0$ can be regarded as a sort of effective friction coefficient for those characteristic modes of motion which involve cooperation of molecular regions separated by one or more coupling points.[27] It is just these modes, with low index p, which contribute substantially all of the viscosity (equation 40).

The coupling points may be regarded as equivalent to transient cross-links separated by an average molecular weight M_e, so that for sufficiently rapid deformations the system behaves as though it had an equilibrium compliance of $J_e = M_e/\rho RT$; hence the leveling, or intermediate region of low slope, in curves for $G(t)$, $J(t)$, G', and J' as illustrated in Figs. 2–1, 2–2, 2–3, and 2–6. The quantity J_e is poorly defined, however, since at very short times there is no distinction between cross-linked and uncross-linked systems anyway, and at intermediate times there is always some motion at the coupling points, which usually prevents $J(t)$ and J' from attaining even what could be called a pseudo-equilibrium value. Where $J(t)$ and J' have a low slope, the relaxation spectrum H is relatively flat, whence the name "plateau zone" for this region of the time scale.

Although the concept of a coupled network explains qualitatively the behavior of uncross-linked polymers of high molecular weight, the nature of the coupling is not well understood. Its simplest interpretation would be as due to temporary cross-links, formed by association of loci with moderately strong secondary attractive forces. The time-dependent viscoelastic properties could then be analyzed in terms of the kinetics of formation and dissociation of such linkages.[63–65] This picture would imply chemical or structural inhomogeneity along the polymer chain, since the loci are so widely spaced, with M_e corre-

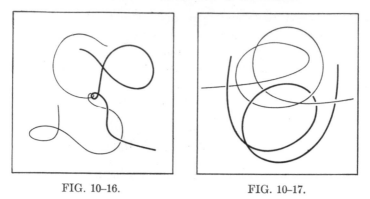

FIG. 10–16.   FIG. 10–17.

FIG. 10–16. Concept of entanglement coupling by local kinking.
FIG. 10–17. Concept of entanglement coupling by long-range contour looping.

sponding [28] to degrees of polymerization from 50 to 500. It is conceivable that specific spots of strong attraction could occur, due to a copolymeric impurity (which can produce marked effects when introduced by design [66]) or regions of tactic ordering.[67] However, the effects of entanglement coupling appear universally; examples include such non-polar polymers as polyisobutylene and polystyrene where the intermolecular attractive forces are small and there is no suspicion of structural heterogeneity. Another possible interpretation of an entanglement is a point where two chains are tightly kinked around each other by bending back on themselves in short-range contour (Fig. 10–16). However, experience [68, 69] shows that stiff, extended chains are more prone to formation of entanglement networks than highly flexible chains; moreover, the presence of bulky side groups does not markedly inhibit the entanglement coupling.[70] It seems probable, therefore, that the coupling involves looping of chains around each other in their long-range contour [71] (Fig. 10–17), and that M_e is related to the minimum length for which the mathematical expectation that a chain will cross itself is unity. If so, it is somewhat misleading to speak of entanglement "points" or "loci." On the basis of steric relations of this nature, Bueche [27, 72] has derived a dependence of viscosity on molecular weight corresponding to equations 67 and 68 with proportionality to $M^{3.5}$, close to the experimentally determined relation with $M^{3.4}$.

For molecular weights of the order of M_e the situation must be very complicated. When M is slightly less than $2M_e$, we can conclude by analogy with the theory of gelation [62] that coupling entanglement should lead to branched aggregates, whose viscoelastic contributions could be treated by a modification of the theory of Ham [29] (Table 10–I). When M is slightly greater than $2M_e$, not all the chains present will on the average participate in the network, but some will be free, corresponding to the "sol fraction" in gelation theory.[62] Because of these features, together with the effects of distribution of chain lengths, no adequate analysis of the effects of entanglement coupling for intermediate molecular weights has been attempted. At sufficiently high M, however, where all the chains are included in the network, several approaches have been made to the problem, and these are described in the following sections.

2. Modification of the Flexible Chain Theory for the Plateau Zone

As a somewhat arbitrary modification of the Rouse theory, Ferry, Landel, and Williams [44] proposed to retain equation 20 but to replace equation 21 by two sets of relaxation times:

$$\tau_p = 6\eta M/\pi^2 p^2 \rho RT, \qquad p \leq p_e \tag{69}$$

$$\tau_p = 6\eta M/Q_e \pi^2 p^2 \rho RT$$

$$= a^2 Z^2 \zeta_0/6\pi^2 p^2 kT, \qquad p > p_e \tag{70}$$

with Q_e given by equation 68 and $p_e = M/2M_e$. Thus the effective friction coefficients for all motions with nodes spaced farther apart than $2M_e$ would be affected by entanglement in the same manner as the steady-flow viscosity. This reproduces the general features of viscoelastic behavior in the plateau zone, but it amounts to a hiatus in relaxation mechanisms between $\tau_{pe} = 6\eta M/\pi^2 p_e^2 \rho RT$ and $6\eta M/Q_e \pi^2 p_e^2 \rho RT$, so that H and L incorrectly vanish in this region.

Bueche [73] has represented the compliance of a high-molecular-weight entanglement network as the sum of one component corresponding to a cross-linked network with $M_c = M_e$ and effective friction coefficient ζ_0 and a second component corresponding to an uncross-linked polymer with effective friction coefficient $Q_e\zeta_0$. This again represents the viscoelastic behavior semi-quantitatively, but with H and L vanishing in the plateau region.

Bueche's calculation would have corresponded, if a spectrum for the uncross-linked structure of the form of equation 7 had been used, to a ladder network as illustrated in Fig. 10–18. Marvin [33] has intro-

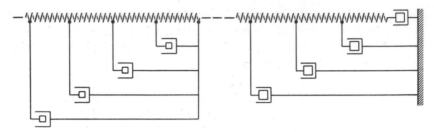

FIG. 10–18. Ladder network corresponding to the Bueche type of calculation for viscoelastic behavior of an entanglement network.

duced the modification shown in Fig. 10–19, where the motions of short segments (*i.e.*, modes with closely spaced nodes) are dissipated against the average medium instead of pulling against the ladder representing the long-segment motions. (In the complete Marvin model, the dashpots ζ_0 are coupled in series with springs ζ_E, as described in Section D above, but the latter are omitted here because they are irrelevant in the time zone concerned.) When the complex shear modulus for Marvin's ladder is calculated in terms of an equivalent continuous function (*cf.* equation 35), it becomes

$$G' + iG'' = (C'_1/M_e)(iC'_2M_e^2\omega)^{1/2}$$

$$\times \frac{\tanh (iC'_2M_e^2\omega)^{1/2} + Q_e^{1/2} \tanh [(M/2M_e) - 1](iC'_2M_e^2Q_e\omega)^{1/2}}{1 + Q_e^{1/2} \tanh (iC'_2M_e^2\omega)^{1/2} \tanh [(M/2M_e) - 1](iC'_2M_e^2Q_e\omega)^{1/2}}$$

$$(71)$$

where C'_1 and C'_2 have the same molecular significance translated into the Rouse theory as in equations 36 and 37. (If the parameter ζ_E is included, the relation is considerably more complicated.[33]) At moderately high frequencies (not so high that ζ_E need be considered), equation 71 reduces just as equation 35 does to equation 27, identical with the familiar limiting square root relation of the Rouse theory. At low frequencies, equation 71 reduces to essentially the same limiting forms

FIG. 10–19. Ladder network for the Marvin calculation for viscoelastic behavior of an entanglement network.

as equation 35 except that ω is multiplied by Q_e, as required by the assumption that the effective friction coefficient is $Q_e \zeta_0$ in this region. A numerical evaluation of equation 71, for several values of $M/2M_e$, is tabulated in Appendix E.

Equation 71 predicts maxima and minima in both G'' and J'' in the plateau zone, as experimentally observed (Figs. 2–4 and 2–7). An approximate evaluation [33] of the maximum in G'' shows its magnitude to be 0.32 $\rho RT/M_e$ and its location on the frequency scale at $\omega = (95kT/a^2\zeta_0 Z^2)(M_e/M)^{\frac{1}{2}}$; thus its height is proportional to the number of network strands per unit volume, and the frequency is proportional to $M_e^{\frac{1}{2}}$ and to $M^{-2.5}$. The magnitude of J'' at its maximum is approximately $0.32 M_e/\rho RT$ and its location on the frequency scale $48M_0^2 kT/a^2\zeta_0 M_e^2$. Thus the height is inversely proportional to the density of network strands, and the frequency is directly proportional to the square of that density. The value of 0.32 for $J''_{max}\rho RT/M_e$ may be compared with the values of 0.42, 0.29, and 0.32 predicted for $J''_{max}\rho RT/M_e$ for *permanently* cross-linked networks by the theories discussed in the preceding section.

A comparison of G' and G'' as predicted by equation 71 and numerically evaluated by a high-speed computer [33] with experimental data for a high-molecular-weight polyisobutylene is shown in Fig. 10–20. The necessary parameters were obtained from reference 28 and the steady-flow viscosity.[33] The agreement is considerably better than in either of the previous formulations, and lends encouragement to this method of representation. However, molecular weight distribution and also the distribution of chain lengths between entanglement points have still to be taken into account.

The subject of molecular weight distribution and its effect on the terminal zone have been qualitatively discussed in Section C. One specific question that arises is what average molecular weight enters the calculation of Q_e in equation 68. It follows from equation 52b that Q_e is proportional to $\eta/\bar{M}_w$, so if η is a function of $\bar{M}_w$ alone [28] Q_e is also. However, there is some recent evidence [74] that higher averages of the molecular weight are involved in η. The distribution of lengths between entanglement points undoubtedly affects the detailed curvature in the plateau zone, which is especially prominent in G''; it may be responsible for the fact that the maximum and minimum in the experimental curve in Fig. 10–20 are less marked than their theoretical predictions, and also for the truly flat plateau which is sometimes observed in H, with no maximum nor minimum (though this shape is less frequent than commonly supposed). The assumption that a monodisperse polymer should

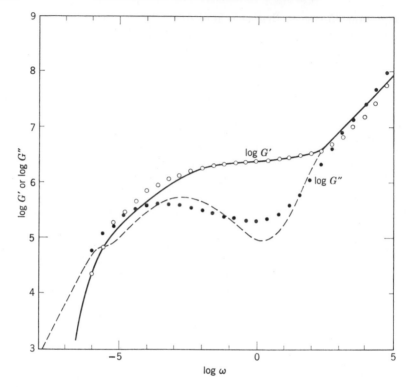

FIG. 10–20. Comparison of calculated curves for G' and G'' as calculated by equation 71 of Marvin for the plateau region with experimental values for a high-molecular-weight polyisobutylene, reduced to 25°C. Points, experimental; lines, theory.

have a truly flat plateau in the relaxation spectrum is the starting point of a theoretical evaluation by Fujita and Ninomiya [74,75] of the relation between the shape of H in the terminal zone and the molecular weight distribution (*cf.* Chapter 13).

3. Estimates of M_e from Viscoelastic Data

The parameter M_e is evidently the most important characteristic of the plateau region, and study of its dependence on temperature and other variables can potentially clarify the nature of entanglement coupling. It can be determined experimentally from the relation between viscosity and molecular weight, as illustrated in Fig. 10–15, with the reservation that the measurement of η involves analysis of a creep curve and possible attendant uncertainty about attainment of steady-state flow (Chapter 5). A second method for gauging it roughly is to estimate a value of G_e for the entanglement network from the inflection in the stress relaxation curve of a single high-molecular-weight fraction in the plateau zone. Under favorable circumstances the estimates from $G(t)$ and corresponding inflections in $J(t)$, J', and G' may agree within 20%, as for Curves III in the figures in Chapter 2. Then according to the theory of rubberlike elasticity [13] $M_e = \rho RT/G_e = \rho RTJ_e$.

Also, M_e can be calculated from the relaxation spectrum of a single sample of high molecular weight and reasonably sharp molecular weight distribution, by measuring the distance between two segments with slope $-\frac{1}{2}$ in the transition and terminal zones respectively (Fig. 10–21). If the intersections of these segments with a horizontal line at a given value of H are τ_{tr} and τ_{te} respectively, it should follow from equations 24 and 68 that:

$$\log \tau_{te} - \log \tau_{tr} = \Delta = \log Q_e = 2.4 \log (M/2M_e) \qquad (72)$$

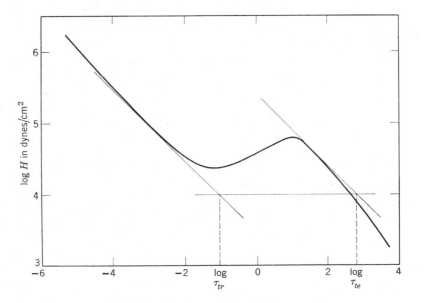

FIG. 10–21. Determination of plateau width for calculation of M_e, illustrated for poly-n-octyl methacrylate (Curve III of Fig. 3-3). Here $\Delta = 3.75$ and $_w = 3.62 \times 10^6$; hence $M_e = 50,000$ (equation 72).

The distance Δ is a quantitative measure of the width of the plateau zone. Recognizing that the molecular weight distribution will inevitably be somewhat non-uniform, $\overline{M}_w$ is perhaps the proper average to use for M. If the distribution is too broad, the terminal zone of the spectrum will sag gradually and no segment with a slope of $-\frac{1}{2}$ on the right side of the plateau will appear (*cf.* Chapter 13).

Still another method for obtaining M_e is to use the expressions given by the Marvin theory, equation 71, for the maxima in J'' and G'' in terms of M_e, together with experimental values for the heights of these maxima.

Unfortunately, values of M_e evaluated by these various methods reveal some discrepancies, as will be shown in Chapter 13. The entire theoretical approach as outlined above must therefore be regarded as being in a rather tentative state.

4. Presence of Abnormally Slow Relaxation Mechanisms

In a permanently cross-linked network, as pointed out in the preceding section, there are small contributions to L and H with relaxation times far in excess of the terminal relaxation time of a single network strand; these may be tentatively ascribed to cooperative motions coupled by network junctions and extending through large regions of the three-dimensional structure.

In an entanglement network, the physical significance of the theoretical terminal relaxation time is less clear. For homogeneous molecular weight, it is $\tau_1 = a^2 Z^2 Q_e \zeta_0 / 6\pi^2 kT$. We have considered Q_e as a factor affecting the average effective friction coefficient for long-range cooperative motions; an alternative interpretation would be the replacement of the single chain of length Z by a larger branched structure with an effective length $ZQ_e^{1/2}$. Thus Q_e could be regarded as a measure of the distance over which the motions of one molecule are coupled to those of its neighbors. By analogy with the permanently cross-linked network, it might be expected that some slight degree of coupling would extend even beyond this distance, producing contributions to H and L at abnormally long times beyond the value of τ_1 given above. There is in fact some experimental evidence for such very slow mechanisms,[76] which will be described in Chapter 13; they may prevent strict attainment of a steady-state compliance in flow, just as the analogous mechanisms in a permanently cross-linked network prevent strict attainment of an equilibrium compliance.

REFERENCES

1. T. Alfrey, Jr., *J. Chem. Phys.*, **12**, 374 (1944).
2. J. G. Kirkwood, *J. Chem. Phys.*, **14**, 51 (1946).
3. W. Kuhn and H. Kuhn, *Helv. Chim. Acta*, **28**, 1533 (1945).
4. W. Kuhn and H. Kuhn, *Helv. Chim. Acta*, **29**, 71 (1946).
5. W. Kuhn and H. Kuhn, *Helv. Chim. Acta*, **29**, 609, 830 (1946).
6. J. G. Kirkwood and R. M. Fuoss, *J. Chem. Phys.*, **9**, 329 (1941).
7. J. G. Kirkwood, *Rec. trav. chim.*, **68**, 649 (1949).
8. J. G. Kirkwood, *J. Polymer Sci.*, **12**, 1 (1954).
9. P. J. Flory, *Principles of Polymer Chemistry*, Cornell University Press, Ithaca, N. Y., 1953, Chapter X.
10. R. Cerf, *Adv. Polymer Sci.*, **1**, 382 (1959).
11. H. Benoît, *J. Polymer Sci.*, **3**, 376 (1948).
12. M. V. Volkenshtein and O. B. Ptitsyn, *Zhur. fiz. Khim. URSS*, **26**, 1061 (1952).
13. L. R. G. Treloar, in H. A. Stuart, *Die Physik der Hochpolymeren*, Vol. IV, Chapter V, Springer-Verlag, Berlin, 1956.
14. P. E. Rouse, Jr., *J. Chem. Phys.*, **21**, 1272 (1953).
15. B. H. Zimm, *J. Chem. Phys.*, **24**, 269 (1956).
16. G. K. Fraenkel, *J. Chem. Phys.*, **20**, 642 (1952).
17. R. Cerf, *J. Chem. Phys.*, **20**, 395 (1952).
18. P. Debye, *J. Chem. Phys.*, **14**, 636 (1946).
19. B. Gross, *J. Polymer Sci.*, **20**, 123 (1956).
20. P. E. Rouse, Jr., and K. Sittel, *J. Applied Phys.*, **24**, 690 (1953).
21. J. D. Ferry, in H. A. Stuart, *Die Physik der Hochpolymeren*, Vol. IV, p. 96, Springer-Verlag, Berlin, 1956.
22. J. G. Kirkwood and J. Riseman, *J. Chem. Phys.*, **16**, 565 (1948).
23. B. H. Zimm, G. M. Roe, and L. F. Epstein, *J. Chem. Phys.*, **24**, 279 (1956).
24. B. H. Zimm, private communication.
25. W. O. Baker, W. P. Mason, and J. H. Heiss, *J. Polymer Sci.*, **8**, 129 (1952).
26. J. G. Kirkwood and P. L. Auer, *J. Chem. Phys.*, **19**, 281 (1951).
27. F. Bueche, *J. Chem. Phys.*, **20**, 1959 (1952).
28. T. G. Fox, S. Gratch, and S. Loshaek, in F. R. Eirich, *Rheology*, Vol. I, p. 446, Academic Press, New York, 1956.
29. J. S. Ham, *J. Chem. Phys.*, **26**, 625 (1957).
30. M. L. Williams and R. F. Landel, unpublished calculations.
31. R. B. Blizard, *J. Applied Phys.*, **22**, 730 (1951).
32. B. Gross and R. M. Fuoss, *J. Polymer Sci.*, **19**, 39 (1956).
33. R. S. Marvin, in J. T. Bergen, *Viscoelasticity—Phenomenological Aspects*, Academic Press, New York, 1960, p. 27, and private communication.
34. A. W. Nolle, *J. Polymer Sci.*, **5**, 1 (1950).
35. S. Takahashi, *J. Colloid Sci.*, **9**, 313 (1954).
36. K. S. Cole and R. H. Cole, *J. Chem. Phys.*, **9**, 341 (1941).
37. J. Schrama, Thesis, Leiden, 1957.
38. J. D. Ferry, unpublished calculations.
39. P. J. Flory, Reference 9, Chapter VIII.

40. J. M. Watkins, R. D. Spangler, and E. C. McKannan, *J. Applied Phys.*, **27,** 685 (1956).
41. J. D. Ferry, M. L. Williams, and D. M. Stern, *J. Phys. Chem.*, **58,** 987 (1954).
42. K. Ninomiya, *J. Colloid Sci.*, **14,** 49 (1959).
43. B. H. Zimm and R. W. Kilb, *J. Polymer Sci.*, **37,** 19 (1959).
44. J. D. Ferry, R. F. Landel, and M. L. Williams, *J. Applied Phys.*, **26,** 359 (1955).
45. A. V. Tobolsky, A. Mercurio, and K. Murakami, *J. Colloid Sci.*, **13,** 196 (1958).
46. R. C. Harper, Jr., H. Markovitz, and T. W. De Witt, *J. Polymer Sci.*, **8,** 435 (1952).
47. W. Philippoff, *J. Applied Phys.*, **25,** 1102 (1954).
48. R. F. Landel and J. D. Ferry, *J. Phys. Chem.*, **59,** 658 (1955).
49. J. D. Ferry, I. Jordan, W. W. Evans, and M. F. Johnson, *J. Polymer Sci.*, **14,** 261 (1954).
50. J. M. Watkins, *J. Applied Phys.*, **27,** 419 (1956).
51. H. Leaderman, R. G. Smith, and L. C. Williams, *J. Polymer Sci.*, **36,** 233 (1959).
52. T. Onishi and M. Yamamoto, *J. Phys. Soc. Japan,* **13,** 1439 (1958).
53. A. Miyake, *J. Polymer Sci.*, **22,** 560 (1956).
54. A. Miyake, *Repts. Liberal Arts Faculty Shizuoka Univ. Nat. Sci.*, **1,** No. 10, 1 (1956).
55. F. Bueche, *J. Chem. Phys.*, **22,** 603 (1954).
56. O. Nakada, *J. Phys. Soc. Japan,* **10,** 804 (1955).
57. W. G. Hammerle and J. G. Kirkwood, *J. Chem. Phys.*, **23,** 1743 (1955).
58. J. Moacanin, *J. Applied Polymer Sci.*, **1,** 272 (1959).
59. J. D. Long, W. E. Singer, and W. P. Davey, *Ind. Eng. Chem.*, **26,** 543 (1934).
60. L. E. Nielsen and R. Buchdahl, *J. Colloid Sci.*, **5,** 282 (1950).
61. H. Mark and A. V. Tobolsky, *Physical Chemistry of High Polymeric Systems,* Interscience Publishers, New York, 1950, Chapter X and p. 344.
62. P. J. Flory, Reference 9, Chapter IX.
63. M. S. Green and A. V. Tobolsky, *J. Chem. Phys.*, **14,** 80 (1946).
64. A. S. Lodge, *Trans. Faraday Soc.*, **52,** 120 (1956).
65. M. Yamamoto, *J. Phys. Soc. Japan,* **11,** 413 (1956).
66. R. Longworth and H. Morawetz, *J. Polymer Sci.*, **29,** 307 (1958).
67. T. G. Fox and others, *J. Amer. Chem. Soc.*, **80,** 1768 (1958).
68. R. F. Landel, J. W. Berge, and J. D. Ferry, *J. Colloid Sci.*, **12,** 400 (1957).
69. F. E. Helders, J. D. Ferry, H. Markovitz, and L. J. Zapas, *J. Phys. Chem.,* **60,** 1575 (1956).
70. P. R. Saunders, D. M. Stern, S. F. Kurath, C. Sakoonkim, and J. D. Ferry, *J. Colloid Sci.,* **14,** 222 (1959).
71. F. Bueche, *J. Polymer Sci.,* **25,** 243 (1957).
72. F. Bueche, *J. Chem. Phys.,* **25,** 599 (1956).
73. F. Bueche, *J. Applied Phys.,* **26,** 738 (1955).
74. H. Fujita and K. Ninomiya, *J. Polymer Sci.,* **24,** 233 (1957).
75. K. Ninomiya and H. Fujita, *J. Colloid Sci.,* **12,** 204 (1957).
76. D. J. Plazek, *J. Colloid Sci.,* **15,** 50 (1960).

CHAPTER 11

Dependence of Viscoelastic Behavior on Temperature

Until now, there has been no explicit discussion of the effect of temperature on any of the viscoelastic functions, although it has been mentioned that below the glass transition temperature the configurations of polymer chain backbones are largely immobilized and the tremendous changes in viscoelastic properties with time or frequency which characterize polymeric systems do not appear (Curves IV in the figures in Chapter 2).

It is in the transition zone between glasslike and rubberlike consistency that the dependence of viscoelastic functions on temperature is most spectacular, just as is the dependence on time or frequency. An example is given in Fig. 11–1 for the real part of the complex compliance of poly-n-octyl methacrylate.[1] Below $-5°$C., the experimental frequency range appears to correspond to the glassy zone; the compliance is quite low, around $10^{-9.5}$ cm^2/dyne, and does not change much with frequency. Above 120°C., the behavior appears to correspond to the plateau zone; the compliance is characteristic of a very soft rubberlike solid ($10^{-5.5}$ cm^2/dyne), and again changes only slowly with frequency. At intermediate temperatures, the transition zone makes its appearance.

This behavior can be understood qualitatively on the basis that the retardation and relaxation times which constitute the viscoelastic spectra decrease rapidly with increasing temperature. At low temperatures, where all $\omega\tau_i \gg 1$, practically no configurational changes occur within the period of deformation; in equation 26 of Chapter 3, the integral over

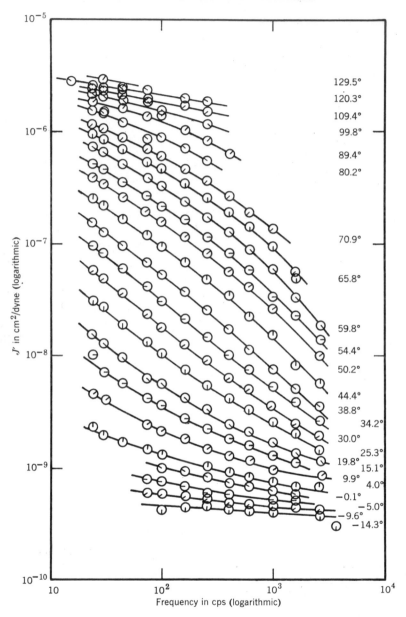

FIG. 11–1. Storage compliance of poly-*n*-octyl methacrylate in the transition zone between glasslike and rubberlike consistency, plotted logarithmically against frequency at 24 temperatures as indicated.

L makes very little contribution, and J' is close to J_g. But at high temperatures, where all $\omega\tau_i$ corresponding to mechanisms in the transition zone are much less than 1, all configurational modes of motion within entanglement coupling points can freely occur. The integral over L then makes a large contribution, and J' is in the region corresponding to the compliance of the entanglement network.

Any attempt to analyze the temperature dependence by seeking an analytical form for $J'(T)$ at constant frequency (or, in a corresponding family of creep curves, for example, $J(t)$ as a function of T at constant time) would lead to very complicated results. Instead, we take recourse in a method of reduced variables or viscoelastic corresponding states. This has already been mentioned as a device for enlarging the effective time or frequency scale available for experimental measurements. It affords a valuable simplification in separating the two principal variables of time and temperature on which the viscoelastic properties depend, and expressing the properties in terms of a single function of each whose form can be determined experimentally whether or not it can be conveniently represented by an analytical expression. We are now prepared to examine this method in detail and to see how the parameters which describe temperature dependence are related to molecular constitution and structure.

A. ORIGIN OF THE METHOD OF REDUCED VARIABLES

1. Deduction from the Flexible-Chain Theories

Although the use of reduced variables developed empirically in advance of the theories which support it, we shall introduce it as a logical consequence of some of the relations in the preceding chapter. In the transition zone between glasslike and rubberlike consistency, where the viscoelastic behavior is due to cooperative motions of individual chains, and all are governed by a single average friction coefficient ζ_0, the Rouse theory applied to an undiluted polymer predicts (equations 1 and 6 of Chapter 10):

$$H = (\rho RT/M)\Sigma\tau_p\delta(\tau - \tau_p) \tag{1}$$

$$\tau_p = a^2Z^2\zeta_0/6\pi^2p^2kT \tag{2}$$

Temperature dependence evidently enters in several ways. Equation 1 contains a factor of T, and also the density which decreases slightly with increasing T because of thermal expansion. In equation 2, there is also a factor of T, and the characteristic dimension a may change slightly, especially if there are strong hindrances to free rotation in the polymer chain; but the effect of temperature appears primarily in ζ_0, which decreases rapidly as the friction opposing segmental motion, being of the nature of a viscosity, diminishes. The last three effects may be lumped together into a factor a_T which describes the ratio of τ_p at temperature T to that at an arbitrary standard temperature T_0:

$$[\tau_p]_T/[\tau_p]_{T_0} = a_T = [a^2\zeta_0]_T T_0/[a^2\zeta_0]_{T_0}T \tag{3}$$

Since this is the same for all τ_p, the effect of a temperature increase from T_0 to T on a logarithmic plot of H such as those in Chapter 3 is to shift the curve *upward* by log $\rho T/\rho_0 T_0$ and to the *left* by log a_T (a negative number, since the change in a_T is dominated by the decrease in ζ_0), while the shape of the curve remains unaltered (Fig. 11–2). In applying these shifts to an experimental curve as in the figure, we are assuming that every contribution to the spectrum is proportional to ρRT and that every relaxation time is proportional to $a^2\zeta_0/T$, whether or not the other features of the Rouse theory may be subject to modification because of molecular weight distribution, hydrodynamic interaction, or other complications.

Alternatively, a curve determined experimentally at temperature T

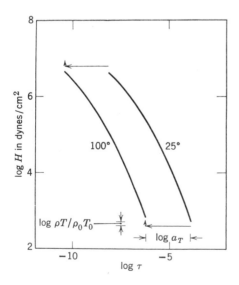

FIG. 11–2. Effect of change in temperature from T_0 to T on the relaxation spectrum H (illustrated by the spectrum for polyisobutylene of low molecular weight, Curve I of Fig. 3–3).

can be "reduced" to the position it would have occupied at temperature T_0 by plotting $H_p = HT_0\rho_0/T\rho$ against τ/a_T, if the thermal expansion coefficient $\alpha = -(1/\rho)\partial\rho/\partial T$) and the factor a_T are known. A series of experimental measurements at several different temperatures, when each is reduced to T_0 using the appropriate value of a_T, should superpose to give a single composite curve representing H at T_0.

The quantities H_p and τ/a_T are not reduced variables in the usual sense of being dimensionless, like those used in treating corresponding states in gases. They could be normalized by dividing respectively by $\rho RT/M$ and by some characteristic time, yielding dimensionless variables, but it is more convenient to leave them in the form designated. Often the normalizing factors are not available; besides, for practical purposes, it is useful to have the actual function H_p as it would appear at T_0. Thus the temperature T_0 serves to designate a standard reference state, somewhat analogous to the standard states used in thermodynamics. If H_p is known at T_0, it can be readily obtained at any other temperature by "un-reducing."

From the relations between H and the other viscoelastic functions, it follows that the latter can also be reduced to T_0 by plotting as follows:

$$L_p = LT\rho/T_0\rho_0, \qquad vs. \qquad t/a_T \qquad (4)$$

$$G_p(t) = G(t)T_0\rho_0/T\rho, \qquad vs. \qquad t/a_T \qquad (5)$$

$$G'_p = G'T_0\rho_0/T\rho, \qquad vs. \qquad \omega a_T \qquad (6)$$

$$G''_p = G''T_0\rho_0/T\rho, \qquad vs. \qquad \omega a_T \qquad (7)$$

$$\eta'_p = \eta'T_0\rho_0/a_T T\rho, \qquad vs. \qquad \omega a_T \qquad (8)$$

$$J_p(t) = J(t)T\rho/T_0\rho_0, \qquad vs. \qquad t/a_T \qquad (9)$$

$$J'_p = J'T\rho/T_0\rho_0, \qquad vs. \qquad \omega a_T \qquad (10)$$

$$J''_p = J''T\rho/T_0\rho_0, \qquad vs. \qquad \omega a_T \qquad (11)$$

Thus, starting from a complicated dependence on both temperature and time (or frequency), as illustrated in Fig. 11–1, these two independent variables can be separated to yield a function of frequency alone—the viscoelastic function reduced to T_0 (Fig. 11–3), and one of temperature alone—a_T vs. T (Fig. 11–4), determined empirically by making everything superpose in Fig. 11–3. The choice of T_0 is purely arbitrary and based on convenience. Figure 11–3 represents J' as it would have been measured at T_0 over an enormous range of frequencies, and it is actually this reduced plot which appeared as a part of Curve III in Fig. 2–6.

The molecular theories based on flexible chains, in any of their forms presented in Chapter 10, predict that a single composite curve such as Fig. 11–3 will be obtained insofar as the motions reflected in the measured quantity are governed by a single average friction coefficient. The experimental criterion for fulfilling the prediction is, in the first place, that the shapes of curves originally determined at different temperatures each over a substantial range of frequencies shall match, so that they coincide after reduction within experimental error. This is evidently satisfied in Fig. 11–3. There are, however, more stringent additional criteria which will be discussed in Section B.

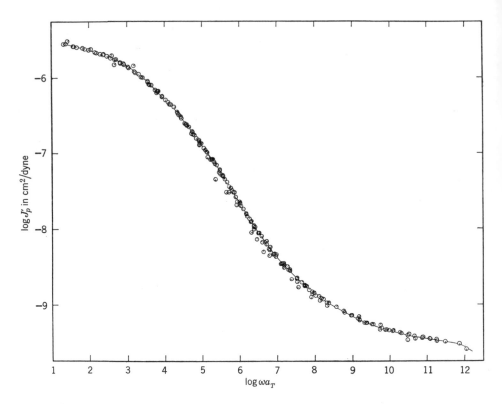

FIG. 11–3. Composite curve obtained by plotting the data of Fig. 11–1 with reduced variables, representing the behavior over an extended frequency scale at temperature T_0.

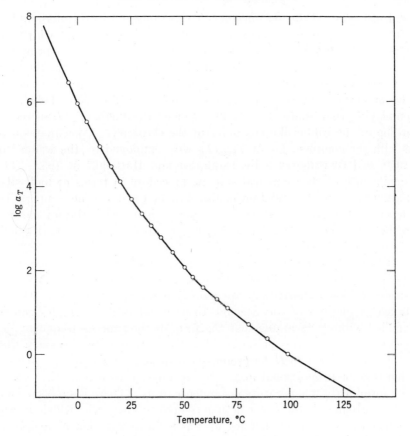

FIG. 11–4. Temperature dependence of the shift factor a_T used in plotting Fig. 11–3. Points, chosen empirically; curve, from equation 19.

When they are not fulfilled, it may be concluded that a single friction coefficient cannot describe all the modes of motion, and that there are effects of temperature in addition to those described previously.

2. Empirical Development of the Use of Reduced Variables

The scheme for construction of a composite curve like Fig. 11–3 by empirical shifts of data obtained at different temperatures along a logarithmic time or frequency axis was applied to dielectric measurements many decades ago.[2] Its application to mechanical, dielectric, and magnetic relaxation phenomena was discussed by Leaderman [3] in 1943. These early treatments ignored the factor $T\rho/T_0\rho_0$, which enters the coordinate schemes 4 to 11 because of the entropy-spring nature of the stored elastic energy in the flexible chain theory; the need for such a factor would usually go unnoticed in the empirical matching of curve shapes, as explained below. Andrews and Tobolsky,[4] employing coordinates 5 in 1943, included the factor T_0/T in recognition of the rubberlike character of the elasticity. Coordinates 6 to 8 with the complete factor $T_0\rho_0/T\rho$ were employed by the writer [5] in 1950, and coordinates 9 by Dahlquist and Hatfield [6] in 1952. The significance of the empirical shifting procedure in terms of molecular parameters, and the relation of the shift factor a_T to the temperature dependence of ζ_0 (equation 3), became evident with the appearance of Rouse's theory [7] in 1953, though it was also inherent in Kirkwood's theory for cross-linked networks [8] in 1946.

It should be noted again that the proportionality of moduli to $T\rho/T_0\rho_0$ (and of compliances to $T_0\rho_0/T\rho$) and the applicability of a single friction coefficient ζ_0 are more general principles than the detailed predictions of any specific theory, and these principles can be applied without assuming that the form of the time or frequency dependence follows any prescribed function. It is only necessary that each contribution to H be proportional to ρRT and that each relaxation time be proportional to ζ_0. No assumption is made, either, about the form of the temperature dependence of a_T. There have been some other schemes [9,6] for constructing composite curves in which it was assumed at the outset that log a_T was a linear function of reciprocal absolute temperature (by analogy with the theory of rate processes [10]), and it has sometimes been erroneously believed that the method of reduced variables implies a specific form such as this for the temperature dependence. On the contrary, the shape of the curve in Fig. 11–4 is determined empirically from the data, although it may be useful to fit it subsequently to a suitable analytical expression (Section B below).

In regions where the modulus or compliance is changing rapidly, as near 40° in Fig. 11–1, it would be possible to match adjacent curves empirically whether they were first shifted vertically in accordance with the factor $T\rho/T_0\rho_0$ or with T/T_0 or not shifted at all. Slightly different values of a_T would be obtained in each case, of course. In regions where the viscoelastic function is flat, however, the influence of a vertical shift is much more apparent, and in several cases [11-13] it has been demonstrated that such a shift is necessary for satisfactory matching. It is impossible to distinguish empirically between the merits of $T\rho/T_0\rho_0$ and T/T_0, since their logarithms are both relatively small and usually differ by only about 20%. However, the former factor is clearly indicated by the flexible chain theory in equation 1 or any other of its various modifications.

The principle on which the use of reduced variables is based has been referred to by various names, such as thermorheological simplicity,[14] the time-temperature superposition principle [15] (not to be confused with the Boltzmann superposition principle!) and time-temperature reducibility; [16] the composite plots with reduced variables have been called master curves.[17]

3. Reduced Variables in Terms of Steady-Flow Viscosity

For uncross-linked polymers of low molecular weight, and for those of high molecular weight with restriction to the terminal zone of time scale, the relation between τ_p and η as given by equation 21 of Chapter 10 leads to the following expression for a_T:

$$a_T = \eta T_0\rho_0/\eta_0 T\rho \tag{12}$$

Thus, if the temperature dependence of the viscosity is known, it is no longer necessary to obtain a_T empirically. The reduced coordinates 5 to 8 become

$$G_p(t) = G(t)T_0\rho_0/T\rho, \qquad vs. \qquad t\eta_0 T\rho/\eta T_0\rho_0 \tag{13}$$

$$G'_p = G'T_0\rho_0/T\rho, \qquad vs. \qquad \omega\eta T_0\rho_0/\eta_0 T\rho \tag{14}$$

$$G''_p = G''T_0\rho_0/T\rho, \qquad vs. \qquad \omega\eta T_0\rho_0/\eta_0 T\rho \tag{15}$$

$$\eta'_p = \eta'T_0\rho_0/T\rho, \qquad vs. \qquad \omega\eta T_0\rho_0/\eta_0 T\rho \tag{16}$$

$$\eta'_r = \eta'/\eta, \qquad vs. \qquad \omega\eta T_0\rho_0/\eta_0 T\rho \tag{17}$$

In the last, a dimensionless reduced variable has been chosen for the ordinate. Similar coordinates can be employed for $J(t)$, J', and J''.

4. Reduced Variables Applied to Polymers of High Molecular Weight

When the molecular weight of an uncross-linked polymer is sufficiently high for entanglement coupling to appear, the effective friction coefficient for the longest relaxation times and for the steady-flow viscosity is $Q_e\zeta_0$, whereas that for short relaxation times is simply ζ_0 (Chapter 10, Section F). The question of whether a_T in the transition zone can be calculated from equation 12—i.e., whether the reduced coordinates of 13 to 17 are applicable in the transition zone—depends on whether or not Q_e changes with temperature. For polyisobutyl-ene,[18] as well as for very concentrated solutions of polystyrene [19] and polyvinyl acetate,[20] Q_e appears to be temperature-independent, since equation 12 holds to a rather close approximation. For some metha-crylate polymers,[21] on the other hand, Q_e evidently decreases with increasing temperature, so that the a_T applicable in the terminal zone is more strongly temperature-dependent than the a_T applicable in the transition zone. This does not prevent successful use of the method of reduced variables within a single zone of the time scale, but in the plateau zone a complicated transition takes place (Section D below).

5. Application of Reduced Variables near the Glassy Zone

At very short times or high frequencies where configurational re-arrangements of the polymer chains do not take place within the ex-perimental time scale, the predictions of the flexible chain theories can no longer be used as guides to a reduction scheme. The factor T/T_0 is not applicable, since the energy storage does not correspond to an entropy spring. Moreover, whatever local motions occur cer-tainly cannot be described in terms of the friction coefficient ζ_0.

In the approach to the glassy zone, the existence of an approxi-mately asymptotic limiting value of the compliance J_g can be taken into account by modifying the coordinates 9 and 10 as follows: [22]

$$J_p(t) = J_g + (J(t) - J_g)T\rho/T_0\rho_0 \qquad vs. \qquad t/a_T \qquad (18)$$

$$J'_p = J_g + (J' - J_g)T\rho/T_0\rho_0 \qquad vs. \qquad \omega a_T \qquad (19)$$

The reduction of J'' remains unchanged, whereas those for the moduli cannot be expressed in simple form. It is implied here that J_g is in-dependent of temperature; alternatively, it has been suggested that J_g should be inversely proportional to ρ, but it is too poorly defined operationally to permit a decision. Coordinates 18 and 19 can be used when J'/J_g or $J(t)/J_g$ lies between 1 and 10; for higher com-pliances, they are indistinguishable from 9 and 10.

When other viscoelastic mechanisms such as those attributed to motions of side groups make contributions comparable in magnitude to those of the backbone configurational motions, there are two types of temperature dependence superposed on each other, as described in Section D below.

B. PROCEDURE AND CRITERIA FOR APPLICABILITY OF THE METHOD OF REDUCED VARIABLES

Exact matching of the shapes of adjacent curves has already been cited as one criterion for the applicability of reduced variables. Two others which should be applied to any experimental example when possible are: (a) the same values of a_T must superpose all the visco-elastic functions; (b) the temperature dependence of a_T must have a reasonable form consistent with experience.

The two components of the complex dynamic modulus (or of the complex compliance) are weighted quite differently with respect to the long-time and short-time contributions to H (or L). For example, as is evident from equations 26 and 27 of Chapter 3, J' at a particular frequency ω is determined primarily by the spectral contributions for which $\omega\tau < 1$, whereas J'' is determined by those for which $\omega\tau \simeq 1$. If for any reason a_T is not the same for long retardation times and short retardation times, not only will the curves for J' and J'' fail to match in shape, but any attempt at a forced fit will provide one set of apparent a_T values for J' and a different set for J''. Whenever this occurs, the method of reduced variables in its simple form as given above must be rejected, no master curves can be drawn without sub-jecting the data to a more complicated analysis.

An example of this sort of test, for the data of Fig. 11–1 and the cor-responding values of J'' which were determined in the same series of measurements, is shown in Table 11–I. The procedure was as follows.[1] First, a reference temperature T_0 somewhere within the range of the experiments was arbitrarily chosen (in this case, 373.2°K.). Then log-arithmic plots of $J'T\rho/T_0\rho_0$ against ω (very similar in appearance to Fig. 11–2, but with slight vertical shifts produced by the $T\rho/T_0\rho_0$ factor) and of $J''T\rho/T_0\rho_0$ were prepared. The horizontal distance between each pair of adjacent curves was measured with a pair of dividers and recorded as $\Delta \log a_T$. (If the curves were not parallel, or if their slopes were such that no reliable measurement could be made, no value was recorded.) Where the values of $\Delta \log a_T$ from J' and J'' were the same within reasonable error, the average was taken. (At low temperatures, the spacings from J'' are often preferred because the nature of the ex-perimental method makes them somewhat more reliable; depending on the experiments, either J' or J'' may be the more reliable measurement in certain regions of frequency and consistency.) The selected values of $\Delta \log a_T$ were then added progressively from T_0 to obtain $\log a_T$ at each temperature.

The next criterion, the form of $\log a_T$ as a function of temperature, was applied first by noting that it was a smooth function with no gross fluctuations or irregularities and then by fitting the empirical values to an expression which has proved to be widely applicable (*cf.* Section C below):

$$\log a_T = -c_1{}^0(T - T_0)/(c_2{}^0 + T - T_0) \qquad (20)$$

For this purpose, $(T - T_0)/\log a_T$ as listed in Table 11–I was plotted against $T - T_0$, and from the slope s and intercept i of the resulting straight line the two empirical constants were calculated:

$$c_1{}^0 = -1/s \qquad (21)$$

$$c_2{}^0 = i/s \qquad (22)$$

The form of equation 19 is independent of the choice of T_0. To check the determination of $c_1{}^0$ and $c_2{}^0$, it is frequently useful to choose a second reference temperature T_1 and repeat the graphical evaluation, which provides coefficients $c_1{}^1$ and $c_2{}^1$ corresponding to T_1. These are then transformed to the values appropriate to T_0 by the relations

$$c_1{}^0 = c_1{}^1 c_2{}^1/(c_2{}^1 + T_0 - T_1) \qquad (23$$

$$c_2{}^0 = c_2{}^1 + T_0 - T_1 \qquad (24)$$

Finally, values of $\log a_T$ were calculated from equation 19 with the selected coefficients $c_1{}^0 = 7.60$, $c_2{}^0 = 227.3$; these are given in the last column of Table 11–I, and amount to a smoothing of the values in the first $\log a_T$ column. They agree quite closely with the initial tentative values. The calculated values were actually used in constructing Fig. 11–3, and also the corresponding reduced plot of the imaginary part of the compliance, which is shown in Fig. 11–5. The criterion that both components be reduced with the same a_T values is clearly satisfied, except for a slight anomaly at the highest reduced frequencies.

Still another criterion for satisfactory reduction is that the coefficients $c_1{}^0$ and $c_2{}^0$ should have magnitudes in accord with experience when they are transformed to the values appropriate to the glass transition temperature T_g as reference temperature. This subject is discussed in Section C below.

There have been many examples where experimental viscoelastic data, both transient and dynamic, superpose with remarkable precision when reduced to a reference temperature in this manner. In other cases, the reduction is successful only in a restricted zone, and deviations occur in other regions of viscoelastic consistency or of temperature. Some examples of the latter and their interpretation are given in Section D below.

Since in a single investigation dynamic measurements usually do not extend over more than three decades of logarithmic frequency, nor transient measurements over more than six decades, specific nu-

Table 11–I

DETERMINATION OF a_T VALUES FOR POLY-n-OCTYL METHACRYLATE FROM FIG. 11–1 AND CORRESPONDING DATA FOR J''

T, °K.	$\log$ $T\rho/T_0\rho_0$	From J'	$\Delta \log a_T$ From J''	Chosen	$\log$ a_T Tent.[a]	$-\dfrac{T-T_0}{\log a_T}$	$\log$ a_T Calc.[b]
268.2	−0.11	0.58 [c]	0.47	0.47	6.45	16.29	6.52
273.1	−0.11	0.43	0.42	0.42	5.98	16.74	5.98
277.2	−0.10	0.62	0.60	0.61	5.56	17.27	5.57
283.1	−0.10	0.45	0.47	0.46	4.95	18.22	4.99
288.3	−0.09	0.35	0.37	0.36	4.49	18.90	4.53
293.0	−0.08	0.41	0.44	0.43	4.13	19.42	4.14
298.5	−0.08	0.31	0.34	0.33	3.70	20.20	3.72
303.2	−0.07	0.29	0.30	0.30	3.37	20.80	3.38
307.4	−0.07	0.29	0.30	0.30	3.07	21.45	3.10
312.0	−0.06	0.35	0.35	0.35	2.77	22.10	2.80
317.6	−0.05	0.32	0.32	0.32	2.42	22.98	2.46
323.4	−0.05	0.22	0.24	0.23	2.10	23.74	2.13
327.6	−0.04	0.27	0.26	0.26	1.87	24.40	1.91
333.0	−0.04	0.27	0.27	0.27	1.61	25.00	1.64
339.0	−0.03	0.22	0.22	0.22	1.34	25.55	1.35
344.1	−0.03	0.37	0.40	0.38	1.12	26.05	1.12
353.4	−0.02	0.34	d	0.34	0.74	e	0.73
362.6	−0.01	0.39	d	0.39	0.40	e	0.37
373.0	0	0.31	d	0.31	0.01	e	0.01
382.6	0.01	d	d				−0.30
393.5	0.02	d	d				−0.62
402.7	0.02						−0.87

[a] Choosing $T_0 = 373.2$°K.

[b] With $c_1{}^0 = 7.60$, $c_2{}^0 = 227.3$.

[c] Poor fit.

[d] Curves too flat to determine $\Delta \log a_T$.

[e] Dividend and divisor too small for precision.

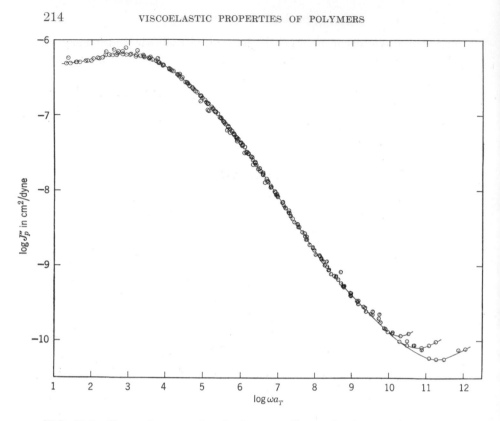

FIG. 11–5. Composite curve for the loss compliance of poly-n-octyl methacrylate, obtained from the same series of measurements as the data of Fig. 11–1 and reduced with the same values of a_T.

merical tests of the accuracy of the reduction procedure are usually limited to distances of this order, although the span of the reduced viscoelastic function may cover twelve decades as in Fig. 11–3 or even more. In a few cases [23, 24] satisfactory agreement has been obtained over a wider distance of time scale by comparing a very high frequency measurement at a high temperature with a transient at long times at a low temperature.

To interpret a reduced curve such as Fig. 11–3 in terms of actual physical behavior at its extremes can become physically or operationally obscure. Thus, Fig. 11–3 could be used to predict the compliance of poly-n-octyl methacrylate at 120°C. at a frequency of 10^{13} cycles/sec. Since this is of the order of molecular vibration frequencies, it can hardly be expected that the calculation would be valid.

At the other extreme, the reduced curves for polyvinyl acetate (curves II) in Chapter 2 could be used to predict its properties at T_g at a frequency of 5×10^{-9} rad./sec. or a time of 2×10^8 sec. This is about six years, and other examples could be cited where the period would transcend historical time. Such paradoxes do not detract, however, from the usefulness of the reduced curve and the accompanying function $a_T(T)$ as an economical expression of data from which the properties can be predicted over wide ranges of temperature and time scale within reasonable limits.

C. THE WLF EQUATION AND THE RELATION OF TEMPERATURE DEPENDENCE OF RELAXATION AND RETARDATION TIMES TO FREE VOLUME

Now that the temperature dependence of viscoelastic properties can be represented for many purposes by a single function $a_T(T)$, it is important to scrutinize the form of this function and its significance. Equation 20, sometimes called the WLF equation, was introduced [25, 26] as an empirical expression for a general curve of $a_T(T)$ in which data for many different polymers had been reduced to standard states in a manner which will be described below. In examining its properties, we shall follow a presentation somewhat different from the chronological development.

1. Reduction to the Glass Transition Temperature

If experimental values for a_T are compared for different polymers all based on the same T_0, as illustrated in Fig. 11–6 for a reference of 373.2°K., the curves of course cross at T_0 but differ widely in steepness. Alternatively, since the only characteristic temperature an amorphous polymer possesses is its glass transition temperature, an obvious way of comparing different polymers in corresponding states is to choose the T_g of each as its reference temperature. To do this directly from experimental data is difficult, because viscoelastic measurements in the transition zone between glasslike and rubberlike consistency (from which the a_T values are obtained) cannot be extended to a temperature as low as T_g without encountering a very prolonged time scale. However, the WLF equation can be used to extrapolate, in effect, 10° or 20° down to T_g from the lowest temperature of measurement. It is only necessary to rewrite equations 23 and

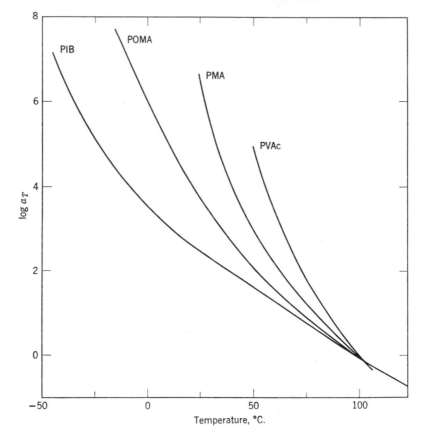

FIG. 11–6. Temperature dependence of a_T for various polymers referred to $T_0 = 373.2°K$. PIB, polyisobutylene; POMA, poly-n-octyl methacrylate (Fig. 11–4); PMA, polymethyl acrylate; PVAc, polyvinyl acetate.

24 to obtain from $c_1{}^0$ and $c_2{}^0$ the WLF coefficients corresponding to T_g:

$$c_1{}^g = c_1{}^0 c_2{}^0 / (c_2{}^0 + T_g - T_0) \qquad (25)$$

$$c_2{}^g = c_2{}^0 + T_g - T_0 \qquad (26)$$

and calculate a_T referred to T_g as:

$$\log a_{T_g} = -c_1{}^g (T - T_g)/(c_2{}^g + T - T_g) \qquad (27)$$

The data of Fig. 11–6 are replotted in this manner in Fig. 11–7. The curves for the two polar polymers and those for the two relatively non-

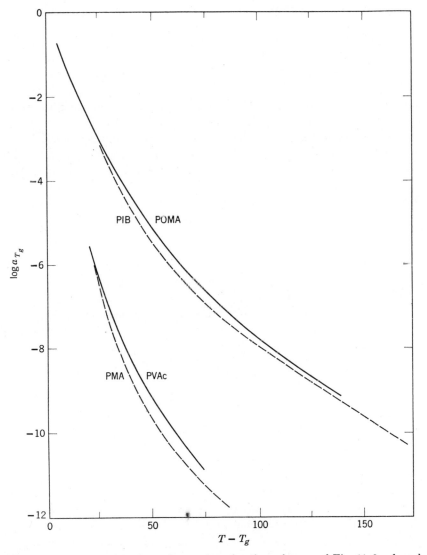

FIG. 11–7. Temperature dependence of a_T for the polymers of Fig. 11–6 referred each to its own glass transition temperature.

polar polymers now lie close to each other; actually, arbitrary adjustments of the values chosen for T_g, within a range of 10°, would make them all nearly coincide. To a rough approximation, $c_1{}^g$ and $c_2{}^g$ were first considered to be approximately universal constants with values of 17.44 and 51.6 respectively.[26] It is evident from the divergences in Fig. 11–7, however, that there is some variation of these coefficients among different polymers. Nevertheless, the form of equation 27 has been found to fit data on many different systems over a temperature range generally from T_g to $T_g + 100°$.

A summary of the two coefficients from various sources in the literature [27–44] is given in Table 11–II, showing a mild variation in $c_1{}^g$ and a somewhat wider one in $c_2{}^g$. For some of the systems, T_g is unknown; in this case, the product $c_1{}^g c_2{}^g$ can still be obtained, since it is temperature-invariant. This quantity varies from 449 to 2305, as compared with the approximate "universal" value of 900. (Where T_g is unknown, values of $c_1{}^0$ and $c_2{}^0$ for an arbitrary reference temperature are given in footnotes, for practical applications.)

The polymers chosen for illustration here are all of sufficiently high molecular weight that the dependence of T_g on molecular weight is slight, and the same is expected to be true for the empirical constants c_1 and c_2. The relation of these constants to molecular structure can be better discussed in terms of certain derived quantities which also appear in the table, and will be introduced below. First, however, we must digress to review the nature of the glass transition.

2. The Glass Transition and Free Volume

In Chapters 1 and 2, the glass transition was described as the point, or narrow region, on the temperature scale where the thermal expansion coefficient α undergoes a discontinuity and below which configurational rearrangements of polymer chain backbones, if they occur at all, are extremely slow. The most unambiguous definition of it is in terms of the discontinuity in α (which is also accompanied by discontinuities in heat capacity and in compressibility [45,46]). It corresponds to a change in slope in a plot of specific volume against temperature, as illustrated schematically in Fig. 11–8.

Many of the properties of liquids, whether polymeric or not, demonstrate the presence of a substantial proportion of free volume, which may be present as holes of the order of molecular (monomeric) dimensions or smaller voids associated with packing irregularities.[47–49] Although the free volume per g., v_f, is poorly defined operationally,[50] it is a useful semi-quantitative concept. In particular, the thermal expansion coefficient of liquids (whether polymeric or not) represents primarily the creation of additional free volume with rising temperature, whereas the much smaller magnitudes characteristic of crystalline solids arise from anharmonicity in the dependence of potential energy on interatomic or intermolecular distances.[51]

Table 11–II

PARAMETERS CHARACTERIZING TEMPERATURE DEPENDENCE
OF a_T FOR VARIOUS POLYMER SYSTEMS

Polymer	T_g °K.	$c_1{}^g$	$c_2{}^g$ deg	$c_1{}^g c_2{}^g$	f_g	α_f deg^{-1} $\times 10^4$	$\Delta\alpha$ deg^{-1} $\times 10^4$	Ref.
General								
Polyisobutylene	202	16.56	104.4	1731	0.026	2.5	5	18,27
Polyvinyl acetate	305	15.6	46.8	732	0.028	5.9	5	28,29
Polyvinyl chloroacetate [a]	296	17.45	40.4	705	0.025	6.2		30,29
Polymethyl acrylate	276	18.1	45.0	815	0.024	5.3	4	31,29
Polyhexene-1	218	22.2	20.2	449	0.020	0.7		32
Poly-3-trifluoro-methoxy-1,1 dihydroperfluorylpropyl acetate		c		1524		2.9		33
Polyurethane [b]	238	15.6	32.6	510	0.028	8.5		34
Hevea rubber	200	16.7	53.6	898	0.026	4.8	4	35
Methacrylate Polymers								
Ethyl	335	17.6	65.5	1152	0.025	3.7	3	36
n-Butyl	300	17.0	96.6	1642	0.026	2.6	3	37
n-Hexyl	268	17.8	129.4	2305	0.025	1.9	2–3	38
n-Octyl	253	16.1	107.3	1730	0.027	2.5	2–3	1
n-Dodecyl		d		1184		3.7		39
Diluted Systems								
Poly-n-butyl methacrylate in diethyl phthalate 30%		e		1565		2.8		40
40%		f		1660		2.6		40
50%	206	17.8	86.1	1531	0.024	2.8	3	40
60%	227	18.1	111.3	2014	0.024	2.2	1	40
Polyvinyl chloride in dimethyl thianthrene 10%				1285		3.4		22,41
Cellulose tributyrate in dimethyl phthalate 21%	188	21.1	42.6	900	0.021	4.8	5	42,43
43%	193	23.3	38.6	900	0.019	4.8	4	42,43
Cellulose nitrate in diethyl phthalate 23%	166	26.2	53.5	1403	0.016	3.1	4	44,43

[a] From dielectric rather than mechanical data.
[b] Copolymer of adipic acid and ethylene and propylene glycols, cross-linked by naphthalene 1,4-diisocyanate and 1,4-butanediol.
[c] At $T_0 = 262°$, $c_1{}^0 = 8.86$, $c_2{}^0 = 101.6$.
[d] At $T_0 = 298.2°$, $c_1{}^0 = 8.52$, $c_2{}^0 = 139.2$.
[e] At $T_0 = 273.2°$, $c_1{}^0 = 9.58$, $c_2{}^0 = 163.3$.
[f] At $T_0 = 273.2°$, $c_1{}^0 = 9.95$, $c_2{}^0 = 166.6$.

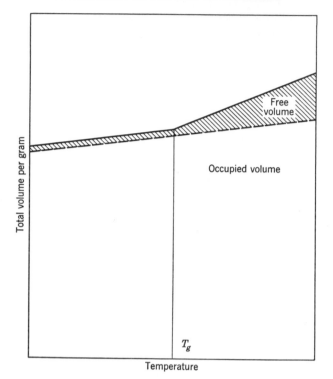

FIG. 11–8. Schematic variation of specific volume, occupied volume, and free volume with temperature for a non-crystallizing liquid (or soft polymeric solid).

At temperatures high enough so that local Brownian motion is rapid in a polymeric liquid or soft solid, a lowering of temperature is accompanied by collapse of free volume as the molecular adjustments take place freely within a normal experimental time scale; α has the magnitude characteristic of liquids, of the order of 10^{-3} deg^{-1}. At lower temperatures, the adjustments are slower, and if crystallization does not occur first a temperature may be reached where the collapse does not occur at all within experimental times. Then the only residual volume contraction is of a solidlike character, and whatever free volume is left presumably remains constant, as illustrated by the shaded area in the figure. It should be emphasized that the dimensional changes correspond to bulk compression with no shear, as mentioned in Chapter 8, so that no long-range contour changes of polymeric molecules are involved. The character of the phenomenon is therefore independent of molecular weight. In fact, the same discontinuity in α has long been known in ordinary non-crystallizing liquids of low molecular weight,[52, 53] and the detailed interrelations among volume, temperature, and time for glucose (for example) and polystyrene or polyvinyl acetate are closely parallel.[54]

It is inherent in the above discussion that T_g must depend on the time scale of the volumetric measurement. It has in fact been demonstrated [55, 56] that a slower measurement pattern leads to a lower value of T_g. The most extensive experiments have been performed by Kovacs.[57] A sample well-equilibrated far above T_g is suddenly cooled to a temperature T_1 near T_g and its specific volume v is followed as a function of time. Representative results are shown in Fig. 11–9 for polyvinyl acetate. Contraction occurs gradually over many hours, and if T_1 is not very far below T_g a stable equilibrium volume $v(\infty)$ is eventually reached. The results here are plotted as $v(t) - v(\infty)$. These data correspond qualitatively to bulk creep experiments; although they do not of course represent contraction under a constant confining pressure, the molecular adjustments responsible for collapse of free volume are similar in nature. The lower the temperature, the slower is the con-

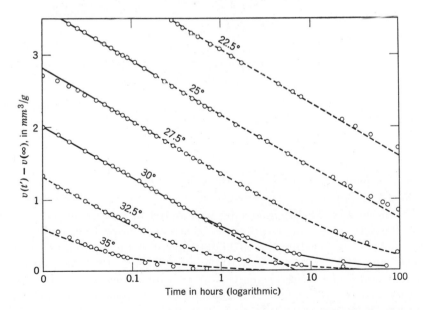

FIG. 11–9. Contraction of polyvinyl acetate plotted against logarithm of time after cooling from well above T_g to the temperature indicated (Kovacs [75]).

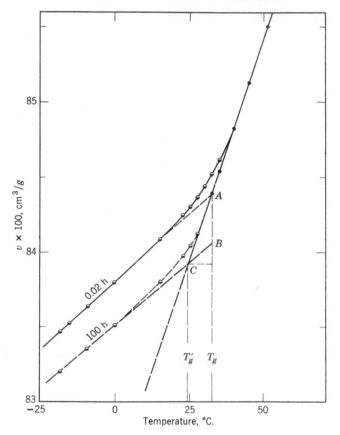

FIG. 11–10. Specific volume $vs.$ temperature for polyvinyl acetate, measured after cooling quickly from well above T_g. Black points, equilibrium values; half black, values measured 0.02 h. and 100 h. after cooling as indicated (Kovacs[75]).

traction process. Intercepts on these curves at $t = 0.02$ hr., when expressed as $v(t)$ instead of $v(t) - v(\infty)$, give the upper line at the left in Fig. 11–10; intercepts at $t = 100$ hr. give the lower line at the left. The intersections of these two respective lines with the volume-temperature line at high temperatures give values of $T_g = 32.5°$ and $24.5°$ at 0.02 h. and 100 h. respectively. (A somewhat different and more accurate analysis gives a difference of about 9° between the two T_g values.[54]) The literature values range from 25° to 33°; in Table 11–II, 32° was selected.[58]

Most T_g values in the literature are based on volumetric measurements with a different experimental pattern, in which the temperature is raised (or lowered) either continuously at a slow rate or intermittently with pauses of the order of an hour between, without strictly controlling the time sequence. Since T_g changes only about three degrees with a change in time scale of a factor of 10 (as exemplified in Fig. 11–8, and by the application of the WLF equation below), these values are significant within a degree or two, and with this reservation will be used for various derived calculations in the sections to follow. It would be preferable, however, to define T_g in terms of an experimental pattern like that on which Fig. 11–10 is based, with a conventional time interval; Kovacs[54] has recommended 3 min. Moreover, the previous thermal history and possible traces of diluents of low molecular weight—in some cases, moisture—can influence the experimental determination. As a result, values of T_g from different laboratories frequently fail to agree, and the proper value to use for correlation with the temperature dependence of viscoelastic properties is sometimes uncertain.

We now examine more closely the details of the volume contraction as portrayed in Fig. 11–9. The isotherms at different temperatures are closely superposable by horizontal translations just as are those for shear deformation in Fig. 11–1. Moreover, if one particular temperature in the transition region is arbitrarily designated as T_g, the translations of logarithmic time expressed as log a_T follow equation 27 closely. This result, obtained by Kovacs for several polymers, indicates that the temperature dependences of the molecular processes in bulk compression and in shear deformation are identical. Moreover, it permits calculation of the effect of experimental time scale on the apparent glass transition temperature, by differentiating equation 27:

$$d \, \Delta T_g/d \log a_T \cong c_2{}^g/c_1{}^g \cong 3^0 \tag{28}$$

The shapes of the curves in Fig. 11–9 can yield information about the retardation spectrum in bulk deformation, as discussed in Chapter 18. From this analysis it follows that their shapes should not be exactly the same at temperatures below $T_g - 8$, but that another somewhat more complicated function of volume when plotted against log t should be exactly superposable by horizontal shifts; this is in fact observed.[54]

The glass transition temperature is thus defined in terms of a kinetic process involving *volume contraction,* at an arbitrary but convenient (and not highly critical) time interval. Efforts have often been made to specify the glass transition in terms of a kinetic process involving shear deformation instead—corresponding to the temperature at which the transition from rubberlike to glasslike consistency as portrayed in Fig. 11–1 reaches a certain stage at an arbitrary time interval; these are so-called softening temperatures, brittle temperatures, Vicat temperatures, etc. They are far more subject to ambiguity because of the more gradual nature of the phenomenon as compared with that of Fig. 11–8, and the difficulty of comparing magnitudes of moduli or compliances in different types of systems. They are not recommended as possessing any significance comparable with that of T_g; it cannot be expected that any kind of transition temperature based on time-dependent mechanical measurements in shear can be substituted for the T_g appearing in equation 27. Only the volumetric transition reflects the temperature below which the free volume no longer collapses, and it is the free volume which determines the rates of relaxation processes, as will become evident below.

The arguments against calling the glass transition in vitrifying liquids a "second-order" transition have been convincingly presented by Flory.[59] However, the existence of a second-order transition in polymers has been predicted theoretically by Gibbs;[60] it may represent a limiting phenomenon approached by the experimental glass transition at very long times of experiment.

3. Relation of Molecular Mobility to Free Volume

The appearance of the glass transition results from the reduction of molecular mobility as the temperature falls, slowing the collapse of free volume. We now introduce the concept that the mobility at any temperature depends primarily on the free volume remaining, so that the rates of both bulk and shear deformations can be advantageously expressed in terms of v_f rather than T as the independent variable. This principle was applied long ago to the shear viscosity of simple liquids by Batchinski,[61] and more recently by Doolittle [62] with a simple empirical equation of high accuracy.

The more common view that the temperature dependence of viscosity (or any other property reflecting molecular rearrangements) is determined by an energy barrier for hole formation [47–50] which is in turn related to intermolecular forces is probably not entirely contradictory,[63, 64] since the difficulty of hole formation must be related to the average free volume present. However, the energy barrier theory in its simple form leads to a viscosity proportional to $e^{\Delta H_\eta/RT}$, where ΔH_η is the activation energy, independent of temperature—an Arrhenius form. This is not compatible with accurate data on simple liquids [62] and it fails spectacularly for supercooled liquids and polymers as T_g is approached. For the latter, ΔH_η can be discussed almost interchangeably with the apparent activation energy for viscoelastic relaxation times, ΔH_a:

$$\Delta H_a = Rd \ln a_T/d(1/T) \tag{29}$$

because differentiation of equation 12 yields

$$\Delta H_\eta = \Delta H_a - RT + \alpha RT^2 \tag{30}$$

in which the last two terms are of minor significance. When the WLF equation holds, differentiation of equation 27 yields

$$\Delta H_a = 2.303Rc_1{}^g c_2{}^g T^2/(c_2{}^g + T - T_g)^2 \tag{31}$$

which increases rapidly with decreasing temperature. In particular, at T_g, $\Delta H_a = 2.303Rc_1{}^g T_g{}^2/c_2{}^g$, corresponding to the enormous values of 62 kcal. at $T_g = 200°$ and 250 kcal. at $T_g = 400°$K.

The sharp increase in ΔH_a or ΔH_η with decreasing temperature, especially near T_g, can be explained qualitatively in terms of the severe decrease in relative free volume, as first clearly pointed out by Fox and Flory,[65] who also proposed that the free volume at T_g should be a constant. The simplest way [26] of obtaining a quantitative expression with free volume parameters which can be related to the WLF coefficients is to modify Doolittle's viscosity equation [49,62]

$$\ln \eta = \ln A + B(v - v_f)/v_f \tag{32}$$

in which A and B are empirical constants, the latter of the order of unity. If the temperature variations of T and ρ in equation 12 are neglected, we obtain for a reference temperature of T_g:

$$\ln a_T = B(1/f - 1/f_g) \tag{33}$$

where f is the volume fraction of free volume, v_f/v. If f increases linearly with temperature in accordance with the relation $f = f_g + \alpha_f(T - T_g)$, this becomes

$$\log a_T = -\frac{(B/2.303\,f_g)(T - T_g)}{f_g/\alpha_f + T - T_g} \tag{34}$$

identical in form with the WLF equation. The same relation has been derived by Bueche [63] from considerations of fluctuations in local free volume and the minimum local fractional free volume f_c necessary for motion of a group of n polymeric segments; here the empirical constant B is replaced by nf_c.

To identify the factors in equations 27 and 34, B has been somewhat arbitrarily set at unity. This is consistent with the magnitude of Doolittle's values for simple liquids, and with Bueche's inference of 5 and 0.2 as reasonable values for n and f_c. On this basis, we obtain

$$f_g = 1/2.303c_1{}^g \qquad (35)$$

$$\alpha_f = 1/2.303c_1{}^g c_2{}^g \qquad (36)$$

(Even if T_g is unknown, α_f can be calculated since $c_1{}^g c_2{}^g = c_1{}^0 c_2{}^0$ for any T_0.) Values of f_g and α_f calculated from these relations for a number of polymeric systems are also listed in Table 11–II.

The fractional free volume at the glass transition temperature, f_g, is 0.025 ± 0.003 for the great majority of the systems. The "universal" value of $c_1{}^g$ from a composite curve of the type of Fig. 11–7 gives $f_g = 0.025$. For the solutions of cellulose derivatives, it is somewhat smaller, but since there are no corresponding values for the pure polymers it is uncertain whether this is an effect of the presence of diluent. The magnitude is reasonable, but no precise significance can be attached to it because the concept of v_f as originally introduced remains operationally undefined. The free volume as used here is probably similar to the fluctuation free volume as defined by Bondi.[66] Some other attempts to estimate f_g from quite different sources have led to similar magnitudes.[54, 60, 67, 68] It should be noted that f_g as calculated from equation 34 depends on the time scale of the experiment in which T_g was determined, and the values in the table refer to the usual scale—unspecified, but probably of the order of an hour. If the time scale were varied sufficiently to lower T_g by 8° (the extreme shown in Fig. 11–10), f_g would be reduced from 0.025 to 0.022.

The thermal expansion coefficient of the free volume, $\alpha_f = df/dT = (1/v)\,dv_f/dT$, shows considerably more variation. However, it is perhaps the most convincing success of the free volume interpretation that α_f does turn out to be the correct magnitude for a thermal expansion coefficient. If the macroscopic expansion coefficient above T_g, α_l, represents creation of free volume together with the thermal expansion of a solidlike structure (α_g) which occurs below T_g, then α_f should be equal to $\alpha_l - \alpha_g = \Delta\alpha$. Values of $\Delta\alpha$ obtained from the slopes of plots such as Figs. 11–8 and 11–10, from various sources in the literature, are included in Table 11–II and in most cases agree fairly well with α_f. The "universal" value of α_f is 4.8×10^{-4} deg^{-1}; individual values range from 1.9 to 9.7×10^{-4} in polymers; the extremes could possibly arise from abnormal values of B. The low values, in some cases, appear in polymers whose shear viscoelastic behavior reveals distinct contributions from chain backbone and side chain motions (cf. Section D below). Possibly the bulk behavior also has distinct mechanisms and the α_f reflects only the contribution from backbone motions. Indeed, $\Delta\alpha$ is also abnormally small for some of the same polymers. (Subsidiary glass transitions with small values of $\Delta\alpha$ have in fact been observed volumetrically in cellulose derivatives.[69])

It should be remarked that α_f and f_g are quite sensitive to the graphical fitting of experimental a_T data as described in the preceding section, and some degree of uncertainty can be expected from this source. For practical purposes, this feature in reverse is an advantage: to predict the function a_T for a new polymer which has not been subjected to detailed experimental measurements, reasonable values of f_g and α_f can be assumed and the prediction will be relatively insensitive to the choice. Only T_g needs to be known for this purpose.

One of the entries in Table 11–II is derived from dielectric rather than mechanical data. In certain cases the dispersion of the complex dielectric constant in undiluted polymers (and concentrated solutions) can be analyzed by the method of reduced variables, and the function $b_T(T)$ analogous to a_T in the mechanical case also follows the WLF equation with coefficients identical with those derived from mechanical data.[25, 30] In such cases it is presumed that the dipole motion involves configurational changes of the chain backbones governed by the same friction coefficient ζ_0 which enters the theories of Chapter 10. In other examples, however, dipole motion involves different molecular mechanisms and the temperature dependence of the electrical relaxation times does not follow the WLF equation.[70, 72]

4. Further Implications of the Free Volume Interpretation

At temperatures near T_g, the WLF equation implies that the temperature dependence of viscosity and relaxation times is the same (except for the minor variations in f_g and α_f) for all systems regardless of molecular structure and intermolecular forces. The validity of this conclusion is evident not only from Table 11–II but also from the applicability of the equation to organic liquids of low molecular weight[26] and to inorganic glasses.[73] (For the latter, the values of f_g are close to those obtained for polymeric and other organic glasses; the values of α_f are often rather small, of the order of 1×10^{-4} deg^{-1}, but agree rather well with $\Delta\alpha$ as measured macroscopically.) Below T_g (more strictly, below the minimum T_g that can be achieved by prolonging the time scale), application of the equation is probably meaningless because free volume collapse does not occur. The prediction of equation 27 that a_T becomes infinite at $T = T_g - c_2^g$ is therefore no cause for concern. If there are subsidiary glass transitions, a separate WLF equation could conceivably be applied to each mechanism.

At high temperatures, the WLF equation reduces to the Arrhenius form, with $\Delta H_a = 2.303\ Rc_1^g c_2^g$ (cf. equation 31). The corresponding value of 4.1 kcal., irrespective of molecular constitution, is certainly incorrect; among liquids far above their freezing (or vitrification) points, where the proportion of free volume is far higher (perhaps 0.3 instead of 0.03) the apparent activation energies vary widely and can be correlated with chemical structure.[50] We must expect, then, the WLF equation to become inapplicable at high temperatures and the temperature dependence of relaxation processes to be governed by more specific features. The upper limit was originally [26] estimated at $T_g + 100°$, although the range of applicability may in fact be wider. Bueche [64] has discussed the temperature dependence over a wide range on the basis of fluctuations in the thermal vibrations of concentric shells surrounding a central molecular segment, with results that are consistent with the WLF form at low and the Arrhenius form at high temperatures.

An alternative form for the apparent activation energy governing the temperature dependence of dielectric relaxation times was proposed by Caillon and Groubert: [74] $\Delta H_a = AT^2/(T - T_0)^2$. This is actually identical with equation 31, with $A = 2.303Rc_1^g c_2^g$ and $T_0 = T_g - c_2^g$.

Kovacs,[54,57] by combining equation 34 with data of the type shown in Figs. 11-9 and 11-10, has shown that $f_g = (\alpha_f[\beta]_g/2.303\ \Delta\alpha\ v_g)^{1/2}$, where $[\beta]_g$ is the slope of the linear plot in Fig. 11-9 at $T_1 = T_g$ and v_g is the specific volume at T_g. If $\Delta\alpha$ is equated to α_f, the values of f_g calculated from measurements of $[\beta]_g$ for several polymers are in the neighborhood of 0.020.

5. Alternative Representations of Individual Differences among Polymeric Systems

In Table 11-II, individual systems are characterized by their values of α_f and f_g. An alternative (earlier) method for fitting experimental a_T data to an equation of the WLF form with a *single* adjustable parameter is to keep c_1^0 and c_2^0 fixed and vary T_0. The form used for this purpose is

$$\log a_T = -8.86(T - T_s)/(101.6 + T - T_s) \qquad (37)$$

Table 11–III

CHARACTERISTIC TEMPERATURES T_s FOR VARIOUS POLYMER SYSTEMS AND OTHER VITRIFYING LIQUIDS

Polymer		T_s °K.	$T_s - T_g$ deg	Ref.
General				
Polyisobutylene		243	41	25
Polystyrene		408–418	35–45	25, 35, 71
Polyvinyl acetate		349–351	44–46	25, 35
Polyvinyl chloroacetate [a]		346	50	25
Polyvinyl acetal [a]		380		25
Polymethyl acrylate		324	48	25
Polymethyl methacrylate		431–435	53–57	25, 35
Polyvinyl chloride		393–396	46–49	35
Polyhexene-1		268		32
Poly-1,1-dihydroperfluoro-butyl acrylate		285		33
Poly-3-trifluoromethoxy-1,1-dihydroperfluoryl propyl acetate		262		33
Copolymers				
Polyurethane [b]		283	45	34
Butadiene-styrene	75/25	268	57	25
	60/40	283		25
	50/50	296		25
	30/70	328		25
Hevea Rubbers				
Unvulcanized		247–251	47–51	35
Lightly vulcanized		251		35
1.5% combined sulfur		251		35
1.7% [a]		251		35
3.0% [a]		254		35
4.3% [a]		259		35
4% sulfur by weight [a]		256–261		35
8% [a]		275		35
10% [a]		283		35
12% [a]		294		35
16% [a]		310		35
Diluted Systems				
Polyvinyl chloride in dimethyl thianthrene	10%	293		25
	40%	313		25
Cellulose tributyrate in dimethyl phthalate	21%	247	59	42
	43%	256	63	42
Polystyrene in Decalin	62%	291		25
Polyvinyl acetate in tricresyl phosphate	50%	293		25
Liquids of Low Molecular Weight				
Glucose		351	46	26
Abietic acid		358		26
Dimethyl thianthrene		288		26
n-Propanol		143	45	26
Propylene glycol		217	57	26
Glycerol		238	51	26

[a] From dielectric data alone.
[b] Copolymer of adipic acid and ethylene and propylene glycols, cross-linked by naphthalene 1,4-diisocyanate and 1,4-butanediol.

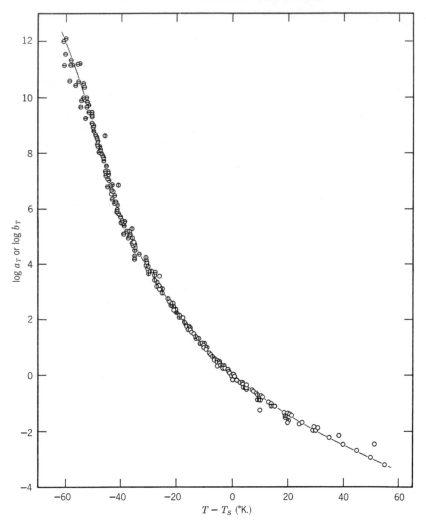

FIG. 11–11. Log a_T (or log b_T from dielectric data) plotted against $T - T_s$, for 17 polymeric systems.[25]

in which T_s was originally chosen arbitrarily for one polymer (243°K. for polyisobutylene) and then determined empirically for other polymers to give the best fit. The fit is accomplished by matching a plot of log a_T against T (for any T_0) against a standard plot of equation 37, using transparent paper, with horizontal and vertical adjustments.[25, 26] Since there is only one empirical parameter T_s, the representation is not quite so accurate as that obtained by the procedure of equations 20 to 24. However, it is convenient and has been applied by several authors. Examples of the plots are shown in Figs. 11–11 and 11–12. Values of T_s obtained for many polymeric systems, as well as several vitrifying liquids of low molecular weight, are listed in Table 11–III. For some of the systems, mechanical data have been supplemented by dielectric data, whereas for others only dielectric data were available.

For each system whose T_g is known, $T_s - T_g$ is also tabulated. This is generally in the neighborhood of 50°. Setting $T_s = T_g + 50°$ in equation 37 is equivalent to using equation 26 with the "universal" values of $c_1{}^g$ and $c_2{}^g$. For practical manipulations, however, equation 37 is more convenient, since it is more difficult to obtain a_T values from viscoelastic data in the neighborhood of T_g. The position of T_s has been selected as an optimum reference point for this purpose.

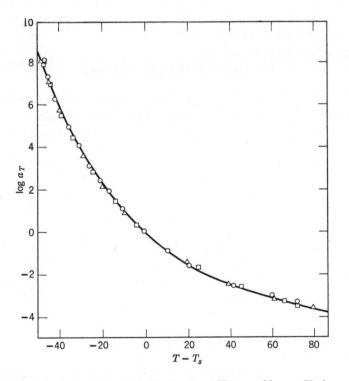

FIG. 11–12. Log a_T plotted against T_s, for three Hevea rubbers. Circles, carbon-black filled vulcanizate; squares, unfilled vulcanizate; triangles, unvulcanized. (After Payne.[35])

Still another method for adjusting the parameters has been proposed by Williams.[75] Assuming that $\alpha_f = \alpha_l$, in other words that the occupied volume $v_o = v - v_f$ is constant and the entire thermal expansion above T_g is attributable to free volume increase, equation 34 can be rewritten

$$\log a_T = -\frac{B/2.303(v_g - v_o)(T - T_g)}{(v_g - v_o)/\alpha_l + T - T_g} \qquad (38)$$

and since v_g and α_l are directly measurable macroscopic quantities, the parameters B and v_o can be determined by numerical analysis. In a study of data on polystyrene fractions [65, 76] of various molecular weights, Williams found $B = 0.91$ (rather than unity as previously assumed) and v_o to increase slightly with molecular weight over a range from 1675 to 134,000. The corresponding values of f_g ranged from 0.022 to 0.028. However, the assumption that $\alpha_f = \alpha_l$ is questionable, since α does not vanish at T_g; and, paradoxically, extrapolation of volume measurements below room temperature indicates that v can attain values smaller than v_o.

6. Effect of Molecular Weight

It is only for relatively low molecular weights—below perhaps of the order of 30,000—that any molecular weight dependence of T_g, ΔH_a, or any of the other parameters characterizing temperature dependence of viscoelastic behavior is to be expected. For very short polymers, several anomalies enter, which were shown by Fox and Flory [65] to be attributable to an enhanced free volume associated with the ends of the molecules. At a given temperature, v increases linearly with $1/M$; T_g is a decreasing linear function of $1/M$; and ΔH_a at a given temperature is an exponential function of $1/M$. The free volume at T_g appears to be substantially independent of molecular weight, however, in harmony with the constancy of f_g for polymers of different chemical structure as shown in Table 11–II. In applying the WLF equation in the form of equation 37, T_s is found to decrease with decreasing molecular weight so that $T_s - T_g$ remains constant.[26]

7. Effects of High Pressure

The presence of free volume in ordinary liquids makes them much more compressible than ordinary solids; for example, the compressibility coefficients β for liquid and solid benzene are about 9 and

3×10^{-11} cm²/dyne respectively. Comparative data [77,78] for polymers above and below their glass transition temperatures are fragmentary and do not permit generalizations. In liquids, it might be expected that increasing pressure would progressively collapse the free volume until a minimum value corresponding approximately to f_g was reached and that the differential compressibility for further pressure increase would correspond more nearly to the glassy or solid state. In fact, the differential compressibility does diminish with increasing pressure, but gradually rather than abruptly. The same effect is seen in polymers; β for a soft rubber-sulfur vulcanizate [79] at room temperature decreases from 2.0 to 0.8×10^{-11} cm²/dyne, and for polyisobutylene [80] from 2.4 to 0.8×10^{-11} cm²/dyne, as the pressure is increased in the range of thousands of atmospheres.

From the free volume interpretation of temperature dependence of viscoelastic properties, it follows that the collapse of free volume under confining pressure should increase the viscosity and all relaxation times. Such an effect is well known in ordinary liquids. In polymers (and other vitrifying liquids) in the range where the WLF equation holds, its magnitude can readily be predicted by analogy with equation 33. For pressure changes, setting $B = 1$ as before,

$$\log a_P = (1/2.303)(1/f - 1/f_0) \tag{39}$$

where a_P is the ratio of viscosities (or relaxation times) at pressure P and at zero or atmospheric pressure, and f_0 is the fractional free volume at atmospheric pressure. If the portion of the total compressibility which reflects collapse of free volume is denoted by β_f (by analogy with α_f), then

$$f = f_0 - \int_0^P \beta_f \, dP$$

where in general β_f is a decreasing function of P. In a moderate range of pressures where β_f is approximately constant, we obtain [81]

$$\log a_P = \frac{\beta_f P}{2.303 f_0 (f_0 - \beta_f P)} \tag{40}$$

and the parameters f_0 and β_f should be obtainable from experimental data by an analysis similar to that of equations 21, 22, 35, and 36. At low pressures, this reduces to

$$(d \log a_P/dP)_{P \to 0} = \beta_f/2.303 f_0^2 \tag{41}$$

It is clear that the effect of confining pressure will diminish rapidly with increasing temperature above T_g, because of the factor $f_0{}^2$ in the denominator of equation 41. By analogy with the limits of applicability of the WLF equation, it cannot be expected that equation 39 or any of its corollaries can hold above $T_g + 100$, or under any circumstances where $f_0 > 0.08$.

Comparison with experimental data is complicated by the latter restriction and by the dependence of β_f on pressure. Increases in viscosity of polystyrene and molten polyethylene under pressure observed by Maxwell and Jung [82] are qualitatively of the magnitude predicted by equation 41.

Another way of gauging the effect of pressure on relaxation times is to measure the increase of temperature which compensates an increase of pressure to bring a measured viscoelastic property to its same position on the time scale. This can be obtained from a dynamic measurement at a single frequency.[80] If it is assumed that constancy of f corresponds to constancy of relaxation times, the condition for simultaneous increase of temperature and pressure is

$$(\partial T/\partial P)_\tau = \beta_f/\alpha_f \tag{42}$$

Some similar expressions have been derived by Singh and Nolle [80] from slightly different starting assumptions, and shown to be in semi-quantitative agreement for longitudinal bulk wave propagation measurements on polyisobutylene at 4 megacycles/sec. and temperatures from 0° to 70°C. The value of the derivative in this case is about 0.025°C./atm. A closely similar value (0.024°/atm.) was obtained for lightly vulcanized natural rubber by McKinney, Belcher, and Marvin.[83]

The predictions of equations 40 to 42 must be regarded as tentative, since there is some evidence [84, 85] that under confining pressure relaxation times (in dielectric dispersion) are not a unique function of volume. However, it is expected that these relations will be most nearly valid at temperatures not too far above T_g. They are of considerable practical importance because of the hydrostatic pressures encountered in injection apparatus and in molds where stresses are annealed out by relaxation processes.[81, 86] Moreover, in tensile deformations of hard solids where extension is accompanied by a perceptible volume expansion on account of Poisson's ratio being less than $\frac{1}{2}$, the resulting increase in free volume might profoundly alter the magnitudes of relaxation times (especially in long-time phenomena observed near T_g).

If the effect of pressure on steady-flow viscosity is known experimentally, the method of reduced variables can be used to predict its effect on dynamic viscoelastic properties, using as an analog of equation 12 the relation $a_P = \eta\rho_0/\eta_0\rho$, where the subscript 0 again refers to atmospheric pressure. This treatment has been successfully applied to high-frequency dynamic data on lubricating oils by Barlow and Lamb.[87]

D. EXAMPLES OF MORE LIMITED APPLICABILITY OF THE METHOD OF REDUCED VARIABLES

The method of reduced variables as outlined in Section B above, including fitting the function $a_T(T)$ to the WLF equation, is appropriate for data in the transition, plateau, and terminal zones of time scale, with the provision that all contributions to the measured viscoelastic properties involve the same friction coefficient ζ_0 and moreover that the internal structure of the system does not change with changing temperature. The latter restrictions are inherent in the development in Section A.

With some modifications, however, reduced variables can also be applied to data on glassy and highly crystalline polymers, and with caution even to systems which do not meet the restrictions stated above.

1. Glassy and Highly Crystalline Polymers

Below T_g, though configurational changes play a minor role, viscoelastic responses exist which are usually attributed to motions of side chains and cover a wide spectrum of relaxation times, as illustrated by Curves IV in the figures of Chapter 2. Such motions can certainly not be described in terms of a monomeric friction coefficient, but if it is assumed that all the relaxation times concerned have the same temperature dependence, reduced variables can be applied to the glassy zone as an entirely separate calculation. The curves in Chapter 2 alluded to were in fact obtained in this way from data on polymethyl methacrylate by Iwayanagi,[88] who combined various viscoelastic measurements. Below T_g, the free volume treatment and the WLF equation cannot be expected to be applicable. In fact, the temperature dependence of a_T follows an equation of the simple Arrhenius form,

$$\log a_T = (\Delta H_a/R)(1/T - 1/T_0) \tag{43}$$

with a moderately low value of ΔH_a (for polymethyl methacrylate, 29 kcal.). Thus the temperature dependence of responses below T_g bears no relation to what would be extrapolated from the behavior above T_g (where ΔH_a is enormous and increasing rapidly with decreasing temperature).

Similarly, for highly crystalline polymers the amorphous segments between crystallites are too short to permit any motions describable in terms of a monomeric friction coefficient. However, at temperatures so far below the melting point that the degree of crystallinity has reached its maximum value consistent with steric limitations—so that further decreases in temperature will not be accompanied by crystal growth and alteration of internal structure—it can again be assumed that the relaxation times concerned in whatever motions do occur have the same temperature dependence as a class. Application of reduced variables on this basis has been successful for a number of highly crystalline polymers, including the high-density polyethylene [89] which was used as an example in Curves VII of Chapter 2. The temperature dependence of a_T again follows equation 43, with $\Delta H_a = 30$ kcal. for polyethylene,[89] 125 kcal. for polychlorotrifluoroethylene,[90] and 88 kcal. for nylon.[91]

2. Multiple Viscoelastic Mechanisms with Different Temperature Dependences

If molecular motions of the sort responsible for viscoelastic behavior in the glass occur above T_g, we are confronted by two classes of relaxation times with entirely different temperature dependences. The viscoelastic contributions attributable to side chains may follow the Arrhenius equation, and those attributable to configurational changes of the polymer chain backbone the WLF equation. Anomalies observed in applying the method of reduced variables to several methacrylate polymers [36–38] have been interpreted in this manner.

For example, in data on poly-n-butyl methacrylate [37] it was observed that the criteria for reduced variables as outlined in Section B were fulfilled over a temperature range from 45° to 135°C. except for some deviations between 55° and 80°. The range of agreement was ample to specify the coefficients c_1^0 and c_2^0 of equation 20, and from the latter a_T was calculated for all temperatures. The resulting reduced plot of J' is shown in Fig. 11–13, revealing a marked anomaly in the points derived from temperatures between 55° and 80°. It was then assumed that the observed compliance is the sum of a contribu-

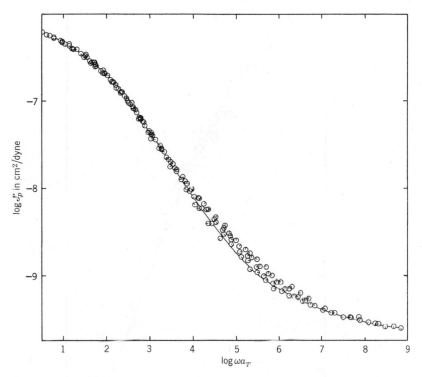

FIG. 11–13. Composite curve for the storage compliance of poly-*n*-butyl methacrylate.

tion J'_α from backbone motions, whose relaxation times follow the WLF equation, and another J'_β from side chain motions (whose maximum value is far smaller than that of J'_α, so it becomes obscured at low reduced frequencies where J'_α is large), and that J'_α could be approximated by the lower envelope of the observed points. By subtraction (not of the logarithms as plotted, of course, but of the actual values) point by point, J'_β was obtained at various temperatures and frequencies and subjected to a *separate* reduction treatment. The reduced plot of J'_β is shown in Fig. 11–14; the temperature dependence of log $a_{T\beta}$ follows the Arrhenius form with $\Delta H_a = 24$ kcal.

This differential treatment pushes the accuracy of the data to its limits, but the results are supported by the conclusion of Hoff [92] from other mechanical and dielectric measurements that there are multiple classes of relaxation times in methacrylates, and that in the *n*-butyl polymer the mechanisms here denoted by α and β (following his termi-

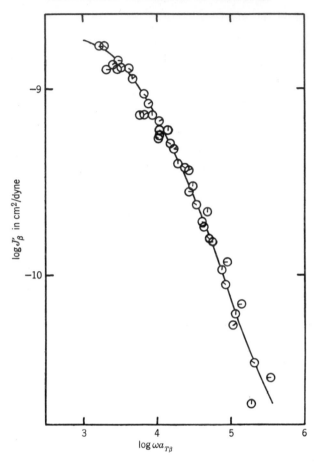

FIG. 11–14. Composite curve for the storage compliance of the β mechanism of poly-n-butyl methacrylate, attributed to motions of the side chains.

nology) are merged somewhat above T_g. Moreover, dielectric measurements by Strella,[72] which reflect dipole orientation due to side group motions, show the same temperature dependence of relaxation times with $\Delta H_a = 24$ kcal.

Contributions from the α mechanism shift much more rapidly along the frequency scale with temperature than do the contributions from the β mechanism. For the α mechanism, ΔH_a is of course a function of temperature in accordance with equation 31, but at 80°C. it is 42 kcal. and at 55° 52 kcal., in contrast with the considerably lower figure for the β mechanism. At high temperatures, therefore, the α mechanism overtakes the β and obscures it. Only where the two mechanisms make contributions of comparable magnitude to J' is the reduction anomaly evident. The exact nature of the side chain motions which cause the viscoelastic response called the β mechanism is still somewhat obscure.

3. Changes in Internal Structure Due to Crystallinity

In a polymer such as polyethylene capable of a high degree of crystallinity, the internal structure changes markedly with decreasing temperature from the melting point down to a temperature where the crystallinity approaches its maximum value. In this range the method of reduced variables is wholly inapplicable, as emphasized by Tobolsky.[93] Empirically, it may appear that horizontal shifts combined with rather large vertical shifts on logarithmic plots might achieve a single composite curve from a family of curves for a given viscoelastic function, but theoretical guides for performing such a manipulation are in a rather tentative stage of development (Chapter 15).

A similar situation may occur in a polymer with side groups long enough to crystallize, as in poly-n-dodecyl methacrylate [39] where the method of reduced variables is applicable in its normal form down to $-28°$ but at lower temperatures large deviations appear. These have been attributed to crystallization of the side groups.

In gels where the network structure is cross-linked by crystallites, the degree of crystallinity is small, and if it changes with temperature the primary structural effect from the standpoint of viscoelastic properties is a variation in the degree of cross-linking. For the polyvinyl chloride gel whose properties were illustrated as Curves VI of Chapter 2, the degree of cross-linking appears to be invariant since reduced variables are applicable over a wide temperature range. This is probably associated with the low tactic order of the polymer, which keeps the degree of crystallinity small even at very low temperatures.[94] In some other gels,[42, 95] however, the degree of cross-linking changes progressively with temperature, and the method of reduced variables cannot be employed without substantial modification.

4. Changes in Entanglement Coupling

One type of structural change whose effects have been successfully incorporated into the method of reduced variables is the change in degree of entanglement coupling with temperature which apparently

occurs in some methacrylate polymers.[21] The phenomenon appears
as a failure of data in the plateau zone to superpose when reduced with
the a_T values derived from the transition zone; it is illustrated for the
loss compliance of four solutions of poly-n-butyl methacrylate [40] in
Fig. 11–15. With increasing temperature, the maximum in J'' shifts
upward and to the left.

This maximum is associated with the presence of a network (Chapter
10, Sections E and F), in this case due to entanglement coupling rather
than permanent cross-links. But since entanglement slippage should be
slight in this zone, the behavior of permanently cross-linked networks
can be used as a guide to the effect of the degree of coupling on J''_{max}.
The Blizard and Bueche theories (Chapter 10, Fig. 10–14 and associated
discussion) predict that J''_{max} should be proportional to Z_c and its
location on the frequency scale inversely proportional to Z_c^2, where Z_c
is the degree of polymerization between linkage points. The theory of
Marvin (Chapter 10, Section F) reaches the same conclusion for an
entanglement network with Z_e, the degree of polymerization between
coupling points, substituted for Z_c. The magnitudes and time constants
associated with all individual contributions to the retardation spectrum
(e.g., Chapter 10, equations 57 and 58) are affected in the same manner,
provided the distribution of strand lengths between linkage points
remains unaltered in form. Hence if, with a change in temperature from
T_0 to T, the number of network strands per cc. n_c is changed by a factor
f (Z_c correspondingly changing by $1/f$), the magnitude of the complex
compliance J^* changes by $1/f$ and its position on the frequency scale by
f^2.

If follows that an additional reduction of the data can be made to take
into account the effect of temperature on network spacing as well as the
local friction coefficient by plotting $\log J''_p f$ against $\log \omega a_T/f^2$. The
data of Fig. 11–15 are shown reduced in this manner in Fig. 11–16, using
f values which fit an equation of the Arrhenius or van't Hoff form with
$\Delta H = 2.1$ kcal. mole. The quantity ΔH is not an activation energy. It
can be formally interpreted as a heat of dissociation of coupling points,
but its molecular significance is obscure. The reduction is quite successful in providing single composite curves; similar results, with similar low
values of ΔH, have been obtained for several undiluted methacrylate
polymers.[21]

The f-shift is in the direction of a slope of $-\frac{1}{2}$ on a logarithmic plot of J'
or J'' against frequency, and hence its effect disappears in the transition zone
where the slopes of these functions themselves approach the value of $-\frac{1}{2}$
predicted by the Rouse and Bueche theories. Indeed, at high frequencies the

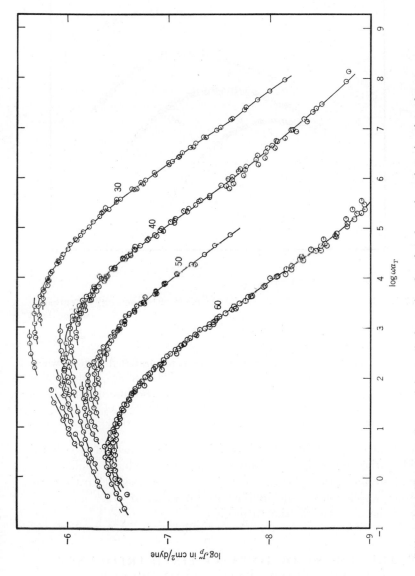

FIG. 11–15. Loss compliance of four solutions of poly-*n*-butyl methacrylate in the plateau zone, reduced to a reference temperature of 273.2° by a_T factors derived from data in the transition zone and fitted to the WLF equation. Numbers denote polymer concentrations in weight per cent.

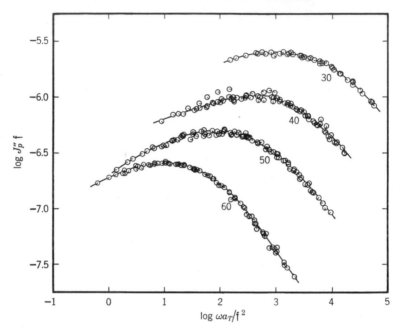

FIG. 11–16. Data of Fig. 11–15 reduced for the effect of temperature on entanglement coupling spacing, as measured by f , in addition to its effect on the local friction coefficient as measured by a_T .

viscoelastic response is governed by short-range configurational motions which should be oblivious of the entanglement spacing. The storage modulus J' is never sharply affected by this entanglement anomaly because it never has a positive slope. The anomaly is most apparent on the left side of the maximum in J'' where the f-shift has a slope of opposite sign to that of the loss compliance.

The above examples illustrate how failures of the method of reduced variables, when applied in its simple form, serve as clues to additional information about the systems treated. They represent characteristic symptoms which may guide in the interpretation of other anomalies that may be observed in the future.

E. TREATMENT OF DATA AT FIXED FREQUENCY OR TIME AND VARYING TEMPERATURE

Critical application of the method of reduced variables requires a series of isotherms as in Fig. 11–1, each covering a wide enough range of frequency or time to specify the shape of the experimental visco-elastic function. In some experimental methods, it is easier to vary the temperature than the frequency, so that data are available instead as isochrones plotted against the temperature at a few selected frequencies, as shown (calculated) for a polyvinylchloride gel in Fig. 11–17. Such curves are *not* superposable by horizontal shifts along the temperature axis; their shapes are quite different, because of the non-linear temperature dependence of a_T. For example, the slopes drawn at log $G' = 8$ in the figure are obviously different for the three isochrones. Such slopes depend on both the steepness of $G'(\omega)$ at the particular frequency and the steepness of $a_T(T)$ at the particular frequency, in accordance with the equation

$$(\partial \log G'/\partial T)_\omega = (\partial \log G'/\partial \log \omega a_T)_T (\partial \log \omega a_T/\partial T)_\omega \qquad (44)$$

Failure to recognize this feature has led to some erroneous conclusions about the applicability of the method of reduced variables.

From a single isochrone, neither the temperature dependence of a_T nor any of the basic viscoelastic functions can be determined. However, if $a_T(T)$ is known from another source (*e.g.*, dielectric measurements under circumstances where a judicious identification can be made) or if a reasonable assumption of its form can be made, the isochrone can be transformed to an effective isotherm [97] sim-

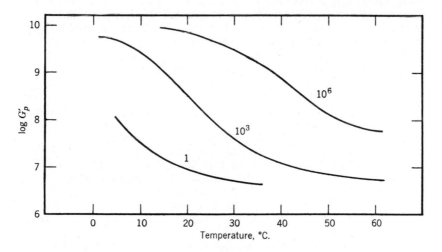

FIG. 11–17. Storage shear modulus of a 40% gel of polyvinyl chloride in dimethyl thianthrene plotted against temperature at 3 frequencies (radians/sec.) as indicated. (Calculated from data of Fitzgerald and Ferry [96].)

ply by plotting against ωa_T, and the viscoelastic functions can be obtained by the methods of Chapter 4. In particular, in the transition zone, $a_T(T)$ can be estimated from the WLF equation in one or another of its forms provided T_g is known.

In certain other experimental methods, notably those involving resonance vibrations (Chapter 7), both temperature and frequency vary simultaneously in a sequence of measurements, and it is even more difficult to obtain basic information. However, such results are useful for exploratory studies, especially in identifying multiple viscoelastic mechanisms.[98]

An interesting treatment has been proposed by Hopkins [99] in which the temperature is changed according to a prescribed function of time *during* a transient viscoelastic experiment (creep or stress relaxation). By comparing the results, $J(t)$ or $G(t)$, with those obtained in a second experiment under conventional isothermal conditions, the factor a_T can be calculated over the temperature range concerned.

REFERENCES

1. W. Dannhauser, W. C. Child, Jr., and J. D. Ferry, *J. Colloid Sci.*, **13**, 103 (1958).
2. K. W. Wagner, *Elektrotechn. Z.*, **36**, 135, 163 (1915).
3. H. Leaderman, *Elastic and Creep Properties of Filamentous Materials and Other High Polymers*, The Textile Foundation, Washington, 1943.
4. A. V. Tobolsky and R. D. Andrews, *J. Chem. Phys.*, **11**, 125 (1943).
5. J. D. Ferry, *J. Amer. Chem. Soc.*, **72**, 3746 (1950).
6. C. A. Dahlquist and M. R. Hatfield, *J. Colloid Sci.*, **7**, 253 (1952).
7. P. E. Rouse, Jr., *J. Chem. Phys.*, **21**, 1272 (1953).
8. J. G. Kirkwood, *J. Chem. Phys.*, **14**, 51 (1946).
9. R. C. Harper, H. Markovitz, and T. W. De Witt, *J. Polymer Sci.*, **8**, 435 (1952).
10. S. Glasstone, K. Laidler, and H. Eyring, *Theory of Rate Processes*, McGraw-Hill, New York, 1941.
11. I. L. Hopkins, *J. Applied Phys.*, **24**, 1300 (1953).
12. W. Philippoff, *J. Applied Phys.*, **25**, 1102 (1954).
13. D. J. Plazek, W. Dannhauser, and J. D. Ferry, *J. Colloid Sci.*, in press.
14. F. Schwarzl and A. J. Staverman, *J. Applied Phys.*, **23**, 838 (1952).
15. A. V. Tobolsky, *J. Applied Phys.*, **27**, 673 (1956).
16. O. Nakada, *J. Phys. Soc. Japan*, **12**, 1218 (1957).
17. J. Bischoff, E. Catsiff, and A. V. Tobolsky, *J. Amer. Chem. Soc.*, **74**, 3378 (1952).
18. J. D. Ferry, L. D. Grandine, Jr., and E. R. Fitzgerald, *J. Applied Phys.*, **24**, 911 (1953).
19. L. D. Grandine, Jr., and J. D. Ferry, *J. Applied Phys.*, **24**, 679 (1953).
20. M. L. Williams and J. D. Ferry, *J. Colloid Sci.*, **10**, 1 (1955).

21. J. W. Berge, P. R. Saunders, and J. D. Ferry, *J. Colloid Sci.*, **14**, 135 (1959).
22. J. D. Ferry and E. R. Fitzgerald, *J. Colloid Sci.*, **8**, 224 (1953).
23. R. S. Marvin, *Proc. 2nd Intern. Cong. Rheology*, Butterworths, London, 1953, p. 156.
24. A. V. Tobolsky and E. Catsiff, *J. Polymer Sci.*, **19**, 111 (1956).
25. M. L. Williams, *J. Phys. Chem.*, **59**, 95 (1955).
26. M. L. Williams, R. F. Landel, and J. D. Ferry, *J. Amer. Chem. Soc.*, **77**, 3701 (1955).
27. D. J. Plazek, M. N. Vrancken, and J. W. Berge, *Trans. Soc. Rheology*, **2**, 39 (1959).
28. M. L. Williams and J. D. Ferry, *J. Colloid Sci.*, **9**, 479 (1954).
29. J. D. Ferry and R. F. Landel, *Kolloid-Z.*, **148**, 1 (1956).
30. J. D. Ferry, M. L. Williams, and E. R. Fitzgerald, *J. Phys. Chem.*, **59**, 403 (1955).
31. M. L. Williams and J. D. Ferry, *J. Colloid Sci.*, **10**, 474 (1955).
32. S. F. Kurath, E. Passaglia, and R. Pariser, *J. Applied Phys.*, **28**, 499 (1957).
33. K. E. Owens and C. F. Dahlquist, *Trans. Soc. Rheology*, **2**, 23 (1958), and private communication.
34. R. F. Landel, *J. Colloid Sci.*, **12**, 308 (1957).
35. A. R. Payne, in *Rheology of Elastomers,* edited by P. Mason and N. Wookey, Pergamon Press, London, 1958.
36. J. D. Ferry, W. C. Child, Jr., R. Zand, D. M. Stern, M. L. Williams, and R. F. Landel, *J. Colloid Sci.*, **12**, 53 (1957).
37. W. C. Child, Jr., and J. D. Ferry, *J. Colloid Sci.*, **12**, 327 (1957).
38. W. C. Child, Jr., and J. D. Ferry, *J. Colloid Sci.*, **12**, 389 (1957).
39. S. F. Kurath, T. P. Yin, J. W. Berge, and J. D. Ferry, *J. Colloid Sci.*, **14**, 147 (1959).
40. P. R. Saunders, D. M. Stern, S. F. Kurath, C. Sakoonkim, and J. D. Ferry, *J. Colloid Sci.*, **14**, 222 (1959).
41. J. D. Ferry, D. J. Plazek, and G. E. Heckler, *J. chim. phys.*, **55**, 152 (1958).
42. R. F. Landel and J. D. Ferry, *J. Phys. Chem.*, **60**, 294 (1956).
43. M. N. Vrancken and J. D. Ferry, *J. Polymer Sci.*, **24**, 27 (1957).
44. D. J. Plazek, *J. Colloid Sci.*, **15**, 50 (1960).
45. W. Kauzmann, *Chem. Rev.*, **43**, 219 (1948).
46. R. O. Davies and G. O. Jones, *Adv. Phys.*, **2**, 370 (1953).
47. H. Eyring and J. O. Hirschfelder, *J. Phys. Chem.*, **41**, 249 (1937).
48. J. Frenkel, *Kinetic Theory of Liquids,* Oxford University Press, 1946.
49. A. K. Doolittle, *J. Applied Phys.*, **22**, 1471 (1951).
50. A. Bondi, *Ann. N. Y. Acad. Sci.*, **53**, 870 (1951).
51. C. Kittel, *Introduction to Solid-State Physics,* John Wiley and Sons, New York, 1956.
52. G. Tammann, *Aggregatzustände,* Leipzig, 1922; *Der Glaszustand,* Leipzig, 1933.
53. G. S. Parks and H. M. Huffman, *Science,* **64**, 363 (1926).
54. A. Kovacs, private communication.
55. T. Alfrey, G. Goldfinger, and H. Mark, *J. Applied Phys.*, **14**, 700 (1943).
56. A. Kovacs, Sc.D. Thesis, University of Paris, 1955.
57. A. Kovacs, *J. Polymer Sci.*, **30**, 131 (1958).

58. Y. Yano and S. Mitsui, *Busseiron Kenkyu,* **75,** 55 (1954).
59. P. J. Flory, *Ricerca Sci., Suppl.,* 1955, p. 3.
60. J. H. Gibbs and E. A. Di Marzio, *J. Chem. Phys.,* **28,** 373 (1958).
61. A. J. Batchinski, *Z. phys. Chem.,* **84,** 644 (1913).
62. A. K. Doolittle and D. B. Doolittle, *J. Applied Phys.,* **28,** 901 (1957).
63. F. Bueche, *J. Chem. Phys.,* **24,** 418 (1956).
64. F. Bueche, *J. Chem. Phys.,* **30,** 748 (1959).
65. T. G. Fox and P. J. Flory, *J. Applied Phys.,* **21,** 581 (1950).
66. A. Bondi, *J. Phys. Chem.,* **58,** 929 (1954).
67. N. Hirai, *J. Chem. Soc. Japan,* **75,** 683 (1954).
68. H. Fujita and H. Kishimoto, *J. Colloid Sci.,* **13,** 418 (1958).
69. L. Mandelkern and P. J. Flory, *J. Amer. Chem. Soc.,* **73,** 3206 (1951).
70. L. de Brouckère and G. Offergeld, *Bull. Soc. Chim. Belg.,* **67,** 96 (1958).
71. K. Ninomiya, private communication.
72. J. D. Ferry and S. Strella, *J. Colloid Sci.,* **13,** 459 (1958).
73. A. B. Bestul, *Glastechnische Berichte,* **32K,** 59 (1959).
74. P. Caillon and E. Groubert, *Compt. rend. Acad. Sci.,* **248,** 2093 (1959).
75. M. L. Williams, *J. Applied Phys.,* **29,** 1395 (1958).
76. T. G. Fox and P. J. Flory, *J. Phys. Chem.,* **55,** 221 (1951).
77. D. S. Hughes, E. B. Blankenship, and R. L. Mims, *J. Applied Phys.,* **21,** 294 (1950).
78. S. Matsuoka and B. Maxwell, *J. Polymer Sci.,* **32,** 131 (1958).
79. C. E. Weir, *J. Res. Nat. Bur. Standards,* **50,** 311 (1953).
80. H. Singh and A. W. Nolle, *J. Applied Phys.,* **30,** 337 (1959).
81. J. D. Ferry and R. A. Stratton, *Bull. Amer. Phys. Soc.,* II, **5,** 203 (1960); *Kolloid-Z.,* **171,** 107 (1960).
82. B. Maxwell and A. Jung, *Modern Plastics,* **35,** 174 (1957).
83. J. E. McKinney, H. V. Belcher, and R. S. Marvin, *Trans. Soc. Rheology,* **4,** 347 (1960).
84. A. Gilchrist, J. E. Earley, and R. H. Cole, *J. Chem. Phys.,* **26,** 196 (1957).
85. W. H. Stockmayer, unpublished work.
86. H. Högberg, private communication.
87. A. J. Barlow and J. Lamb, *Proc. Roy. Soc.,* **A253,** 52 (1959).
88. K. Sato, H. Nakane, T. Hideshima, and S. Iwayanagi, *J. Phys. Soc. Japan,* **9,** 413 (1954); S. Iwayanagi, *J. Sci. Res. Inst. Tokyo,* **49,** 4 (1955).
89. J. A. Faucher, *Trans. Soc. Rheology,* **3,** 81 (1959).
90. K. Nagamatsu and T. Yoshitomi, *J. Colloid Sci.,* **14,** 377 (1959).
91. T. Yoshitomi, K. Nagamatsu, and K. Kosiyama, *J. Polymer Sci.,* **27,** 335 (1958).
92. E. A. W. Hoff, D. W. Robinson, and A. H. Willbourn, *J. Polymer Sci.,* **18,** 161 (1955).
93. A. V. Tobolsky and J. R. McLoughlin, *J. Phys. Chem.,* **59,** 989 (1955).
94. B. D. Coleman, *J. Polymer Sci.,* **31,** 155 (1958).
95. P. R. Saunders and A. G. Ward, in F. R. Eirich, *Rheology,* Vol. II, Chapter 8, Academic Press, New York, 1958.
96. J. D. Ferry and E. R. Fitzgerald, *Proc. 2nd Intern. Cong. Rheology,* Butterworths, London, 1953, p. 140.
97. S. Onogi and K. Ui, *J. Colloid Sci.,* **11,** 214 (1956).

98. A. E. Woodward and J. A. Sauer, *Fortschr. Hochpolym. Forschung*, **1**, 114 (1958).
99. I. L. Hopkins, *J. Polymer Sci.*, **28**, 631 (1958).

Additional References

100. F. H. Müller, *Kolloid-Z.*, **114**, 2 (1949).
101. M. Mooney, *Trans. Soc. Rheology*, **1**, 63 (1957).
102. R. H. Norman and A. R. Payne, to be published.
103. T. Hideshima, *Prog. Theor. Phys. (Japan)*, Suppl. 10, 174 (1959).
104. R. B. Beevers and E. F. T. White, *Trans. Faraday Soc.*, **56**, 744 (1960).
105. M. H. Cohen and D. Turnbull, *J. Chem. Phys.*, **31**, 1164 (1959).

CHAPTER **12**

The Transition Zone from Rubberlike to Glasslike Consistency

Having examined the nature of the temperature dependence of the relaxation and retardation times, we now turn attention to the details of the time and frequency dependence of the basic viscoelastic functions and their correlation with chemical structure. Each zone of time scale represents a separate problem. The one most characteristic of polymers is the transition from rubberlike to glasslike consistency, the subject of this chapter.

The shapes of the functions in the transition zone are grossly similar for all polymers, as illustrated by the curves in Chapter 2, being qualitatively in accord with the predictions of the flexible chain theories outlined in Chapter 10. The most striking feature which varies among polymers is therefore the position of the transition zone on the time or frequency scale, when different systems are examined either all at the same temperature or at suitable corresponding temperatures. This comparison will first be undertaken, both in terms of directly measured quantities and in terms of the monomeric friction coefficient ζ_0 whose magnitude sets the time scale according to theory. Subsequently, detailed differences in the shapes of the spectra will be scrutinized.

In practically all cases, composite functions are utilized, obtained by reduction of data from experiments at various temperatures as described in the preceding chapter. Since cross-linking affects the transition zone only to a minor degree, both uncross-linked and cross-linked systems are included.

A. THE LOCATION OF THE TRANSITION ZONE ON THE TIME SCALE

As an example of the effect of chemical structure on the time scale of the transition zone, the storage modulus reduced to 100°C. is plotted logarithmically against frequency in Fig. 12–1 for polymers of five n-alkyl methacrylates [1-5] whose ester groups contain respectively 2, 4, 6, 8, and 12 carbon atoms. With increasing side group length, the position of the transition shifts to higher frequencies, at first rapidly and then more slowly, traversing more than six decades of the logarithmic frequency scale. The displacement reflects a decrease in all the relaxation times which is in turn caused by a decrease in the monomeric friction coefficient. At the same time, the level of G' approached at low frequencies (representing roughly the

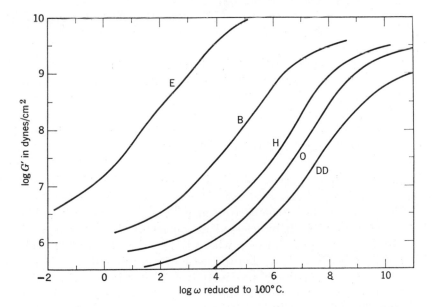

FIG. 12–1. Storage modulus plotted against frequency reduced to 100°C., for five n-alkyl methacrylate polymers.[1-5] E, ethyl; B, butyl; H, hexyl; O, octyl; DD, dodecyl.

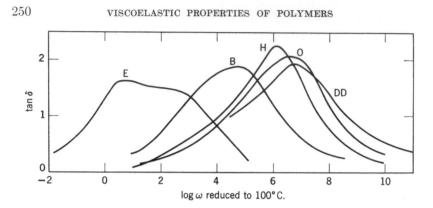

FIG. 12–2. Loss tangent plotted against frequency reduced to 100°C., for the same polymers as in Fig. 12–1, similarly identified.

pseudo-equilibrium modulus of the entanglement network and therefore inversely proportional to the average molecular weight between coupling points) appears to fall with increasing side group length, and so does the level approached at high frequencies (representing roughly the modulus in the glassy state). It should be mentioned that for the first three members of the series the effect of a β mechanism has already been separated out as described in Section D of the preceding chapter.

The loss tangent, $G''/G' = J''/J'$, is plotted against frequency for the same series in Fig. 12–2. This quantity, whose maximum occurs roughly near the middle of the transition zone, shifts to higher frequencies in the same manner. It also experiences minor changes in shape, its sharpness first increasing slightly and then decreasing with increasing side group length. It will be recalled that the loss tangent is not susceptible of direct molecular interpretation, but it is important in determining various physical properties of practical interest. (The maxima in G'' and J'' occur at quite different locations.)

For a more extensive comparison of polymers, two quantities have been somewhat arbitrarily selected as gauges of the location of the transition zone: the frequency where $G' = 10^8$ dynes/cm², a value intermediate between those characteristic of the rubberlike and glasslike states (corresponding approximately to the reciprocal time where $G(t) = 0.8 \times 10^8$ dynes/cm², since tan $\delta \cong 1$ in this region—cf. equation 53 of Chapter 10), and the frequency where tan δ is a maximum. These are summarized for the polymers of Figs. 12–1 and 12–2 and a number of others from data taken from the literature [6–21] at

Table 12–I

FREQUENCIES (CYCLES/SEC.) CHARACTERIZING THE TRANSITION ZONE FOR VARIOUS POLYMERS

Polymer	T_g	log ν at which $G' = 10^8$			log ν for Max. tan δ			Ref.
		298°	373°	398°	298°	373°	398°	
Methacrylate Polymers								
Methyl	378	—	—	0.5	—	—	—	6
Ethyl	335	—	0.5	2.6	—	1.0	3.1	1
n-Butyl	300	—	4.0	5.2	—	3.7	4.9	2
n-Hexyl	268	1.4	5.9	6.8	0.8	5.3	6.2	3
n-Octyl	253	3.2	6.8	7.5	2.2	5.8	6.5	4
n-Dodecyl	—	5.6	7.5	—	4.1	6.0	—	5
General								
Polyisobutylene	202	4.4	6.7	7.2	3.9	6.2	6.7	7
Polystyrene	373 {	—	—	2.6	—	—	2.1	9
		—	—	2.9	—	—	—	10
Polyvinyl acetate	305 {	—	5.3	6.4	—	5.2	6.3	11
		—	5.3	6.4	—	5.0	6.1	12
Polymethyl acrylate	276	0.0	6.3	7.2	−0.3	6.0	6.9	13
Polyvinyl chloride	347	—	2.2	—	—	2.6	—	14
Polyhexene-1	218	5.4	—	—	4.4	—	—	15
Poly-1,1-dihydroperfluorobutyl acrylate		4.4	—	—	4.5	—	—	16
Poly-3-trifluoromethoxy-1,1-dihydroperfluoryl propyl acrylate		5.0	—	—	4.1	—	—	16
Hevea rubber, unvulcanized	200 {	7.0	—	—	7.1	—	—	17
		7.2	—	—	7.2	—	—	18
Hevea rubber, cross-linked [a]	{	6.35	—	—	6.2	—	—	17
		6.9	—	—	6.1	—	—	19
Copolymers								
Butadiene-styrene	80/20 (unv.)	7.3	—	—	7.7	—	—	18
	60/40 (vulc.)	4.3	—	—	—	—	—	20
	50/50 (vulc.)	3.4	—	—	—	—	—	20
	30/70 (vulc.)	−0.8	—	—	—	—	—	20
Polyurethane [b]	238	4.9	—	—	5.7	—	—	21

[a] Lightly vulcanized pure gum stock.

[b] Copolymer of adipic acid and ethylene and propylene glycols, cross-linked by naphthalene 1,4-diisocyanate and 1,4-butanediol.

several different reference temperatures in Table 12–I. For practical orientation, the frequencies are given in *cycles/sec.* rather than the rad./sec. (ω) used in Figs. 12–1 and 12–2. In several cases, values are available from more than one experimental source, usually obtained by entirely different methods of measurement, and the agreement is gratifying.

The values for the methacrylate series show the effect of side chain length already observed. Those for the butadiene-styrene copolymers

show a progressive shift to lower frequencies with increasing proportion of styrene. The remaining polymers do not fit into any comparative series. They show that a low T_g is generally associated with a
high frequency for the transition zone, but this is not the only controlling parameter as evidenced by a comparison of polyisobutylene
and unvulcanized Hevea rubber at 298°K. Although T_g is nearly the
same, the transition lies at higher frequencies by about 3 logarithmic
decades in the rubber. Such differences will be discussed in more
detail in terms of the monomeric friction coefficient in Section B below.

An alternative means of comparing the locations of the transition
zone in various polymers is to specify the temperature at which a
characteristic feature of the transition is reached for a fixed time or
frequency scale. For example, at fixed frequency G' drops rapidly
with increasing temperature, and the lower the chosen frequency the
steeper the drop (cf. Fig. 11–17). At approximately 1 cycle/sec., most
of the change from the glasslike to the rubberlike level is accomplished
within 5° or 10°, and an inflection point can be chosen with relatively
little ambiguity to represent the mid-point temperature, corresponding
usually to G' somewhere between 10^8 and 10^9; near this point, tan δ
as a function of temperature goes through a rather sharp maximum,
as illustrated in Fig. 12–3 from data of Schmieder and Wolf [22] for
three isomeric polybutyl ethers. (The logarithmic decrement Δ is
approximately (tan δ)/π.) Data of this sort have been adduced by
several investigators,[22-27] mostly from compound resonance devices,
especially the torsion pendulum (Chapter 6). It is ordinarily impossible to obtain data at strictly constant frequency, but in those of
Schmieder and Wolf the frequency at the transition mid-point has
been kept within a narrow range for purposes of comparison.

Mid-point temperatures T_M determined in this way at about 1
cycle/sec. for a variety of polymers are listed in Table 12–II, together with the glass transition temperatures where available. In
the homologous series of the acrylates and vinyl ethers, increasing
the length of flexible side groups shifts T_M to lower temperatures, corresponding to the shifts to higher frequencies in the methacrylate
series in Figs. 12–1 and 12–2 and Table 12–I. However, branched side
groups are less effective and may even raise T_M (cf. also other data
on methacrylates [27,28]). In the vulcanized rubbers with sulfur, the
changes of T_M are attributable primarily to the alteration in chemical
composition and not to the cross-linking, as shown by later experiments on rubbers cross-linked by radiation,[24] where T_M is independent

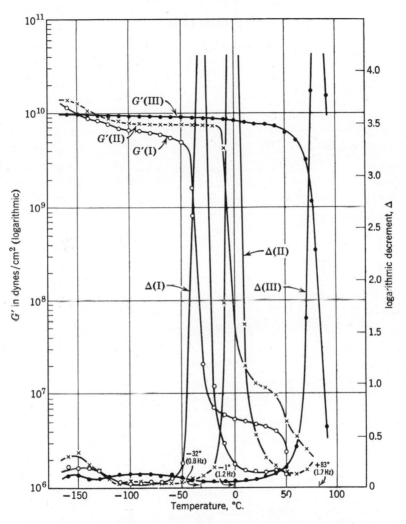

FIG. 12–3. Storage modulus G' and logarithmic decrement Δ (approximately proportional to loss tangent), plotted against temperature at frequencies near 1 cycle/sec., for three polyvinylbutyl ethers.[22] I, n-butyl; II, i-butyl; III, t-butyl.

of the degree of cross-linking until the latter becomes very high. In general, T_M is from 1° to 25° higher than T_g, but since the difference between them is variable one cannot be predicted from the other.

If a higher frequency is chosen for comparing such data, the ambiguity in specifying T_M becomes more serious because the transition occurs at higher

Table 12–II

TEMPERATURES CORRESPONDING TO TRANSITION MID-POINTS FOR G'
AT FREQUENCIES NEAR 1 CYCLE/SEC. (SCHMIEDER AND WOLF)

Polymer		T_M, °K.	Freq. of Measurement cycles/sec.	T_g, °K.
Acrylate Polymers				
Methyl		298	1.2	276
Ethyl		268	1.6	
n-Butyl		241	0.8	
Vinyl Ether Polymers				
Methyl		263	2.7	
Ethyl		256	1.1	
Propyl		246	1.1	
n-Butyl		241	0.8	
i-Butyl		272	1.2	
t-Butyl		356	1.7	
General				
Polyisobutylene		225	1	202
Polystyrene		389	0.9	373
Polyvinyl acetate		306	1.9	305
Polyvinyl chloride		363	0.7	347
Polymethyl methacrylate		393	0.12	
Polyvinyl propionate		285	1.5	
Rubbers				
Hevea, unvulcanized		223	1.2	200
Vulcanized with	0.5% S	223	1.9	
	1.5	223	1.9	
	2.0	224	5.4	
	2.5	226	3.1	
	3.0	228	2.1	
	5.0	233	1.5	
	10	253	2.8	
	15	274	2.0	
	20	296	1.7	
	30	336	1.8	

temperatures where log a_T is less temperature-dependent; as a result the transition is broader on the temperature scale (*cf.* Fig. 11–17).

As long as the molecular weight is sufficiently high that the friction coefficient is uninfluenced by molecular ends, *i.e.*, M of the order of 20,000 or more, the position of the transition zone on the time scale is quite independent of molecular weight. This expectation was embodied in the schematic plots of molecular weight dependence in Figs. 10–5 and 10–6; it has been demonstrated experimentally not only by determining T_M at constant frequency for polyisobutylenes,[22] but by showing the virtual coincidence of entire viscoelastic functions throughout the transition zone for different molecular weights of polyisobutylene,[29] polymethyl methacrylate,[6] polyethyl methacrylate,[1] poly-*n*-butyl methacrylate,[2] and polyvinyl acetate,[12] covering wide ranges of molecular weight up to several million.

B. THE MONOMERIC FRICTION COEFFICIENT

The position of the transition zone on the time scale reflects the absolute magnitudes of the relaxation and retardation times, and hence that of the monomeric friction coefficient upon which (according to the flexible chain theories of viscoelasticity) they all depend. It is therefore of interest to examine the friction coefficient ζ_0 as a basis for more quantitative considerations.

The friction coefficient has usually been calculated by applying equation 24 of Chapter 10 to the relaxation spectrum H, as follows:

$$\log \zeta_0 = 2 \log H + \log \tau + \log (6/kT) + 2 \log (2\pi M_0/a\rho N_0) \quad (1)$$

At the long-time end of the transition zone, there is a segment of H which conforms to the theoretical slope of $-\frac{1}{2}$ on a doubly logarithmic plot, between the steeper slope which prevails at short times and the flattening or minimum characteristic of the plateau region. This feature is illustrated in Fig. 12–4 for the five methacrylate polymers of Figs. 12–1 and 12–2. From the position of a tangent in this region, ζ_0 is calculated. It is necessary to know the density ρ and monomer molecular weight M_0, as well as a, the root-mean-square end-to-end length per square root of the number of monomer units. The latter is usually taken as the value determined in dilute solution in a Θ-solvent,[30] under the assumption that the molecular configuration in the undiluted polymer is unperturbed by long-range effects.

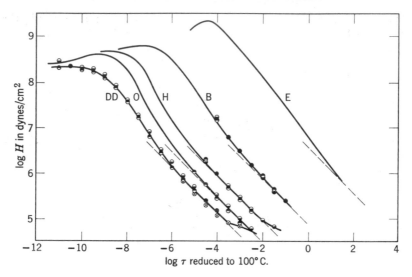

FIG. 12–4. Relaxation spectrum in the transition zone for the five methacrylate polymers of Fig. 12–1, similarly identified, to illustrate calculation of ζ_0.

Since the retardation spectrum L provides in principle the same information as the relaxation spectrum H, it might be expected that ζ_0 could be calculated from L also, using equation 25 of Chapter 10. However, a substantial segment of L with a slope of ½ on a logarithmic plot does not appear in polymers of high molecular weight; in the appropriate region of the time scale, L is changing slope rapidly, approaching the maximum which characterizes the entanglement network (Fig. 3–4).

The reason for this apparent paradox is the difference in weighting of H and L by mechanisms in different regions of the time scale. In L, the magnitudes of the contributions increase rapidly with increasing retardation time. For spectra conforming to the Rouse theory, this feature is evident in comparing equations 1 and 7 of Chapter 10, and in Fig. 10–2. And regardless of the precise form of the spectra, the long-time contributions to L will always be strongly weighted relative to their contributions to H, as shown by the general relations of the phenomenological theory.[31]

At the long-time end of the transition zone in a polymer of high molecular weight, the deviations from the simple flexible chain theory caused by entanglement coupling thus appear in L sooner and more strongly than in H. As a result, in this region where H is making its closest fit to the simple theory and permitting calculation of ζ_0, L is entering the maximum which provides information about the entanglement network as discussed in the following chapter.

1. Comparisons at Constant Temperature

Values of log ζ_0 for most of the polymers of Table 12–I, together with the constants M_0 and a used for their calculation, are given in Table 12–III. It is impossible to compare all the systems at any one temperature, but at 398°, where a majority are comparable, ζ_0 in dynes-sec/cm ranges from the order of 1 to 10^{-7}. The friction coefficient, measuring the average force per monomer unit required for a chain segment to push its way through its local surroundings at unit velocity, must depend upon the free volume and/or intermolecular forces and steric hindrances to rotations around free bonds. Comparisons in the methacrylate series show the familiar effect of long side chains in diminishing friction. Comparison of log ζ_0 for polymethyl methacrylate (0.66) with that for polymethyl acrylate (-6.83) at 398° shows the marked steric blocking of the extra methyl group in the former. In the methacrylate series, with steric blocking near the backbone and some degree of polarity in intermolecular forces, it is necessary to have an ester side group with 12 carbon atoms (log $\zeta_0 = -4.69$ at 298°) to achieve the same mobility as in polyhexene-1 with a hydrocarbon group of 4 atoms and no extra methyl substituent (log $\zeta_0 = -4.72$ at 298°). Hevea rubber is in a class by itself with respect to mobility, having a friction coefficient at 298° two orders of magnitude smaller than the smallest among those polymers with saturated backbones (poly-n-dodecyl methacrylate, polyhexene, and the urethane and fluorinated butyl acrylate polymers).

2. Relation of Friction Coefficient to Free Volume in the Methacrylate Series

Since the dependence of the friction coefficient on temperature, and probably also on pressure, can be described in terms of the free volume, it is of interest to examine whether its variation with chemical composition in a homologous series such as that of the methacrylates can be explained in a similar manner. With increasing side group length, the local packing undoubtedly becomes less efficient, and of the rather large increase in specific volume progressing from the ethyl to the dodecyl polymeric ester ($v = 0.917$ to $v = 1.127$ cc./g. at 100°C.) some can be attributed to an increase in empty space.[32]

The effect of increased free volume due to side group extension on the friction coefficient may be inferred by analogy with equations 32

Table 12–III

MONOMERIC FRICTION COEFFICIENTS OF VARIOUS POLYMERS

Polymer	T_g	M_0	a cm$\times 10^8$	log ζ_0(dynes-sec/cm) at 298°	373°	398°	T_g
Methacrylate Polymers							
Methyl	378	100	6.9			0.66	(5.47) [e]
Ethyl	335	114	5.9		−0.21	−2.35	6.22
n-Butyl	300	142	6.4		−3.44	−4.66	3.81
n-Hexyl	268	170	7.5	−0.75	−5.25	−6.16	2.59
n-Octyl	253	198	7.0	−2.29	−5.93	−6.65	2.39
n-Dodecyl		254	8.75	−4.69	−6.57		
n-Docosyl		394			[c]		
General							
Polyisobutylene	202	56	5.9	−4.35	−6.66	−7.17	3.97
Polystyrene	373	104	7.4			−2.54	(3.10) [e]
Polyvinyl acetate	305	86	6.9		−4.87	−5.98	4.29
Polymethyl acrylate	276	86	6.8	0.32	−5.99	−6.83	6.24
Polyvinyl chloride	347	62.5	6			−4.57	(4.05) [e]
Polyhexene-1	218	84	7	−4.72			
Poly-1,1-dihydroperfluorobutyl acrylate		308	8	−4.7			
Hevea rubber, unvulcanized	200	68	6.8	−6.74 [f]			3.94
				−6.87 [g]			3.81
Hevea rubber, cross-linked [a]	203 [i]	68	6.8	−5.90 [f]			4.66
	212 [i]			−5.64 [h]			4.53
Polyurethane [b]	238	[d]	[d]	−4.33			3.51

[a] Lightly vulcanized pure gum stock.
[b] See footnote b, Table 12–I.
[c] Estimated to be −7.2 at 335°K.
[d] M_0/a estimated to be 12×10^8.
[e] Difficult to estimate reliably because c_1^g and c_2^g uncertain; based on "universal" c_1^g and c_2^g values.
[f] From data of Payne.[17]
[g] From data of Zapas, Shufler, and DeWitt.[18]
[h] From data of Cunningham and Ivey.[19]
[i] Estimated from effect of sulfur vulcanization on T_s (cf. Table 11–III).

and 38 of Chapter 11 to be

$$\Delta_i \log a^2\zeta_0 \equiv \log (a^2\zeta_0)_i - \log (a^2\zeta_0)_R = (1/2.303)(1/f_i - 1/f_R) \quad (2)$$

where $\Delta_i \log a^2\zeta_0$ is the analog of a_T or a_P, since all relaxation times are proportional to $a^2\zeta_0/T$ (equation 3 of Chapter 11) and we are now considering comparisons at constant temperature; f_i is the fractional free volume of the ith member of the series, and f_R that of a particular member chosen as a reference. On this basis, the data for the methacrylate series have been analyzed by Dannhauser, Child, and Ferry [4] and by Fujita and Kishimoto.[33] The two treatments differ somewhat; the latter, being more general, is employed here. If the reference polymer is chosen as that with the highest T_g and the latter temperature is chosen for the comparisons, it can be shown from equation 2 (provided f_g is the same for all members of the series) that

$$-1/\Delta_i \log a^2\zeta_0 = 2.303f_g + 2.303f_g{}^2/\Delta\alpha_i \, \Delta T_{gi} \quad (3)$$

where $\Delta\alpha_i$ is the change in thermal expansion coefficient at T_g for the ith polymer, and $\Delta T_{gi} = T_{gR} - T_{gi}$. It follows that a plot of the left side of equation 4 against $1/\Delta\alpha_i \, \Delta T_{gi}$ should be linear and f_g should be calculable from both its intercept and its slope.

Data for this purpose (not the same set originally used by Fujita and Kishimoto) are assembled [5] in Table 12–IV. It may be remarked that the quantity $a^2\zeta_0$ is directly obtainable from the intercepts of the tangents in Fig. 12–4 without specification of the somewhat uncertain parameter a, and is therefore better determined experimentally than ζ_0 itself. The quantity $\Delta\alpha_i$ was taken as 2.4×10^{-4} for all the polymers. The results are plotted in Fig. 12–5, and a moderately good line is obtained; from its intercept, f_g is calculated to be 0.026, and from its slope 0.018. The reasonable agreement between these values

Table 12–IV

DATA FOR FUJITA-KISHIMOTO PLOT FOR POLY-n-ALKYL METHACRYLATES

Polymer	Ethyl	Butyl	Hexyl	Octyl	Dodecyl
$\log a^2\zeta_0$ at T_g for ethyl	-8.19	-15.03	-17.60	-18.71	-19.45
ΔT_{gi}	0	35	67	82	108
$f_i - f_R$ at T_g for ethyl	0	0.008	0.016	0.020	0.026
$v_i - v_R$ at T_g for ethyl	0	0.073	0.117	0.122	0.141
$(f_i - f_R)/(v_i - v_R)$		0.11	0.14	0.16	0.18

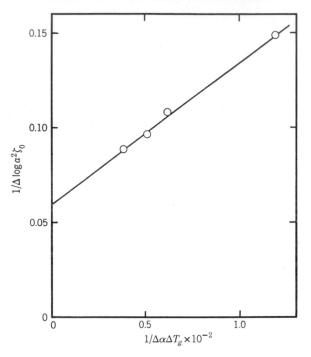

FIG. 12–5. Fujita-Kishimoto plot for the methacrylate series, with the ethyl polymer as reference.

and those of 0.025 to 0.027 obtained from the analysis of temperature dependence (Table 11–II) lends confidence to the view that the enhancement of mobility with increasing side group length is primarily due to the increase in free volume.

In the table, values for the increase in f and in v with side group length are also given, leading to the conclusion that of the order of 15% of the increase in v is attributable to f. This estimate had already been made by Rogers and Mandelkern[32] and formed the basis of the analysis of Dannhauser, Child, and Ferry,[4,5] in which the free volumes at 100° (far above T_g for all the polymers) were calculated both from equation 2 and from dilatometric measurements, with reasonable agreement.

3. The Monomeric Friction Coefficient at T_g

If ζ_0 were strictly a function of free volume alone, all polymers should have the same ζ_0 when compared each at its own T_g, since f_g is so nearly a universal constant (Table 11–II).

This is not quite a fair statement since ζ_0 is the coefficient per monomer unit and a large monomer should encounter more frictional force, other things being equal, than a small one. However, by analogy with Stokes' law we should expect the effects of size to be proportional to the cube root of the molecular volume—a small variation among the systems in Table 12–III, and in the opposite direction to most of the substantial deviations which are actually encountered.

To calculate ζ_0 at T_g, it is necessary to reduce the time scale by extrapolation, since experimental measurements in the transition zone cannot be made at T_g directly. In most cases the extrapolation can be made with confidence by the WLF equation and the coefficients of Table 11–II. The results are given in the last column of Table 12–III, and show that even when compared each at its own T_g polymers can still have monomeric friction coefficients differing by several orders of magnitude. In particular, ζ_{0g} decreases with increasing side chain length in the polymethacrylate series, although it appears to be approaching a limiting value.

Interpretations of the differences in ζ_0 at T_g are still speculative; two possibilities may be mentioned. One is that ζ_0 is correlated with the strength of intermolecular forces or cohesive energy density. The other [34] introduces the concept of *local* free volume, reflecting detailed aspects of packing geometry which remain unclarified. Although at T_g the *average* fractional free volume is always close to 0.025, in some polymers (*e.g.*, Hevea and polyurethane rubbers) this free volume may be disposed in such a way as to greatly facilitate configurational changes while in others (polyvinyl acetate, polymethyl acrylate) the geometry is such that the free volume is less effective. One interpretation is primarily energetic, the other steric, and at present it appears to be impossible to decide between them.

It may be of interest to make a very crude calculation of the effective local viscosity η_e at the glass transition temperature based on Stokes' law for an isolated sphere of radius r: $\zeta_0 = 6\pi\eta_e r$. For a molar volume of 100 cc. and log $\zeta_0 = 6$, the effective viscosity is 1.6×10^{12} poises, which is not far from the level of 10^{13} often specified as the *macroscopic* viscosity characteristic of the glass transition.[35] This suggests that 10^6 dynes-sec./cm may be nearly an upper limit for ζ_0 at T_g. By contrast, Stokes' law estimates at temperatures well above T_g give local viscosities far smaller than the macroscopic viscosity, as will be seen in the comparisons with diffusion data which follow.

4. Correlation of ζ_0 with Data from Diffusion of Small Foreign Molecules

Because of the importance of the quantity ζ_0, which fixes the time scale for all viscoelastic behavior in the transition zone, it would be desirable to obtain information about it from other types of physical measurements than mechanical. At present, there seems to be no alternative method for obtaining ζ_0 for the polymeric chain itself. However, it is possible from diffusion measurements to obtain the translatory friction coefficient of a small foreign molecule similar in size to the monomeric unit and dissolved in the polymer.

When such a foreign molecule diffuses down a concentration gradient, its maximum concentration being very small (of the order of 1% or less), the molecules may be regarded as pushing their way individually through the polymer matrix. The diffusion constant D_0 at vanishing concentration of the low-molecular-weight component can be expressed without complications arising from thermodynamic non-ideality [36,34] or ambiguity of frames of reference; [37] the translatory friction coefficient for the foreign molecule is simply

$$\zeta_1 = kT/D_0 \tag{4}$$

If D_0 is measured (by transpiration, absorption-desorption, or radioactivity of tagged molecules [38,39]), ζ_1 can be easily calculated and compared with the friction coefficient per monomer unit of the polymer chain itself.

Naturally ζ_1 depends on the size and shape of the foreign molecule, and for very large molecules the dependence can be quite marked.[40,41] However, for normal paraffin chains ζ_1 is approximately directly proportional to molecular length,[39] corresponding to the principle that the friction encountered by a polymer segment is proportional to its length, upon which the definition of ζ_0 is based; and for quite short chains the dependence appears to be somewhat less.[42] Thus by choosing a foreign molecule similar in structure and length to the monomeric unit of the polymer, a comparison can be obtained between an isolated unit and one which is an integral part of the polymer backbone.

Some information collected from the literature for this purpose [34] is given in Table 12–V. In some cases, the chemical similarity between foreign molecule and polymer is not very close because of the paucity of available data. However, it appears that for temperatures *far above* T_g, as in the polyisobutylene and rubber, the friction coefficients ζ_0 and ζ_1 for the chain unit and for a foreign molecule of like size are closely similar. This leads to the conclusion that the monomeric friction coefficient reflects almost wholly the force of pushing aside neighboring chains of the environment, and to a negligible extent the difficulty of articulating the chain in which the monomer unit is located.

When the temperature is not far above T_g, however, the friction coefficient is considerably smaller for the foreign molecule than for the chain unit, and the discrepancy appears to increase as T_g is ap-

Table 12–V

MOLECULAR FRICTION COEFFICIENTS FROM DIFFUSION IN POLYMERS
COMPARED WITH MONOMERIC FRICTION COEFFICIENTS

Polymer	Temp. °K.	$T-T_g$	Diffusing Unit	Mol. Wt.	$\log \zeta_1$	$\log \zeta_0$	Ref.
Polyisobutylene	298	96	n-Butane	58	−4.46		43
			i-Butane	58	−4.11		43
			n-Pentane	72	−4.42		43
			Chain unit	56		−4.35	a
Hevea rubber	303	103	n-Butane	58	−6.74		42
			i-Butane	58	−6.56		42
			n-Pentane	72	−6.74		42
			Chain unit	68		−6.90	a
Polymethyl acrylate	323	47	Ethyl alcohol	58	−3.69		44
			Chain unit	86		−3.15	a
Polyvinyl acetate	313	8	n-Propyl alcohol	60	−1.41		45
			n-Propyl chloride	79	−1.48		45
			Chain unit	86		1.75	a
Polyvinyl acetate	343	38	Ethyl chloride	65	−4.63		44
			Ethyl bromide	109	−4.37		44
			Chain unit	86		−2.63	a

a From the values in Table 12–III, reduced where necessary to different temperatures by the data of Table 11–II.

proached, as judged by the data on polyvinyl acetate. This effect has been tentatively attributed [34] to additional local free volume in the immediate vicinity of a foreign molecule due to inefficient packing.[46] For a vanishing concentration of the low-molecular-weight component, the extra space is too small to affect the over-all average free volume perceptibly, but it occurs in just the right places to facilitate motion of the small molecules. Near T_g, where the average free volume is small, this is supposed to be a very important influence. Far above T_g, on the other hand, where f may be several times as large as its value near T_g, the small molecule has no significant advantage over the polymeric chain unit; the friction coefficient is determined by f alone.

The effect attributed to excess local free volume is also apparent [34] in comparing the temperature dependence of the respective friction coefficients ζ_0 and ζ_1. For polyisobutylene near 25° (about 100° above T_g), ΔH_a from the temperature variation of a_T (equations 28 and 30 of Chapter 11) and the apparent activation energy for diffusion are closely similar. For polyvinyl acetate only 8° above T_g, however, ΔH_a from viscoelastic data is considerably larger than that obtained from the temperature dependence of the diffusion constant.

It is of particular interest to compare polyisobutylene and rubber, both hydrocarbons with almost identical glass transition temperatures. At 25°, the monomeric friction coefficient of the latter is smaller by more than two orders of magnitude. Exactly the same difference appears in the friction coefficients for small foreign molecules. Thus the higher flexibility of the rubber backbone appears as a decrease in the effective local viscosity surrounding a given chain segment rather than an "internal" viscosity of the chain segment itself. If crude Stokes' law estimates of the effective viscosity are made as described above, they provide values of 80 and 0.2 poises, respectively, for the polyisobutylene and the rubber. These clearly bear no relation to the macroscopic viscosity, which depending on the molecular weight might be as high as 10^{10} for the former, and for the latter (if cross-linked) essentially infinite.

If Stokes' law is applied to translational friction, in a polymer matrix, of spherical bodies with various sizes increasing from molecular up to macroscopic dimensions, the effective viscosity η_e must increase by many orders of magnitude and eventually attain the macroscopic value. This phenomenon has been observed in measurements of diffusion [40, 47] as well as centrifugation.[41, 48] Kuhn [49] has pointed out that the increase in η_e with the size of the moving unit is analogous to the increase in the (macroscopic) dynamic viscosity η' with decreasing frequency as it reflects configurational rearrangements coordinated over increasingly large distances.

C. SHAPES OF THE SPECTRA AND VISCOELASTIC FUNCTIONS IN THE TRANSITION ZONE

We are now prepared to examine the detailed shapes of the viscoelastic functions. For this purpose, it is convenient to reduce different polymers to corresponding states in which those portions of their relaxation spectra conforming to the flexible chain theories coincide.

1. Relaxation Spectra Reduced to Corresponding States

In equation 24 of Chapter 10, the time scale is set by the product $a^2\zeta_0/T$ (*cf.* also the discussion associated with equation 2 of the present chapter); in fact, $a^2\zeta_0/kT$ has the dimensions of time. The other quantities in equation 24 of Chapter 10 which may vary from one polymer to another appear as the ratio $T\rho/M_0$, *i.e.*, temperature times the moles of monomer units per cc., which may be regarded as determining the magnitudes of contributions to H. Decreasing ρ/M_0 by having a smaller density or larger monomeric molecular weight is equivalent to diluting the concentration of polymer chains and decreasing the magnitudes of all contributions to H proportionally; decreasing T also decreases H in proportion because of the entropy character of the elastic contributions.

Accordingly, the equation can be rearranged as follows:

$$[\log H - \log T\rho/M_0] = \log (R/2\pi)(\tfrac{1}{6})^{\frac{1}{2}} - \tfrac{1}{2}[\log \tau - \log a^2\zeta_0/kT] \quad (5)$$

a universal function of the variables expressed in brackets. Although this theoretical equation is valid only for the linear segment of the relaxation spectrum which conforms to the Rouse slope of $-\frac{1}{2}$ on a doubly logarithmic plot, where data for all polymers will coincide if plotted with the above reduced variables, it is of interest to examine how far coincidence will occur over wider ranges where deviations from the Rouse slope appear.

The relaxation spectra of the five methacrylate polymers of Fig. 12–4 are plotted in this manner [4,5] in Fig. 12–6. Their shapes coincide rather closely throughout the transition zone, though the maxima for the ethyl (experimentally uncertain) and for the dodecyl are some-

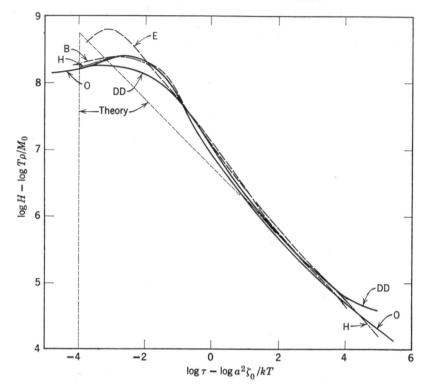

FIG. 12–6. Relaxation spectra of Fig. 12–4 reduced to corresponding states in which the Rouse segments at the long-time end of the transition zone coincide. Dotted line is the prediction of simple flexible chain theory with cutoff at minimum relaxation time of Marvin model.[50]

what higher and lower, respectively, than the others. The straight line predicted by the Rouse theory up to the minimum relaxation time specified by the modified model of Marvin [50] (Chapter 10, Section D) is drawn in for comparison. For the latter purpose, $\log G_g M_0/\rho$ was taken as 11.80, an approximation based on inspection of Fig. 12–1. It is evident that the deviations from the simple theoretical shape are of much the same character for all the methacrylates. It may be inferred that these deviations are characteristic primarily of the polymer chain backbone rather than side group packing or cohesive energy density, both of which vary greatly in progressing from the ethyl to the dodecyl ester.

A wider variety of such comparisons is shown in Fig. 12–7, where the deviations from the simple linear spectrum appear to fall into three classes. The smallest upward curvature is exhibited by the group consisting of a polyurethane rubber,[21] polyisobutylene,[7] poly-hexene-1,[15] and the methacrylate series (from Fig. 12–6). Sharper deviations are shown by polyvinyl acetate[11] and polymethyl acrylate;[13] whereas the Hevea rubbers,[17] cross-linked and uncross-linked, show very marked deviations with steep slopes far removed from the theoretical value of $\frac{1}{2}$. The first group (except for polyhexene-1, which appears anomalous because the maximum is abnormally low) is characterized by doubly substituted carbon atoms in the backbone (polyisobutylene, polymethacrylates) or essentially no substitution at all (polyesters composing polyurethane). The second is characterized by monosubstituted backbone atoms (with presumably less hindrance to rotation than the disubstituted), whereas the third is characterized by the unusual rotational freedom of the unsaturated polybutadiene chain which has already been emphasized. Thus the shapes of the spectra appear again to be determined primarily by the nature of the chain backbone. It is still impossible, however, to go very far in making generalizations, and there is no theoretical guide to the magnitudes of the divergences.

It may be noted that the shape of the relaxation spectrum in the transition zone is also modified by the presence of diluent (Chapter 16) and also by cross-linking if the latter is made sufficiently dense.

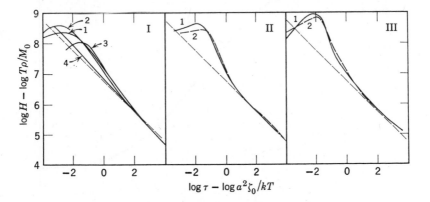

FIG. 12–7. Relaxation spectra of various polymers reduced to corresponding states. Panel I: 1, composite methacrylate polymers; 2, polyisobutylene; 3, polyhexene-1; 4, polyurethane rubber. Panel II: 1, polyvinyl acetate; 2, polymethyl acrylate. Panel III: Hevea rubber, (1) unvulcanized and (2) vulcanized. Dotted line is the prediction of the flexible chain theory as in Fig. 12–6.

2. Analytical Expressions for the Relaxation Spectrum and Other Viscoelastic Functions

In advance of the Rouse theory, it was proposed by Tobolsky[51] that H in the transition zone could be approximated by a wedge with the slope of $-\frac{1}{2}$ on a doubly logarithmic plot, equivalent to the dotted lines in Figs. 12–6 and 12–7, and equations for experimental viscoelastic properties calculated from this function by the relations of Chapter 3 were presented. Subsequently, a much closer analytical representation was given in terms of the relaxation modulus in extension, $E(t)$, using three parameters—E_g, E_e (the equilibrium modulus for a cross-linked network, or the modulus corresponding to the entanglement network in an uncross-linked polymer of very high molecular weight), and a numerical coefficient h related to the steepness of the transition. The empirical relation is (for deformation in extension)

$$\log E(t) = (\log E_g + \log E_e)/2 - [(\log E_g - \log E_e)/2]\mathrm{erf}\, h \log (t/K)$$

$$(6)$$

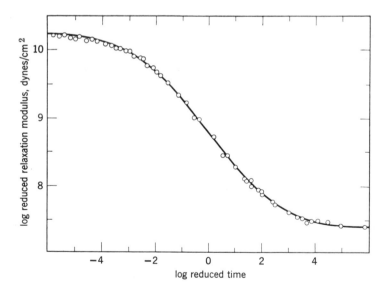

FIG. 12–8. Comparison of the relaxation modulus (in extension) of polymethyl methacrylate in the transition zone with the empirical equation of Tobolsky ($h = 0.31$). Points, experimental; curve, calculated (equation 6).

where erf is the error function and K is the value of t corresponding to $E(t) = (E_g E_e)^{1/2}$. Stress relaxation data on several polymers fit this equation very closely, as illustrated in Fig. 12–8. Values of h are given in Table 12–VI, together with values of n, the negative slope of a plot such as that of Fig. 12–8 at its inflection point.[52] Qualitatively, increasing h corresponds to increasing upward curvature in the relaxation spectra as in progressing from the first to the third panel in Fig. 12–7. The implications of equation 6 for the shapes of the other viscoelastic functions have been examined.[8,53] No theoretical basis for its form has been proposed, however.

Other expressions which have been applied by Smith[54] to describe the shape of the relaxation modulus in the transition region are

$$E(t) - E_e = (E_g - E_e)/[1 + (t/t_0)^b] \tag{7}$$

and, alternatively,

$$E(t) - E_e = (E_g - E_e)/(1 + t/t_0)^\beta \tag{8}$$

where t_0, b, and β are empirical constants. Analogous expressions can be written for the extensional creep compliance $D(t)$ and for the dynamic quantities $E'(\omega)$ and $D'(\omega)$. The relaxation spectrum corresponding to equation 8 has the analytical form

$$H_l = (E_g - E_e)(\tau/t_0)^{-\beta} e^{-t_0/\tau}/\Gamma(\beta) \tag{9}$$

Both equations 7 and 8 are capable of representing experimental data in the middle of the transition region and through the region of the maximum in H rather closely.

3. Relation of the Shape of H to Those of Other Viscoelastic Functions

Even without analytical expressions such as can be derived from equations 6–8, it is clear that increasing steepness of H in the transition zone as portrayed in Fig. 12–7 will be accompanied by a compression of the transition from rubberlike to glasslike consistency into a narrower region of logarithmic time scale. Plots of both transient and dynamic moduli and compliances, as exemplified in Chapter 2, rise and fall with steeper slopes. Perhaps the most sensitive index of the sharpness of the transition is the loss tangent, which is plotted in Fig. 12–9 for several prototypes: the polyurethane rubber, poly-n-octyl methacrylate, polyvinyl acetate, and unvulcanized Hevea rubber.

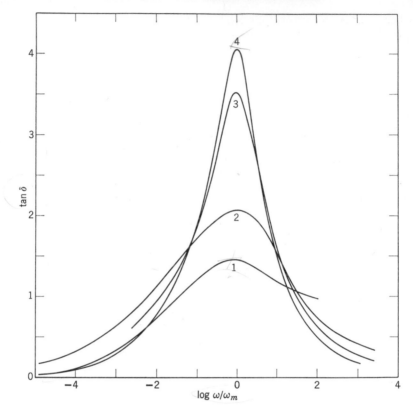

FIG. 12–9. Loss tangent in the transition zone plotted against frequency for
(1) polyurethane rubber, (2) poly-n-octyl methacrylate, (3) polyvinyl acetate,
and (4) unvulcanized Hevea rubber.

Here the frequency scale has been arbitrarily selected to make the
maxima coincide.

The sharpness with which the transition is achieved with changing
temperature at constant time or frequency depends both on the steepness with respect to time as illustrated in Fig. 12–7 or Fig. 12–9 and
the rate of change of a_T in the particular temperature range concerned.

4. Behavior of Copolymers and Polymer Mixtures

Data on several copolymers have already been included in Tables
12–I, 12–III, and 12–VI. Insofar as the chemical heterogeneity is on
a sufficiently local basis that regions with the dimensions of a Rouse

submolecule have the same average chemical composition, the effect of varying the monomer ratio is primarily to change the local friction coefficient. This is illustrated by the butadiene-styrene copolymers investigated by Tobolsky and associates,[20, 52] which have nearly equal values of the parameters n and h characterizing the shapes of their viscoelastic functions (Table 12–VI), though the positions of their transition zones on the time scale are widely different. A similar effect can be seen in isochronal or pseudo-isochronal studies such as those in Fig. 12–3. Thus, Jenckel and Herwig[55] found in copolymers of styrene and methyl acrylate that the maximum in tan δ (measured in torsion at a frequency of 0.14 sec.$^{-1}$) on the temperature scale shifted from about 20° to 110° with increasing proportions of styrene; the sharpness of the maximum was not much affected. On the other hand, recent work by Kawai[56] on copolymers of methyl acrylate and methyl methacrylate shows differences in both the shape and the location of the relaxation modulus.

In a copolymer polymerized by carrying the conversion to completion, there is another aspect to the heterogeneity besides the local fluctuations in chemical composition; the average compositions of polymer molecules formed at the beginning and at the end of the conversion may be quite different, depending on the relative rates at at which the monomer units add to the growing chain.[57] It was found by Nielsen[58] in pseudo-isochronal measurements on copolymers of polyvinyl chloride and methyl acrylate that increasing degrees of

Table 12–VI

PARAMETERS h AND n CHARACTERIZING THE SHAPE OF THE RELAXATION MODULUS IN THE TRANSITION ZONE [52]

Polymer	h	n
Polymethyl methacrylate	0.31	0.525
Paracril	0.415	0.63
GR-S	0.45	0.71
Butadiene-styrene, 60/40	0.40	0.505
50/50	0.364	0.545
30/70	0.36	0.55
Polyisobutylene	0.367	0.745
Hevea rubber unvulcanized	0.495	1.07
Hevea rubber, vulcanized	0.555	1.10

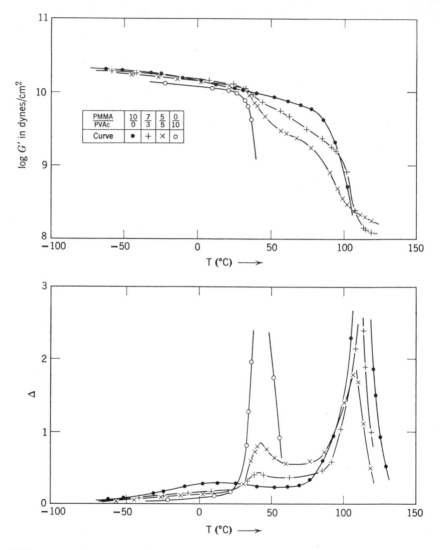

FIG. 12–10. Storage modulus and logarithmic decrement (approximately proportional to loss tangent) plotted against temperature, for physical mixtures of polymethyl methacrylate and polyvinyl acetate, with compositions as indicated. (After Jenckel and Herwig [55].)

this kind of molecular heterogeneity caused a broadening of the transition zone on the temperature scale; G' decreased less steeply near its inflection, and the maximum in tan δ was lower.

The extreme case of the molecular heterogeneity resulting from different monomeric ratios is simply a mixture of two pure homopolymers. Such mixtures, with few exceptions, are incompatible, representing physical blending rather than solution. For the exceptional case (e.g., polyvinyl chloride and butadiene-acrylonitrile rubber,[58] where the severe thermodynamic requirements[59] for compatibility appear to be met) a single broad transition is noted. For the more common case of incompatibility, however, physical blending leaves moderately large regions of homogeneous composition (which often show their presence by opacity), and each type of region experiences its own transition. This is illustrated in isochronal plots of G' and tan δ for mixtures of polymethyl methacrylate and polyvinyl acetate in Fig. 12–10, from data of Jenckel and Herwig.[55] Similar behavior has been found for mixtures of polystyrene with butadiene-styrene copolymer[58] and others.[59,60] There appear to be no isothermal viscoelastic functions available for such systems, however.

REFERENCES

1. J. D. Ferry, W. C. Child, Jr., R. Zand, D. M. Stern, M. L. Williams, and R. F. Landel, *J. Colloid Sci.*, **12**, 53 (1957).
2. W. C. Child, Jr., and J. D. Ferry, *J. Colloid Sci.*, **12**, 327 (1957).
3. W. C. Child, Jr., and J. D. Ferry, *J. Colloid Sci.*, **12**, 389 (1957).
4. W. Dannhauser, W. C. Child, Jr., and J. D. Ferry, *J. Colloid Sci.*, **13**, 103 (1958).
5. S. F. Kurath, T. P. Yin, J. W. Berge, and J. D. Ferry, *J. Colloid Sci.*, **14**, 147 (1959).
6. J. R. McLoughlin and A. V. Tobolsky, *J. Colloid Sci.*, **7**, 555 (1952).
7. J. D. Ferry, L. D. Grandine, Jr., and E. R. Fitzgerald, *J. Applied Phys.*, **24**, 911 (1953).
8. A. V. Tobolsky and E. Catsiff, *J. Polymer Sci.*, **19**, 111 (1956).
9. L. D. Grandine and J. D. Ferry, *J. Applied Phys.*, **24**, 679 (1953).
10. H. Fujita and K. Ninomiya, *J. Polymer Sci.*, **24**, 233 (1957).
11. M. L. Williams and J. D. Ferry, *J. Colloid Sci.*, **9**, 479 (1954).
12. K. Ninomiya and H. Fujita, *J. Colloid Sci.*, **12**, 204 (1957).
13. M. L. Williams and J. D. Ferry, *J. Colloid Sci.*, **10**, 474 (1955).
14. G. W. Becker, *Kolloid-Z.*, **140**, 1 (1955).
15. S. F. Kurath, E. Passaglia, and R. Pariser, *J. Applied Phys.*, **28**, 499 (1957).
16. K. E. Owens and C. F. Dahlquist, *Trans. Soc. Rheology*, **2**, 23 (1958).

17. A. R. Payne, in *Rheology of Elastomers,* edited by P. Mason and N. Wookey, Pergamon Press, London, 1958, p. 86.
18. L. J. Zapas, S. L. Shufler, and T. W. De Witt, *J. Polymer Sci.,* **18,** 245 (1955).
19. J. R. Cunningham and D. G. Ivey, *J. Applied Phys.,* **27,** 967 (1956).
20. E. Catsiff and A. V. Tobolsky, *J. Applied Phys.,* **25,** 1092 (1954).
21. R. F. Landel, *J. Colloid Sci.,* **12,** 308 (1957).
22. K. Schmieder and K. Wolf, *Kolloid-Z.,* **134,** 149 (1953).
23. K. Schmieder and K. Wolf, *Kolloid-Z.,* **127,** 65 (1952).
24. K. Schmieder, unpublished measurements.
25. L. E. Nielsen, R. Buchdahl, and G. C. Claver, *Ind. Eng. Chem.,* **43,** 341 (1951).
26. E. Jenckel, *Kolloid-Z.,* **136,** 142 (1954).
27. A. B. Thompson and D. W. Woods, *Trans. Faraday Soc.,* **52,** 1383 (1956).
28. T. P. Yin and J. D. Ferry, *J. Colloid Sci.* (in press).
29. A. V. Tobolsky and J. R. McLoughlin, *J. Polymer Sci.,* **8,** 543 (1952).
30. P. J. Flory, *Principles of Polymer Chemistry,* Cornell University Press, Ithaca, 1953, Chapter XIV.
31. B. Gross, *Mathematical Structure of the Theories of Viscoelasticity,* Hermann et Cie., Paris, 1953.
32. S. S. Rogers and L. Mandelkern, *J. Phys. Chem.,* **61,** 985 (1957).
33. H. Fujita and A. Kishimoto, *J. Colloid Sci.,* **13,** 418 (1958).
34. J. D. Ferry and R. F. Landel, *Kolloid-Z.,* **148,** 1 (1956).
35. E. Jenckel, in H. A. Stuart, *Die Physik der Hochpolymeren,* Vol. III, p. 615, Springer-Verlag, Berlin, 1955.
36. A. T. Hutcheon, R. J. Kokes, J. L. Hoard, and F. A. Long, *J. Chem. Phys.,* **20,** 1232 (1952).
37. A. W. Adamson and R. Irani, *J. chim. phys.,* **55,** 102 (1958).
38. G. S. Park, *Proc. 2nd Radioisotope Conf.,* Butterworths, London, 1954, p. 11.
39. I. Auerbach, S. D. Gehman, W. R. Miller, and W. C. Kuryla, *J. Polymer Sci.,* **28,** 129 (1958).
40. F. Grün, *Experientia,* **3,** 490 (1947).
41. S. D. Morton and J. D. Ferry, *J. Phys. Chem.,* **63,** 1335 (1959).
42. A. Aitken and R. M. Barrer, *Trans. Faraday Soc.,* **51,** 116 (1955).
43. S. Prager, E. Bagley, and F. A. Long, *J. Amer. Chem. Soc.,* **75,** 1255 (1953).
44. S. N. Zhurkov and G. Ya. Ryskin, *Zhur. Tekh. Fiz.,* **24,** 797 (1954).
45. R. J. Kokes and F. A. Long, *J. Amer. Chem. Soc.,* **75,** 6142 (1953).
46. J. B. Wilkens and F. A. Long, *Trans. Faraday Soc.,* **53,** 1146 (1957).
47. Y. Nishijima and G. Oster, *J. Polymer Sci.,* **19,** 337 (1956).
48. H. K. Schachman and W. F. Harrington, *J. Amer. Chem. Soc.,* **74,** 3965 (1952).
49. W. Kuhn, *Makromol. Chem.,* **6,** 224 (1951).
50. R. S. Marvin, in J. T. Bergen, *Viscoelasticity—Phenomenological Aspects,* Academic Press, New York, 1960, p. 27.
51. A. V. Tobolsky, *J. Amer. Chem. Soc.,* **74,** 3786 (1952).
52. A. V. Tobolsky, *J. Applied Phys.,* **27,** 673 (1956).
53. J. Bischoff, E. Catsiff, and A. V. Tobolsky, *J. Amer. Chem. Soc.,* **74,** 3378 (1952).
54. T. L. Smith, unpublished calculations.
55. E. Jenckel and H. U. Herwig, *Kolloid-Z.,* **148,** 57 (1956).
56. K. Fujino, K. Senshu, and H. Kawai, unpublished work.

57. P. J. Flory, *Principles of Polymer Chemistry*, Cornell University Press, Ithaca, 1953, Chapter V.
58. L. E. Nielsen, *J. Amer. Chem. Soc.*, **75**, 1435 (1953).
59. R. Buchdahl and L. E. Nielsen, *J. Polymer Sci.*, **15**, 1 (1955).
60. E. B. Atkinson and R. F. Eagling, in *The Physical Properties of Polymers*, Soc. Chem. Ind. Monograph, No. 5, 1959, p. 197.

CHAPTER 13

The Rubbery State

In the transition zone treated in the preceding chapter, viscoelastic properties are dominated by configurational rearrangements of individual molecules as described approximately by the flexible chain theories of Rouse and others. In the rubbery or plateau zone now to be discussed, the properties are dominated by a quite different feature: the presence of a network, due either to actual cross-links or to entanglement coupling, which necessitates coordination of the configurational motions of neighboring molecules or molecular strands. For the slower relaxation processes, the influence of the environment can no longer be described solely in terms of an average friction coefficient.

The shapes of the viscoelastic functions are grossly similar for all polymers in the plateau zone, just as they are in the transition zone. For cross-linked polymers at low frequencies (corresponding to long times), G' changes very little with frequency, and G'' is also nearly frequency-independent, with a magnitude considerably below that of G'. This behavior, exemplified by the curves for lightly vulcanized Hevea rubber in Figs. 2–3 and 2–4, was emphasized by Kuhn[1] and Philippoff,[2] and its implications in terms of the form of the relaxation spectrum H were demonstrated.[1] That spectrum is, of course, also a flat plateau, which has given the latter name to this region of the time scale. The smaller the ratio G''/G' (or H/G', since to a close approximation here $H = 2G''/\pi$), the more "rubbery" or "elastomeric" the behavior. For uncross-linked polymers of high molecular weight, G' and G'' also pass through a region where their slopes are relatively small, though more complicated in shape than for the cross-linked case. A representative comparison is shown in Fig. 13–1 for natural

276

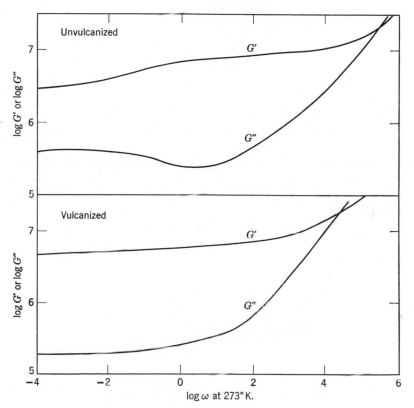

FIG. 13-1. Dynamic shear moduli in the rubbery or plateau zone for natural rubber before and after vulcanization.[3] Upper curves, G'; lower, G''. (The molecular weight before vulcanization was not specified, but must have been very high.)

rubber before and after vulcanization, taken from the measurements of Payne[3] (data tabulated in Appendix D). For the cross-linked polymer, G'' is smaller than G' by a factor of about 0.025. (In the data of Figs. 2–3 and 2–4, taken from another source, this ratio for the vulcanized rubber is about 0.01.) For the uncross-linked polymer, the ratio G''/G' is of the order of 0.04, but varies as G'' passes through a shallow maximum and shallow minimum.

The corresponding plots of the relaxation spectra are given in Fig. 13–2. At long times, both are flat, the level for the cross-linked polymer being lower by a factor of 0.46. At shorter times, they cross, and enter the transition zone parallel but displaced by about 0.8

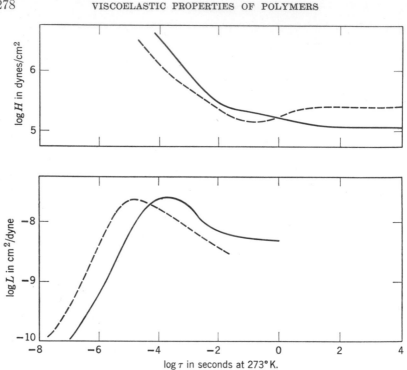

FIG. 13–2. Relaxation and retardation spectra in the plateau zone, calculated from the data of Fig. 13–1. Solid curves, vulcanized; dashed curves, unvulcanized.

unit on the logarithmic time scale, as reflected in the difference in their friction coefficients (Table 12–III).

Perhaps the most striking manifestation of a network structure in viscoelastic properties is the maximum in J'', and the corresponding maximum in L, which appear roughly at the boundary between the transition and plateau zones of the time scale. The maximum in the loss compliance was discussed in Chapter 10 in connection with the theoretical predictions which were compared in Fig. 10–14. The maximum in L, which appears at almost the same position (τ corresponding to $1/\omega$) as that in J'', is plotted also in Fig. 13–2 for the vulcanized and unvulcanized rubbers. We shall first examine the features of these characteristic maxima.

A. THE MAXIMA IN THE LOSS COMPLIANCE AND RETARDATION SPECTRUM

Although the maximum in the loss compliance occurs at the high-frequency end of the plateau zone, in fact slightly beyond it corresponding to the point where H is just beginning to abandon the Rouse slope of $-\frac{1}{2}$ and level out into the plateau zone (cf. the discussion relevant to equation 1 in Chapter 12), it is really characteristic of the network structure; its height and position depend on the number and distribution of the network strands. According to the theories presently available, which do not take into account distributions of strand lengths, we have for the location of the maximum (cf. Chapter 10):

Cross-linked (Bueche):

$$J''_m = 0.42 Z_c M_0 / \rho R T = 0.42 J_e \qquad (1)$$

$$\omega_m = 29.6 k T / a^2 Z_c{}^2 \zeta_0 \qquad (2)$$

Uncross-linked (Marvin):

$$J''_m = 0.32 Z_e M_0 / \rho R T \qquad (3)$$

$$\omega_m = 48 k T / a^2 Z_e{}^2 \zeta_0 \qquad (4)$$

where the symbols have their usual significance as in Chapter 10; in particular, $Z_c \ (= M_c / M_0)$ and $Z_e \ (= M_e / M_0)$ are the average degrees of polymerization per network strand in the cross-linked and entanglement networks respectively. The similarity of these equations implies that the maximum in J'' does not depend much on whether the chains are coupled by entanglements or by true cross-links. It may be noted that in an uncross-linked polymer the maximum in J'' is independent of the molecular weight, as long as $M \gg M_e$; this feature makes it a valuable source of information about M_e. The existence of maxima somewhat lower than predicted by equations 1 and 3 may be at least in part attributed to non-uniformity of strand lengths in the networks (but not, of course, to non-uniformity in M, as long as $M \gg M_e$).

It is of interest to eliminate Z_c and Z_e from equations 1 and 2 and 3 and 4 respectively, obtaining the following expressions for ζ_0:

$$\zeta_0 = 5.22 \, M_0{}^2 / a^2 \rho^2 N_0 R T \omega_m J''_m{}^2, \text{ cross-linked} \qquad (5)$$

$$\zeta_0 = 4.91 \, M_0{}^2 / a^2 \rho^2 N_0 R T \omega_m J''_m{}^2, \text{ uncross-linked} \qquad (6)$$

These equations could be used as alternative means for calculating ζ_0 from experimental data; but they are less reliable than equation 1 of Chapter 12, since they contain the assumption that the network strands are all of uniform length.

Since the value of the retardation spectrum L corresponding to the maximum in J'' (where the derivative of J'' is zero) is related to that of J'' simply by a factor of $2/\pi$ or $e^2/4\pi$, according to equations 25, 26, and 27 of Chapter 4, the maximum in L should also be independent of M and its position should depend on Z_c or Z_e in the same manner as given by equations 1 to 4. The fact that equations 1 and 2 are based on a discontinuous retardation spectrum does not prevent applying this conclusion to the spectra obtained from experiments, which are always continuous because of the distribution of network strand lengths. In practice, in examining the maximum, we shall use the function L rather than J''.

1. Comparisons of Cross-Linked Polymers

In Fig. 13–3, the retardation spectrum in the neighborhood of its maximum has been drawn for several cross-linked systems after reduction to corresponding states where, according to equations 1 and 2, their positions should coincide: L/J_e is plotted logarithmically against $(29.6kT/a^2Z_c^2\zeta_0)\tau$. The data for the reduction are summarized in Table 13–I. Here ζ_0 is obtained from the data of Table 12–III and M_c is calculated from J_e. Because of the paucity of experimental data, two plasticized systems have been included.

Table 13–I

DATA FOR REDUCTION OF L TO CORRESPONDING STATES
(CROSS-LINKED SYSTEMS)

Polymer System	Ref.	$\log J_e$	M_c	$\log M_0^2/a^2\zeta_0$
Hevea rubber, 0°C.	3	−6.68	4280	24.75
Polyurethane rubber, 0°C.	4	−7.17	1960	20.48
40% Polyvinyl chloride in dimethyl thianthrene, 25°C.	5	−6.70	2780	19.40
43% Cellulose tributyrate, −25°C. in dimethyl phthalate	6	−7.38	440	18.84

In view of the approximate equivalence of the maxima in J'' and L, the location of the latter would be expected from equation 2 to be at zero on the reduced logarithmic time scale. This is fulfilled for all of the systems except the cellulose tributyrate, which is so densely cross-linked (M_c of 440 in Table 13–I) that the strand configurations probably do not follow the Gaussian statistics assumed in all the theories. The shapes of the maxima are also roughly the same. Their heights vary from 0.115 to 0.19, as compared with the value of about 0.26 predicted from equation 1 by applying the factor $2/\pi$. From the detailed shape, it should be possible in principle to obtain information about the distribution of strand lengths (Chapter 10, Section E).

2. Comparisons of Uncross-Linked Polymers

Since for an uncross-linked polymer M_e and Z_e are not unambiguously obtainable, reduced variables analogous to those of Fig. 13–3 cannot be used for comparing the shapes of the maxima in L. How-

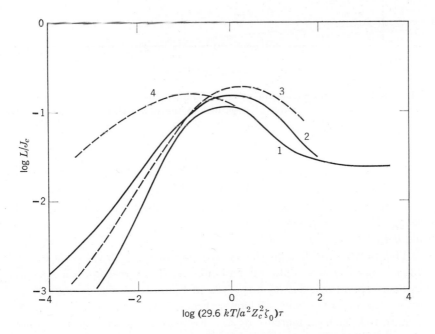

FIG. 13–3. Retardation spectra of cross-linked systems, near their maxima, reduced to corresponding states in accordance with equations 1 and 2. Curve 1, Hevea rubber; 2, polyurethane rubber; 3, 40% polyvinyl chloride in dimethyl thianthrene; 4, 43% cellulose tributyrate in dimethyl phthalate.

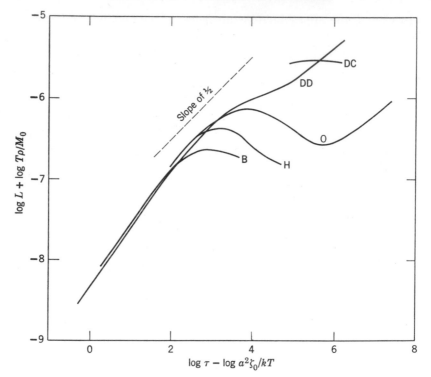

FIG. 13–4. Retardation spectra of uncross-linked methacrylate polymers,[7,8] reduced to corresponding states as described in the text. B, butyl; H, hexyl; O, octyl; DD, dodecyl; DC, docosyl.

ever, a corresponding-state plot analogous to that of Fig. 12–6 reduces out the differences in ζ_0, M_0, and ρ, leaving only the variable parameter Z_e in equations 3 and 4, whose influence can then be clearly seen. For this purpose, we plot $\log L + \log T\rho/M_0$ against $\log \tau - \log a^2\zeta_0/kT$.

The results for five methacrylate polymers [7,8] are shown in Fig. 13–4. The reduced data all coincide in the transition zone as did the corresponding relaxation spectra in Fig. 12–6. The maxima, however, shift upward and to longer times with increasing side group length, reflecting an increase in Z_e. From equations 3 and 4 it follows that L_m should be proportional to Z_e and τ_m to Z_e^2, so an increase in Z_e should shift the maximum along a direction with a slope of $\frac{1}{2}$ on a logarithmic plot; this is approximately the direction observed.

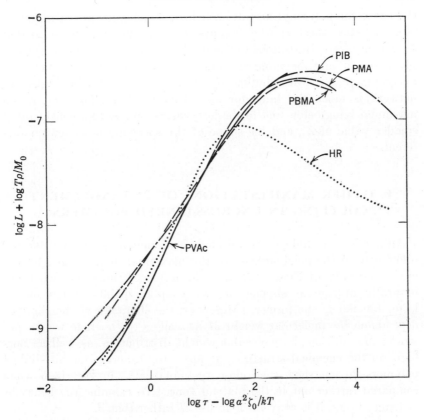

FIG. 13–5. Retardation spectra of various uncross-linked polymers reduced to corresponding states as in Fig. 13–4. PBMA, poly-n-butyl methacrylate from Fig. 13–4; PMA, polymethyl acrylate;[9] PVAc, polyvinyl acetate;[10] PIB, polyisobutylene;[11] HR, Hevea rubber.[3]

(*Cf.* also the effects of an inferred change of Z_e with temperature as discussed in Chapter 11, Section D.) For the poly-n-dodecyl methacrylate, the ratio M/M_e is evidently not high enough for a maximum in L to appear, although there is an inflection at the appropriate point; the fragmentary data on the docosyl polymer portray the immediate neighborhood of the maximum only.

A wider assortment of uncross-linked polymers is compared in the same way in Fig. 13–5, based on data which have already been cited in the preceding chapter.[3, 9–11] The maxima in L for poly-n-butyl methacrylate, polymethyl acrylate, and polyisobutylene, as well as the curve for polyvinyl acetate, which does not quite reach its maximum, lie close together when reduced to corresponding states, so that Z_e is apparently (fortuitously) about the same for all these polymers. Moreover, it may be inferred from the similarity in shape near the maximum that the distribution of strand lengths in the entanglement network is much the same for all. Hevea rubber, however, has a maximum lying below and to the left, corresponding to a considerably smaller value of Z_e, and the shape of the spectrum is somewhat different.

B. OTHER MANIFESTATIONS OF ENTANGLEMENT COUPLING IN UNCROSS-LINKED POLYMERS

Although cross-linked and entanglement networks behave not too differently in the neighborhood of the maximum in L, judged by the gross similarity of Figs. 13–3 to 13–5, at longer times the two types naturally diverge as slippage of the coupling points occurs in the latter but not in the former. Moreover, the character of the slippage depends on the molecular weight M as well as the average weight per strand M_e, and on the molecular weight distribution, as well as perhaps on the chemical structure; at any rate, different uncross-linked polymers do not show such close resemblance as in Fig. 13–5 when compared farther out in the plateau zone. To examine the behavior at longer times, it is convenient to use H rather than L.

1. The Relaxation Spectrum in the Plateau Zone

To illustrate the effect of molecular weight at long times, the relaxation spectrum for extension ($H_l = 3H$) is plotted in Fig. 13–6 for six fractions of polyvinyl acetate, from data of Ninomiya.[12] As the spectrum enters the plateau zone, the lowest molecular weight deviates the most from the Rouse slope, and the magnitude of the spectrum increases with decreasing molecular weight. Qualitatively, perhaps, this deviation may be attributed to more substantial relaxation processes caused by greater slippage of entanglement points, but there is no precisely formulated theory. At longer times, the curves all cross so that entering the terminal zone the magnitude of the spectrum increases with *increasing* molecular weight, as well as extending to much longer times in accordance with the expectation that the terminal relaxation time should be proportional to $M\eta$ and hence to something like $M^{4.4}$ (equation 21, Chapter 10) for fractions homogeneous with respect to molecular weight. Actually, no fraction is strictly homogeneous, and the terminal relaxation times are not quite encompassed in the experimental time range.

The fact that such curves must cross somewhere in the plateau zone can be predicted by the phenomenological theory as presented in Chapter 3. At some point well into the transition zone where the curves all coincide, e.g., at log $\tau = -3$ in Fig. 13–6, all the viscoelastic properties are independent of molecular weight (cf. Chapter 12, Section A, where experimental evidence is cited). For example, the relaxation modulus at $t = 10^{-3}$, given by

$$G(10^{-3}) = \int_{-\infty}^{\infty} H e^{-10^{-3}/\tau} \, d \ln \tau$$

is the same for all the fractions. The exponential factor is essentially unity throughout the plateau zone. Since for high molecular weights

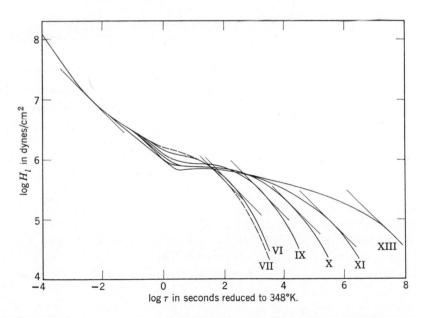

FIG. 13–6. Relaxation spectrum in extension, H_l, for various polyvinyl acetate fractions reduced to 75°C. (data of Ninomiya[12]). Weight-average molecular weights: VII, 7.9×10^4; VI, 8.5×10^4; IX, 1.9×10^5; X, 3.0×10^5; XI, 4.1×10^5; XIII, 7.6×10^5. Tangents are drawn with theoretical slope of $-\frac{1}{2}$.

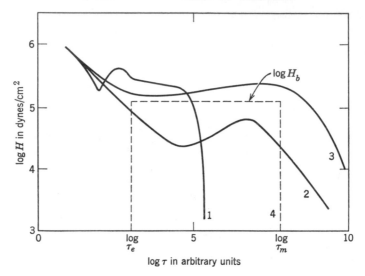

FIG. 13–7. Examples of shapes of the relaxation spectrum in the plateau zone:
1, polystyrene with very narrow molecular weight distribution; 2, poly-*n*-octyl
methacrylate, moderately sharp fraction (Curve III, Fig. 3–3); 3, polyisobutylene, broad distribution; 4, box idealization.

H is larger at long times, it must be smaller at short times to keep
the integral constant. In fact, if the relaxation spectrum in the
plateau zone is approximated by a flat-topped box [1,13] as schematically
illustrated in Fig. 13–7, its height H_b (absolute, not logarithmic)
should be inversely proportional [14] to its width on the logarithmic
time scale, $\log \tau_m/\tau_e$.

Experimentally observed spectra in the plateau zone, as exemplified
in Fig. 13–7 (*cf.* also Fig. 13–2), vary in shape from an extended level
region resembling the idealized box, but with a minimum at the short-
end, as observed for a polystyrene sample with a very sharp distribution of molecular weights,[15] to an undulating form with broad minimum and maximum as predicted by the model of Marvin [16] (Fig. 10–
13). It is not clear at present what is responsible for these differences.
For the box approximation, all the viscoelastic functions can be calculated as rather simple expressions in terms of the parameters H_b,
τ_m, and τ_e shown in Fig. 13–7. For example, the relaxation modulus
is given by

$$G(t) = H_b[\mathrm{Ei}(-t/\tau_e) - \mathrm{Ei}(-t/\tau_m)] \qquad (7)$$

where Ei is the exponential integral function. In some cases, moderately good agreement with experimental data is achieved.[1, 13, 17, 18]

If it is assumed that the box approximation is valid for a polymer homogeneous with respect to molecular weight, then a monotonically decreasing relaxation spectrum in the plateau region (such as all but Curve XIII in Fig. 13–6) can be interpreted in terms of molecular weight distribution; in fact, the distribution $\varphi(M)$ as discussed in Chapter 10, Section C can be calculated from the shape of the spectrum.[14] However, this treatment cannot account for the minima which often appear in the relaxation spectrum.

2. Estimates of the Average Strand Molecular Weight in the Entanglement Network

In the current conceptual scheme of entanglement coupling, the most important parameter is M_e, the average molecular weight of a network strand, or Z_e $(= M_e/M_0)$. Methods for calculating M_e from experimental data were summarized in Chapter 10, Section F. One of these employs the width of the plateau zone of H as measured by Δ, the distance on the logarithmic time scale between two tangents drawn with the theoretical slope of $-\frac{1}{2}$ in the terminal and transition zones respectively. Thus, equation 72 of Chapter 10 can be rewritten

$$\log M_e = \log (M/2) - \Delta/2.4 \qquad (8)$$

Although this calculation is applicable strictly only to a sample homogeneous with respect to molecular weight, its use may be illustrated with the data of Fig. 13–6, where the appropriate tangents have been drawn in. For this purpose, the weight-average molecular weights, which are slightly higher than the number-average, have been used. A plot of Δ against $\log M_w$, which according to equation 8 should have a slope of 2.4, is shown in Fig. 13–8. The predicted slope is followed closely except for the two samples of highest molecular weight. (These two samples appear also to deviate from the proportionality of steady-flow viscosity to $M^{3.4}$, from which the exponent of 2.4 is derived.) The intercept of the line with slope 2.4 provides a value for M_e of 7400, or $Z_e = 86$.

Values of Z_e can also be obtained from the maximum in J'' according to the Marvin model, either its magnitude by equation 3 or its position on the frequency scale by equation 4. These have the advantage that a sharp distribution of molecular weights is not required,

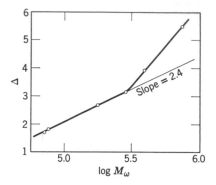

FIG. 13–8. Plot of Δ against log M_w to determine M_e in accordance with equation 8, for the data of Fig. 13–6.

nor is knowledge of the average molecular weight so long as it is high. The same remarks apply to estimation of Z_e from the magnitude of $G(t)$ at its inflection point in the rubbery zone. For determination from the dependence of η on M, on the other hand, M must of course be known for several samples, and they should be sharp fractions.

In Table 13–II, values of Z_e calculated by all of these methods are summarized for a number of polymers, based on data from the literature as cited.[3, 7–12, 15, 19, 20, 23]   For each polymer, the estimates from various sources are of the same order of magnitude. The values confirm the statement that the coupling occurs at widely separated points. There are systematic differences according to source, some of which can be qualitatively interpreted.

First, the frequency of the maximum in J'' generally gives a value about 50% higher than that derived from the height of the maximum. Intuitively this seems reasonable, since the latter should yield something like a number-average (by analogy with the properties of cross-linked networks—Chapter 10, Section E), whereas the former should give some kind of higher average. Next, the estimate from the width of the plateau in H (equation 8) is smaller than the others. This may arise from the rather arbitrary procedure of drawing a tangent in the terminal zone as illustrated in Fig. 13–6. Finally, that from the inflection in the modulus agrees roughly with the estimates from the maximum in J'', except for the case of Hevea rubber.

To compare different polymers, the calculation from J''_m may be taken since it is available for nearly all of them and is the most

Table 13–II

ESTIMATES OF THE DEGREE OF POLYMERIZATION BETWEEN ENTANGLEMENT POINTS, FROM VARIOUS SOURCES

	Maximum in J''		Z_e from Plateau in H	Dep. of η on M	Infl. in $G(t)$ or G'	Ref.
Polymer	J''_m	ω_m				
Hevea rubber	34	50			159	62
					125 [a]	64
					100	3
Polyisobutylene	125	210		152	220	11, 20
Polystyrene	>100		96	180	330	15, 20
Polyvinyl acetate	170	290	86	132 [b]	200	10,12,23
Polymethyl acrylate	100	190				9
Polymethyl methacrylate					86 [a]	19
					102	21
Poly-n-butyl methacrylate	92	160				22
Poly-n-hexyl methacrylate	180	270				22
Poly-n-octyl methacrylate	330	580	250			22
Poly-n-dodecyl methacrylate			650			7
Poly-n-docosyl methacrylate	1250	4800				8

[a] From inflection in $J(t)$.
[b] At 100°C.

easily obtainable from experimental data without ambiguity. In the methacrylate series, there is a progressive increase in Z_e with increasing side group length; this may be attributed primarily to dilution of the polymer backbones per unit volume, as will be discussed in Chapter 16. For Hevea rubber Z_e appears to be remarkably small, but of course the monomer unit, taken as isoprene, contains four chain bonds instead of the usual two. For all the remaining polymers it is of similar magnitude, as inferred already from Fig. 13–5. By comparing the latter polymers with poly-n-butyl methacrylate, it appears that the strands are somewhat shorter in this methacrylate than in polymers with monosubstituted carbon chains. The information is not yet sufficient, however, to draw further generalizations or conclusions.

3. Effects of Blending Different Molecular Weights

In a study of stress relaxation in polyvinyl acetate samples prepared by blending pairs of fairly sharp fractions, Ninomiya [12] showed
that the relaxation modulus of a blend could be expressed in terms
of those of the original components by the relation

$$E_b(t) = w_1 E_1(t/\lambda_1) + w_2 E_2(t/\lambda_2) \tag{9}$$

where the subscripts 1 and 2 refer to the components of lower and
higher M respectively, the w's are weight fractions, and the λ's are
numerical coefficients; $\lambda_1 > 1$ and $\lambda_2 < 1$. (The results are expressed
here as Young's modulus because the experiments were in extension.)
Equation 9 is equivalent to the prediction from the flexible chain theory
as given for example by equation 47 of Chapter 10 in terms of H, pro-
vided that $\lambda_i = \eta_b M_i / \eta_i \bar{M}_w$, where $\bar{M}_w$ is the weight-average molecular
weight in the blend. If η is proportional to $\bar{M}_w^{3.4}$, this is equivalent to
$\lambda_i = (\bar{M}_w / M_i)^{2.4}$. As an alternative form for λ_i, Ninomiya [12, 24] has
proposed a more complicated expression involving $\bar{M}_n$ for the blend.
Regardless of the exact relation between λ_i and molecular weight, however, the success of equation 9 in fitting the results for blends indicates
that the slow relaxation processes in the entanglement network can be
described in terms of an average effective friction coefficient $Q_e \zeta_0$, where
Q_e depends on the molecular weight distribution of the blend in some
characteristic manner. It may be noted [24] that symmetry considerations
(interchangeability of the subscripts 1 and 2) in equation 9 require that
for any pair of components the ratio λ_1 / λ_2 be independent of the composition of the blend (w_i). This conclusion can be derived directly if
$\lambda_i = \eta_b M_i / \eta_i \bar{M}_w$, and it corresponds to the qualitative interpretation of
the ratio λ_1 / λ_2 as the ratio of the average monomeric friction coefficients
in the pure components 2 and 1 respectively (Chapter 10, Section C).

C. BEHAVIOR OF NETWORKS AT VERY LONG TIMES

1. Cross-Linked Networks

The failure of cross-linked networks to achieve true elastic equilibrium at constant stress or strain has been mentioned in Chapters 2
and 10. It may be illustrated by creep curves for various vulcanized
rubbers obtained by Martin, Roth, and Stiehler [25] in Fig. 13–9, and
some related recovery curves in Fig. 13–10. The slow continued de-

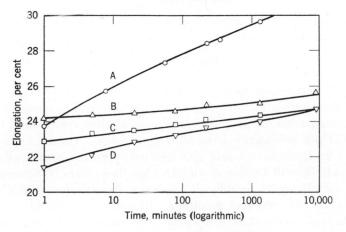

FIG. 13–9. Creep of vulcanized rubbers over a prolonged time. A, Neoprene; B, Hevea; C, GR-I; D, GR-S. (Martin, Roth, and Stiehler [25].)

formation amounts to several per cent, at least, of the pseudo-equilibrium strain, and it is essentially all recoverable.

For the Hevea rubber the slow deformation is approximately a linear function of log t, corresponding to a constant value of L throughout the pseudo-equilibrium zone; in fact, the plots of L and H shown in Figs. 3–3 and 3–4 for this region were derived from the data of Fig. 13–9.

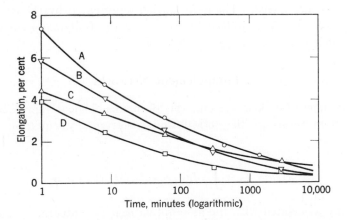

FIG. 13–10. Creep recovery of vulcanized rubbers after creep for 1400 minutes. A, Neoprene; B, GR-S; C, Hevea; D, GR-I. (Martin, Roth, and Stiehler [25].)

Alternatively, it has been proposed [26] that the creep in this region be fitted to the relation

$$J(t) = J_A + \beta t^{\frac{1}{3}} \tag{10}$$

originally introduced in slightly different form by Andrade [27] to describe the creep of metals. Here J_A (the "Andrade intercept") might be regarded as an extrapolated pseudo-equilibrium compliance, though it would not necessarily have this significance. On a plot such as Fig. 13–9, equation 10 would give upward curvature, and is evidently incompatible with Curves A and D. For the others, the creep is so slight that it would be difficult to decide the relative merits of the logarithmic and cube root functions. In such measurements, previous thermal and mechanical history is very critical; [25, 28] and chemical degradation, which would produce non-recoverable deformation,[29] must be avoided.

Equation 10 has been found to describe the creep of cellulose nitrate [30] and that of a 23% cellulose nitrate gel [31] over a wide range of time scale. In the latter case, the temperature dependence of the processes reflected in the $\beta t^{\frac{1}{3}}$ term is identical with that for the configurational rearrangements characterizing the transition zone; when referred to a standard reference temperature T_0, the ratio $\beta_0 T_0 \rho_0 / \beta T \rho$ is found to be identical with $a_T^{\frac{1}{3}}$ as determined from dynamic measurements in the transition zone. Thus, whatever molecular processes are responsible for the slow creep appear to be governed in rate by the monomeric friction coefficient which governs ordinary configurational rearrangements. The deformation represented by the $\beta t^{\frac{1}{3}}$ term is fully recoverable as judged by tests with the Boltzmann superposition principle (equation 19 of Chapter 1).

2. Entanglement Networks

In an uncross-linked system, the phenomenological representation of creep in terms of the retardation spectrum, by equation 20 of Chapter 3,

$$J(t) = J_g + \int_{-\infty}^{\infty} L(1 - e^{-t/\tau}) \, d\ln \tau + t/\eta \tag{11}$$

is usually associated with the assumption that the integral approaches a maximum limiting value of J_e and thereafter $J(t)$ is a linear function of t (cf. Fig. 1–11). Of course, for high molecular weights, a very long period under stress must be required to attain the limiting steady state. However, Plazek [31] has shown that data on a cellulose nitrate solution and also on high molecular weight polyisobutylene [11, 32] can be fitted with high accuracy in the region where viscous flow is beginning to predominate by the relation

$$J(t) = J_A + \beta t^{\frac{1}{3}} + t/\eta \tag{12}$$

For the cellulose nitrate solution, the coefficient β is a smooth function of temperature down through the presumed gelation point where η becomes infinite and equation 12 becomes equation 10. These relations imply that the integral in equation 11 does not converge and that strictly there is no steady-state compliance. Such a statement is very difficult to test experimentally; at long times, the t/η term dominates the creep, but the question of when linear time dependence of the deformation is reached remains doubtful. In any case, the deformation represented by the $\beta t^{\frac{1}{3}}$ term again appears to be fully recoverable.

Whether or not the $\beta t^{\frac{1}{3}}$ term in equation 12 applies at very long times and causes the elastic compliance to increase in principle without limit, its applicability in a range where the last two terms are of similar magnitude provides a valuable simplification in calculating η from creep measurements.[31] It is not necessary to wait until $J(t)$ is a strictly linear function of time. A plot of $J(t)$ against $t^{\frac{1}{3}}$ is made, and J_A and β are determined from its linear portion at intermediate times; then $J(t) - J_A - \beta t^{\frac{1}{3}}$ is found to be strictly proportional to t, thus providing a determination of $1/\eta$.

In certain cases uncross-linked polymers, whose linear character is evident in their solubility in suitable solvents, behave mechanically like cross-linked systems, owing perhaps to widely spaced loci of rather strong associative forces. Such networks may be regarded as intermediate in character between permanently cross-linked and entanglement networks. Examples are polyurethane elastomers containing urea groups [33] which presumably associate with hydrogen bond formation, and polydimethyl siloxanes of high molecular weight [34] in which the nature of the associative loci is unknown. In the latter polymers the Andrade form of creep at long times is closely followed, as illustrated in Fig. 13-11.

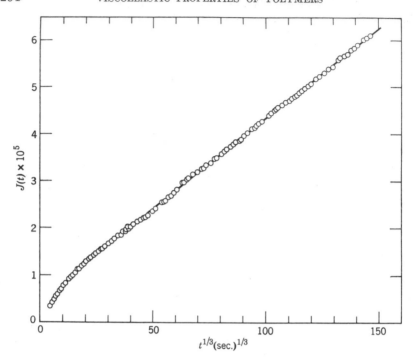

FIG. 13–11. Andrade plot of the creep of polydimethyl siloxane, weight-average molecular weight 2.7×10^6, at 25°C. for 36 days.[34]

3. Molecular Interpretation of Response at Very Long Times

In Chapter 10, very slow mechanisms in networks were tentatively ascribed to cooperative motions of groups of strands coupled through linkage points. Bueche[35] has calculated the compliance contribution of a strand which at its end is linked to 3 others, each of which is linked to 3 others, and so on indefinitely, using the continuous dynamic functions of Gross and Fuoss[36] (Chapter 10, Section B). The result is of the form $dJ(t)/d \ln t$ proportional to $t^{-1/2}$, so that a plot such as in Fig. 13-9 should have downward curvature (but more marked than found in Curves A and D). Imperfection in the network would increase the magnitude of this slow creep without altering the form of its time dependence.

Despite the discrepancies between this treatment and the experimental data, it seems probable that an approach of this kind will eventually explain the very slow mechanisms treated in the section.

D. NON-LINEAR BEHAVIOR

The subject of time-dependent mechanical phenomena outside the range of linear viscoelastic behavior, where the Boltzmann superposition principle and the phenomenological theory of Chapter 3 are not valid, is in a very early stage of development. However, a few remarks can be made about non-linear behavior in the rubbery zone.

1. Non-Linear Elasticity at Equilibrium

There have been numerous investigations[37] of departures from linearity in equilibrium or pseudo-equilibrium deformations of cross-linked rubbers (with the usual reservations about neglecting slight residual effects at long times as described in the preceding section). The original statistical theory of rubberlike elasticity predicts non-linearity in extension, as expressed by equation 4 of Chapter 6, which can be rewritten

$$\sigma = (\lambda E/3)(\lambda - 1/\lambda^2) \tag{13}$$

where σ is the stress calculated on the actual cross-section, and $\lambda = L/L_0$. (The very small deviation of Poisson's ratio from $\frac{1}{2}$ in a soft rubberlike solid is neglected, so the ratio of the original cross-section area A_0 to the strained cross-section area is λ.) Beyond an extension of 20% to 30%, however, experimental data have been fitted to a more complicated expression, the simplest form of which is derivable from a phenomenological theory of Mooney:[38]

$$\sigma = 2\lambda(C_1 + C_2/\lambda)(\lambda - 1/\lambda^2) \tag{14}$$

in which C_1 is identifiable with $E/6$ in equation 13. Although still more complicated relations may be required to describe data under a wide variety of conditions,[39] equation 14 holds up to simple extensions of the order of 140% ($\lambda = 2.4$). It may be noted that, unlike equation 13, it predicts non-linear stress-strain behavior in shear as well as extension. Deviations from equation 14 at higher extensions have been attributed to complete extension of the shorter network strands, which then store energy by bending chemical bonds rather than as entropy springs.[40]

Since C_1 corresponds to $E/6$, it would be expected from the statistical theory of rubberlike elasticity that $C_1 = \rho RT/2M_c$, and this is confirmed by the experiments of Mullins.[40]   The physical significance of C_2 has not been elaborated in detail, but it has been attributed by Ciferri and Flory [41] to time-dependent effects associated with failure to obtain true mechanical equilibrium.   This interpretation is supported by the dynamic experiments described below.

2. Small Dynamic Strains Superimposed on Large Static Strains

Equation 14 has been adapted to differential time-dependent deformations at finite static extensions by Mason.[42]   If a differential Young's modulus is defined as $\mathcal{E} = d\sigma/d\epsilon = \lambda d\sigma/d\lambda$, equation 14 becomes

$$F_1 \mathcal{E} = C_1 + F_2 C_2 \tag{15}$$

where
$$F_1 = \lambda/2(2\lambda^3 + 1) \tag{16}$$

and
$$F_2 = (\lambda^3 + 2)/\lambda(2\lambda^3 + 1) \tag{17}$$

For differential dynamic deformations, as for example in the propagation of a longitudinal wave of small amplitude down a rubber strip stretched at high fixed extension, equation 15 has the counterparts

$$F_1 E' = C'_1 + F_2 C'_2 \tag{18}$$

$$F_1 E'' = C''_1 + F_2 C''_2 \tag{19}$$

where the primed coefficients are all functions of frequency.   In the language of models, these coefficients represent summations of the type of equation 17 of Chapter 3 over a group of Maxwell elements with non-Hookean springs, each characterized by its own C_{1i} and C_{2i} by analogy with equation 15.

From wave-propagation measurements at various temperatures and extensions, but mostly at constant frequency, Mason has shown that equations 18 and 19 are closely followed again up to an extension of about 140%, as shown in Figs. 13–12 and 13–13.   From such plots of $F_1 E'$ against F_2, and $F_1 E''$ against F_2, the dynamic coefficients can be evaluated.   Over a range of temperatures embodying both rubberlike behavior and the major part of the transition from rubberlike to glasslike consistency, C'_1 was found to be of the order of 10^6 dynes/cm^2 and C''_1 was near 10^5 dynes/cm^2—zero within the precision of measurement.   Both C'_2 and C''_2 increased rapidly with decreasing temperature, however, qualitatively similar to the behavior of E' and E'' as directly measured.   Hence it may be concluded that the time-dependent mechanical properties are not associated with C_1 and the

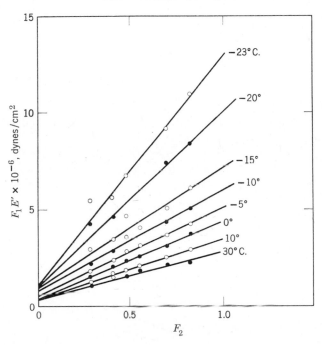

FIG. 13–12. Plot of F_1E' against F_2, for longitudinal wave measurements on vulcanized natural rubber at 1 kc/sec., at various temperatures as indicated.[42]

elastic features treated by the statistical theory, but rather with the quantity C_2 which in static experiments appears at high strains. Thus, in the extensional analog of equation 23 of Chapter 3,

$$E' = E_e + \int_{-\infty}^{\infty} [H_l \omega^2 \tau^2 / (1 + \omega^2 \tau^2)] \, d \ln \tau \tag{20}$$

E_e is related to C_1 as in the static case and H_l is related to C_2. Further development of these connections between static and time-dependent phenomena should clarify the physical significance of C_2.

It should be noted that a stretched strip such as the subject of the above experiments is an anisotropic body and has different viscoelastic behavior in different directions. Thus, the moduli E' and E'' measured in the direction of stretch by differential extension are not the same as those which would be measured by a lateral deformation of the strip. Also, the shear moduli measured in torsion of the strip, corresponding to a direction of slide perpendicular to the direction of

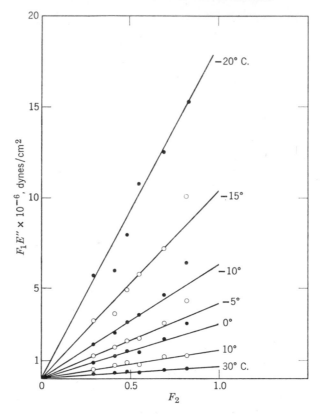

FIG. 13–13. Plot of F_1E'' against F_2 from measurements described in Fig. 13–11.

stretch, would differ from that for slide in the same direction. Dynamic torsion measurements of stretched rubber strips by Kuhn[43] showed that G'' and η' decreased with increasing degrees of static extension; *cf.* also recent experiments of Mason.[44]

3. Large Time-Dependent Strains

Experiments in which the time-dependent deformations themselves are large must usually be limited to the transient type, since dynamic deformations with high amplitude require substantial power input and generate heat; moreover, their strict interpretation is complicated since under non-linear conditions a sinusoidally varying stress implies a non-sinusoidal strain and vice versa.

In the slow creep of cross-linked networks in the pseudo-equilibrium zone (Section C above), the creep rate on a logarithmic time scale (*cf.* Fig. 13–9) increases with stress at high stresses.[45, 46] Perhaps the most spectacular effect of stress non-linearity in creep is the failure of creep recovery to coincide with the creep function when plotted as a mirror image (equation 23 of Chapter 1), as illustrated in Fig. 13–14 by data of Leaderman.[45] In fact, the recovery rate on a logarithmic time scale is the *smaller*, the higher the stress applied during the creep.[46] Thus the predictions of the Boltzmann superposition principle are wholly inapplicable.

Leaderman [45] has shown that the qualitative aspects of this behavior can be interpreted in terms of a mechanical model with non-Hookean springs and Newtonian dashpots. On the other hand, the stress relaxation in concentrated polymer solutions after cessation of steady-state flow, which is also non-linear—the relaxation occurring more rapidly, the higher the rate of shear during the flow (Fig. 13–15)—

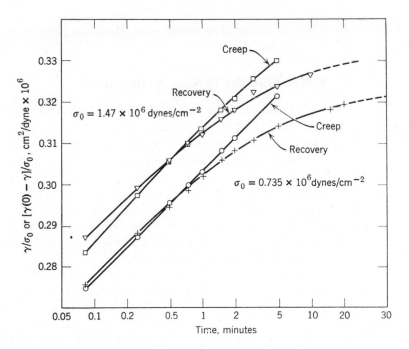

FIG. 13–14. Creep and creep recovery of vulcanized natural rubber at −40°C. at two high stresses as indicated.[45]

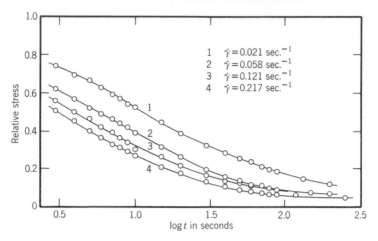

FIG. 13–15. Stress relaxation after cessation of steady-state flow in a 16.5% solution of polyisobutylene in Decalin, for various rates of shear ($\dot{\gamma}$) preceding the relaxation, as indicated.[47]

has been described in terms of a model with Hookean springs and non-Newtonian dashpots.[47, 48]

4. Non-Linearity of Stress-Strain Curves

For a solid devoid of time-dependent mechanical behavior, non-proportionality of stress and strain implies failure of Hooke's Law. For a viscoelastic material, however, any plot of stress *vs.* strain based on measurements within a finite time pattern will in general be non-linear because of relaxation or retardation effects, even if the *viscoelastic* behavior is linear in the sense that it can be duplicated with Hookean springs and Newtonian dashpots. Specifically, for a stress-strain curve determined by deformation at constant rate, the shape of the stress-strain curve is defined in terms of the relaxation spectrum H by equation 57 of Chapter 3.

The form of this equation permits the use of reduced variables at different straining rates to construct composite curves, as demonstrated by Smith.[49] For extension, in which elastic linearity holds up to moderate strains (in spite of the complications discussed in the preceding paragraphs) as shown by equation 6 of Chapter 6, the stress-strain curve takes the following form:

$$\sigma/\dot{\epsilon} = \int_{-\infty}^{\infty} \tau H_l (1 - e^{-\epsilon/\dot{\epsilon}\tau}) \, d\ln \tau \qquad (21)$$

where σ is the stress (calculated on the instantaneous cross-section area), $\dot{\epsilon}$ the rate of strain, and H_l the relaxation spectrum in extension; $\epsilon/\dot{\epsilon} = t$, the time elapsed after starting the deformation. It follows that measurements at different temperatures and rates of strain should be superposable by plotting a reduced stress, $\sigma T_0/\dot{\epsilon} T a_T$, against a reduced strain, $\epsilon/\dot{\epsilon} a_T$. The success of this procedure is illustrated by Fig. 13–16 for data on polyisobutylene [49] at ten different temperatures and four different strain rates. From such a curve, the relaxation modulus can be derived by differentiation in accordance with equation 59 of Chapter 3, and the relaxation spectrum by a second differentiation. Thus a non-linear stress-strain curve does not necessarily mean non-linear visco-elastic behavior. The presence of the latter can be distinguished most readily by the simpler transient or periodic experimental patterns.

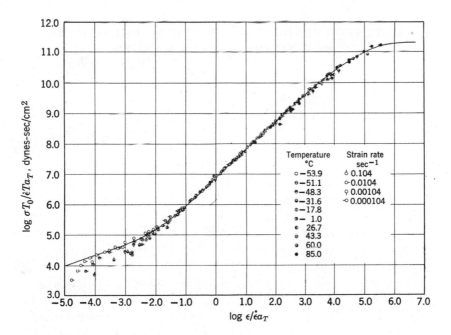

FIG. 13–16. Stress-strain curves for polyisobutylene at constant rate of elongation, for 4 different rates and 10 different temperatures, plotted with reduced variables as described in the text.[49]

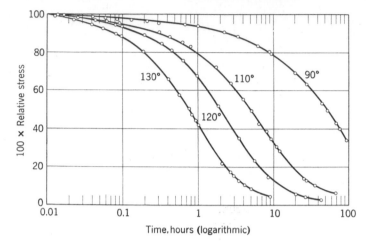

FIG. 13–17. Stress relaxation of a polyester rubber (Vulcollan A) due to chemical scission of network strands, at 4 temperatures as indicated.[50]

E. TIME-DEPENDENT MECHANICAL PHENOMENA DUE TO CHEMICAL CHANGES

If the chemical structure of a polymer is altered during a viscoelastic experiment—in particular, if a cross-linked network is subjected to a reaction which increases or decreases the number of network strands while it is being investigated in the rubbery zone of viscoelastic behavior—the apparent mechanical properties will be profoundly influenced. For example, scission of the network strands will cause stress relaxation at constant strain [29, 50] (Fig. 13–17) or creep under constant stress. Formally, if a single first-order chemical reaction is responsible, the relaxation may be described by a single relaxation time which is the reciprocal of the chemical rate constant, instead of the broad spectra which are characteristic of the usual mechanical processes.

The effects of chemical stress relaxation (sometimes referred to as chemorheology) depend on whether the network scissions occur at the original cross-links or are randomly disposed at all points along the network strands. [51, 52] They also depend on whether the broken bonds join again to leave the same number of network strands but with an undistorted distribution of configurations, or remain permanently cut.[53, 54] In some cases the reaction may be a bond interchange.[55, 56]

This subject is beyond the scope of the present discussion, but is mentioned here to refer the reader to other sources of information.[57-60]

F. PRACTICAL ASPECTS OF BEHAVIOR IN THE RUBBERY ZONE

For practical purposes, it is usually desirable in a cross-linked rubbery polymer that G''/G' be as small as possible at frequencies corresponding to deformation rates experienced in use, and that the creep rate at very long times be extremely small. Unfortunately, the molecular features governing these quantities are still incompletely understood.

For vulcanized natural rubber, G''/G' in the plateau zone may vary from 0.01 to 0.025 depending on the source (and probably the details of the vulcanization process).[61] For many synthetic rubbers, it is substantially larger, for example about 0.1 for GR-S with 25% styrene. The higher loss in the latter has been attributed to entanglement coupling in between the chemical cross-links (which is not supposed to occur in the Hevea rubber because the coupling points in the unvulcanized polymer are farther apart);[62,63] alternatively, to imperfections in the network arising from loose ends on account of the relatively low molecular weight prior to vulcanization.[64] It is also possible that the degree of heterogeneity of strand lengths in the network influences the behavior.

To achieve a very low long-time creep rate, aside from the obvious necessity of avoiding chemical degradation, the requirements are also obscure. The heterogeneity of the network and the degree of connectivity are probably important factors. Experimental work with networks of known topology is needed.

REFERENCES

1. W. Kuhn, O. Künzle, and A. Preissmann, *Helv. Chim. Acta,* **30,** 307, 464 (1947).
2. W. Philippoff, *J. Applied Phys.,* **24,** 685 (1953).
3. A. R. Payne, in *Rheology of Elastomers,* edited by P. Mason and N. Wookey, Pergamon Press, London, 1958, p. 86.
4. R. F. Landel, *J. Colloid Sci.,* **12,** 308 (1957).
5. J. D. Ferry and E. R. Fitzgerald, *J. Colloid Sci.,* **8,** 224 (1953).
6. R. F. Landel and J. D. Ferry, *J. Phys. Chem.,* **60,** 294 (1956).

7. S. F. Kurath, T. P. Yin, J. W. Berge, and J. D. Ferry, *J. Colloid Sci.*, **14**, 147 (1959).
8. P. R. Saunders and J. D. Ferry, *J. Colloid Sci.*, **14**, 239 (1959).
9. M. L. Williams and J. D. Ferry, *J. Colloid Sci.*, **10**, 474 (1955).
10. M. L. Williams and J. D. Ferry, *J. Colloid Sci.*, **9**, 479 (1954).
11. J. D. Ferry, L. D. Grandine, and E. R. Fitzgerald, *J. Applied Phys.*, **24**, 911 (1953).
12. K. Ninomiya, *J. Colloid Sci.*, **14**, 49 (1959).
13. R. D. Andrews, R. Hofman-Bang, and A. V. Tobolsky, *J. Polymer Sci.*, **3**, 669 (1948).
14. H. Fujita and K. Ninomiya, *J. Polymer Sci.*, **24**, 233 (1957).
15. A. V. Tobolsky, A. Mercurio, and K. Murakami, *J. Colloid Sci.*, **13**, 196 (1958).
16. R. S. Marvin, in J. T. Bergen, *Viscoelasticity—Phenomenological Aspects*, Academic Press, New York, 1960, p. 27.
17. R. D. Andrews and A. V. Tobolsky, *J. Polymer Sci.*, **6**, 221 (1951).
18. A. V. Tobolsky, *J. Amer. Chem. Soc.*, **74**, 3786 (1952).
19. F. Bueche, *J. Applied Phys.*, **26**, 738 (1955).
20. T. G. Fox and S. Loshaek, *J. Applied Phys.*, **26**, 1080 (1955).
21. A. V. Tobolsky and J. R. McLoughlin, *J. Amer. Chem. Soc.*, **74**, 3378 (1952).
22. J. W. Berge, P. R. Saunders, and J. D. Ferry, *J. Colloid Sci.*, **14**, 135 (1959).
23. H. Nakayasu and T. G. Fox, presented at the 137th meeting of the American Chemical Society, Cleveland, April 13, 1960.
24. K. Ninomiya and M. Sakamoto, *J. Phys. Chem.*, **64**, 181 (1960).
25. G. M. Martin, F. L. Roth, and R. D. Stiehler, *Trans. Inst. Rubber Ind.*, **32**, 189 (1956).
26. A. J. Kennedy, *Mech. Phys. Solids,* **1**, 172 (1953).
27. E. N. da C. Andrade, *Proc. Roy. Soc.*, **A84**, 1 (1910).
28. P. Thirion and R. Chasset, in *Rheology of Elastomers*, edited by P. Mason and N. Wookey, Pergamon Press, London, 1958, p. 17.
29. A. V. Tobolsky, I. B. Prettyman, and J. H. Dillon, *J. Applied Phys.*, **15**, 380 (1944).
30. K. E. Van Holde, *J. Polymer Sci.*, **24**, 417 (1957).
31. D. J. Plazek, *J. Colloid Sci.*, **15**, 50 (1960).
32. A. V. Tobolsky and E. Catsiff, *J. Polymer Sci.*, **19**, 111 (1956).
33. R. F. Landel, private communication.
34. D. J. Plazek, W. Dannhauser, and J. D. Ferry, *J. Colloid Sci.*, in press.
35. F. Bueche, personal communication.
36. B. Gross and R. M. Fuoss, *J. Polymer Sci.*, **19**, 39 (1956).
37. L. R. G. Treloar, in *Rheology of Elastomers*, edited by P. Mason and N. Wookey, Pergamon Press, London, 1958, p. 1.
38. M. Mooney, *J. Applied Phys.*, **11**, 582 (1940).
39. R. S. Rivlin and D. W. Saunders, *Phil. Trans. Roy. Soc.*, **A243**, 251 (1951).
40. L. Mullins, Ph.D. Thesis, University of London, 1958.
41. A. Ciferri and P. J. Flory, *J. Applied Phys.*, **30**, 1498 (1959).
42. P. Mason, *J. Applied Polymer Sci.*, **1**, 63 (1959).
43. W. Kuhn and O. Künzle, *Helv. Chim. Acta,* **30**, 839 (1947).

44. P. Mason, *Trans. Faraday Soc.*, **55**, 1461 (1959); *Physical Properties of Polymers*, Macmillan Company, New York, p. 262.
45. H. Leaderman, *J. Polymer Sci.*, **16**, 261 (1955).
46. A. N. Gent, private communication.
47. F. W. Schremp, J. D. Ferry, and W. W. Evans, *J. Applied Phys.*, **22**, 711 (1951).
48. J. D. Ferry, M. L. Williams, and D. M. Stern, *J. Phys. Chem.*, **58**, 987 (1954).
49. T. L. Smith, *J. Polymer Sci.*, **20**, 89 (1956).
50. J. A. Offenbach and A. V. Tobolsky, *J. Colloid Sci.*, **11**, 39 (1956).
51. A. M. Bueche, *J. Chem. Phys.*, **21**, 614 (1953).
52. J. P. Berry and W. F. Watson, *J. Polymer Sci.*, **18**, 201 (1955).
53. R. S. Stein and A. V. Tobolsky, *Textile Res. Jr.*, **18**, 302 (1948).
54. R. D. Andrews, A. V. Tobolsky, and E. E. Hanson, *J. Applied Phys.*, **17**, 352 (1946).
55. M. D. Stern and A. V. Tobolsky, *J. Chem. Phys.*, **14**, 93 (1946).
56. M. Mochulsky and A. V. Tobolsky, *Ind. Eng. Chem.*, **40**, 2155 (1948).
57. A. V. Tobolsky, *J. Applied Phys.*, **27**, 673 (1956).
58. J. Scanlan, in *Rheology of Elastomers*, edited by P. Mason and N. Wookey, Pergamon Press, London, 1958, p. 58.
59. J. P. Berry and L. R. G. Treloar, in H. A. Stuart, *Die Physik der Hochpolymeren*, Vol. IV, p. 361, Springer-Verlag, Berlin, 1956.
60. A. V. Tobolsky, *Properties and Structure of Polymers*, John Wiley and Sons, 1960.
61. W. P. Fletcher and A. N. Gent, *Brit. J. Applied Phys.*, **8**, 194 (1957).
62. L. J. Zapas, S. L. Shufler, and T. W. De Witt, *J. Polymer Sci.*, **18**, 245 (1955).
63. E. Catsiff and A. V. Tobolsky, *Office of Naval Research Technical Report*, RLT-21, Contract Nonr-1858(07), 1956.
64. F. Bueche, *J. Polymer Sci.*, **25**, 305 (1957).

CHAPTER 14

The Glassy State

It has been mentioned in several previous chapters that below the glass transition temperature the convolutions of polymer chain backbones are largely immobilized. Thus, most viscoelastic properties in the glassy state must reflect limited local molecular motions. Such motions are often ascribed to rearrangements in the side groups pendant from the backbone. Unfortunately, this assignment cannot be easily tested by studying polymers without side groups, because the latter almost invariably crystallize instead of vitrifying.

As far as backbone immobility is concerned, viscoelastic measurements well above T_g at very high frequencies should be approximately equivalent to those below T_g at low frequencies or in transient experiments. In fact, the shear storage moduli are of the same order of magnitude [1-3]—around 10^{10} dynes/cm². But the nature of the local motions of side groups may perhaps be different, and there appear to be no studies of the same system under both sets of conditions from which a detailed comparison can be made.

Below T_g, viscoelastic behavior can be easily demonstrated not only in amorphous polymers but also in vitrifying liquids of low molecular weight. The bulk viscoelastic properties, as evidenced by the course of volume contraction with decreasing temperature near T_g which was described in Chapter 11, seem to be very similar for both large and small molecules (cf. Chapter 18). But in shear there are marked differences, and it is instructive to examine the behavior of small molecules first.

A. AMORPHOUS SOLIDS OF LOW MOLECULAR WEIGHT

The dynamic mechanical properties of 2'-hydroxy-2:4:4:6:5' penta-methyl flavan

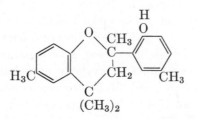

in the glassy state have been extensively investigated by Benbow.[4] Over a range of at least three logarithmic decades, from 10^{-3} to 1 cycle/sec., the storage and loss shear moduli follow the frequency dependence prescribed for a single Maxwell element, equations 3 and 4 of Chapter 3.

Because of the manner in which the results are calculated, the quantities termed "dynamic elasticity" and "dynamic viscosity" by Benbow are in our language the reciprocal of the storage compliance ($1/J'$) and the reciprocal of the loss compliance times frequency ($1/\omega J''$) respectively. For a Maxwell element, these quantities are independent of frequency (equations 6 and 7 of Chapter 3).

This behavior corresponds to a retardation spectrum with a single line; the retardation time is $\tau_1 = 0.15$ sec. at 16°C., and over the range from 10° to 20° it varies in accordance with the Arrhenius form with an apparent activation energy of 75 kcal. (Over such a short range, it would be impossible to distinguish between the Arrhenius and WLF types of temperature dependence.) At frequencies well below $1/\tau_1$, G'' is directly proportional to frequency, and η' is essentially a constant (approximately equal to the steady flow viscosity,[5] indicating that no other viscoelastic mechanisms enter at lower frequencies); the magnitude of η' is in the range from 10^8 to 10^{10} poises in the temperature range from 10° to 18°C. If a rough Stokes' law calculation is made for the effective local viscosity η_e governing a rotatory relaxation of a spherical body with the same molecular volume, using the equation $\eta_e = \rho R T \tau / 3M$, the result is $\eta_e = 4 \times 10^6$ at 16°C., as compared with 2.7×10^8 poises for the limiting low-frequency value of η'. Similar discrepancies are found in the dielectric relaxation times of roughly spherical dipolar molecules in liquids,[6] and it seems reasonable to postulate that the single contribution to the retardation spectrum corresponds to a rotatory motion of the molecule as a whole.

Other organic glasses formed from bulky-shaped molecules of low molecular weight were found by Benbow and Wood [5] to behave similarly, as shown in Fig. 14–1 where tan δ is plotted against frequency. (In the original figure, the ordinate is "internal friction" which in our language is the logarithmic decrement Δ of equation 15, Chapter 6.) For a Maxwell element, tan δ is inversely proportional to frequency (equation 8 of Chapter 3), and this is followed as evidenced by a slope of −1 on a logarithmic plot at low frequencies for the hydroxypentamethylflavan as well as 2-phenyl-3-p-tolylindanone and glycerol sextol phthalate.

At high frequencies, however, there is a transition (abrupt in the hydroxypentamethylflavan at about $\omega \tau_1 = 10$, more gradual in the others) to a region where tan δ becomes nearly independent of fre-

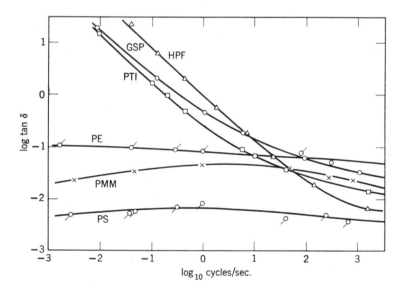

FIG. 14–1. Loss tangent plotted against frequency for three glasses of low molecular weight and two polymeric glasses. HPF, hydroxypentamethyflavan; GSP, glycerol sextol phthalate; PTI, 2-phenyl-3-p-tolylindanone; PMMA, polymethyl methacrylate (calculated from data of Lethersich [16]); PS, polystyrene. (After Benbow and Wood.[5])

quency. Here, G'' is approximately constant (instead of directly proportional to ω) and η' is approximately inversely proportional to ω (instead of constant); the retardation spectrum is a flat plateau instead of a single line. The limiting high-frequency value of tan δ for these and a number of other glasses of low molecular weight [5] ranges from 0.03 to 0.11 when they are compared at temperatures of equal steady-flow viscosity (4×10^9 poises). Its magnitude apparently increases with the degree of internal flexibility of the molecule,[5] indicating that the broad retardation spectrum in this region of short times is associated with internal molecular motions.

B. POLYMERS IN THE GLASSY ZONE

The characteristic retardation spectrum of a polymeric glass has already been portrayed as Curve IV in Fig. 3–4 as a relatively flat plateau. The loss tangent in Fig. 2–8 is correspondingly relatively independent of frequency. In Fig. 14–1, loss tangents for two polymers in the glassy state are included; their magnitudes are everywhere similar to those of the simple glasses at high frequencies, and presumably they reflect the same kind of intramolecular motions. The macromolecular structure of course prevents any motion of the type characterizing the simple glasses at low frequencies.

The loss tangent curves for the polymers show shallow maxima, often designated as secondary viscoelastic mechanisms to distinguish them from the much larger maximum in tan δ which occurs above T_g when the transition from rubberlike to glasslike consistency is traversed (Figs. 12–3 and 12–9)—the so-called primary or α mechanism. The existence of such maxima, which of course change their positions on the frequency scale with temperature, makes it difficult to draw any significant comparisons among the general magnitudes of the losses in different polymers. However, tan δ in glassy polymers rarely falls below the level indicated in Fig. 14–1 for polystyrene, of the order of 3×10^{-3}. Attention has been devoted primarily to determining the number of secondary maxima and their location with respect to temperature and frequency.

1. Viscoelastic Functions at Constant Temperature

Only in a few cases have measurements been made at enough frequencies or over a sufficient range of time scale to define isothermal viscoelastic functions. It may be remarked that such measurements require careful control of certain variables which are not so critical in the transition and rubbery zones treated in previous chapters. The absorption of a trace of diluent—in some cases, moisture [7]—can shift the time scale to shorter values, while the same effect can be obtained [7,8] by rapid quenching from above the glass transition temperature, thereby leaving a slightly larger proportion of uncollapsed free volume.[9] These difficulties may be responsible for some lack of agreement among investigations in different laboratories.

An unusually extensive study of the viscoelastic functions through a secondary mechanism in polymethyl methacrylate by Koppelmann [10] is shown in Fig. 14–2. Dynamic measurements of G', E', G''/G', and E''/E' are plotted against frequency over seven logarithmic decades. The results illustrate, in the first place, that for glassy polymers shear and elongation do not give equivalent information, as emphasized in Chapter 7; unlike the situation for the softer systems described in the preceding two chapters, elongation includes a perceptible volume change. With increasing frequency both G' and E' undergo gradual

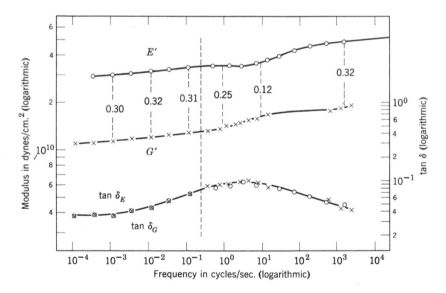

FIG. 14–2. Storage moduli in shear and extension, and loss tangents, of polymethyl methacrylate near 25°C., plotted logarithmically against frequency. The numbers between E' and G' denote values of Poisson's ratio. (After Koppelmann.[10])

increases of the order of 50%, but the inflection in the former lies at a lower frequency by about one power of ten. However, the loss tangents appear within experimental error to be identical, although in principle some difference would be expected from the non-equivalence of G' and E'. The maximum in tan δ is of the order of 0.1, somewhat higher than that appearing in Fig. 14–1 for the same polymer; the discrepancy probably represents a difference between the two samples investigated. The location of the maximum on the frequency scale (about 1 cycle/sec. near room temperature) is in approximate agreement, however, and has been confirmed by various other investigators.[11–14] The shift in position on the frequency scale with temperature [11–14] corresponds to an apparent activation energy variously estimated between 20 and 30 kcal. This mechanism, being the first secondary maximum in tan δ (as the temperature is decreased below T_g, or the frequency is increased at a given temperature near T_g) is often designated the β mechanism following the terminology of Hoff.[11]

In principle, the frequency dependence of the complex bulk modulus could be obtained from the data for E', E'', G', and G''. In Fig. 14–2, the shear and extension data have been combined to calculate Poisson's ratio μ as a function of frequency. The values indicated show that μ passes through a minimum between the inflections in the dispersion of G' and of E'.

Although the data of Fig. 14–2 have not been used to calculate relaxation and retardation spectra, it is clear from the very gradual frequency dependence of the moduli and tan δ that the spectra are relatively flat over a wide range of frequency scale, as already illustrated as Curves IV in Figs. 3–3 and 3–4 for this same polymer in the glassy state. The latter were derived from shear creep data of Iwayanagi,[15] confirmed by comparison with similar data of Lethersich.[16]

The shape of the retardation spectrum for the mechanism in polymethyl methacrylate [15,16] can now be compared with those of two other homologs, the ethyl and n-butyl polymers, derived from the analysis of dynamic data somewhat above T_g, in which the α and β mechanisms can be separated and resolved by their different temperature dependences [17,18] (Chapter 11, Section D). The three spectra are plotted in Fig. 14–3 with an arbitrary logarithmic time scale, and there is evidently a considerable sharpening with increasing side group length. However, as Hideshima [19] has pointed out, the curve for the methyl polymer may not be directly comparable with the others, having been determined *below* T_g. The apparent activation energies gov-

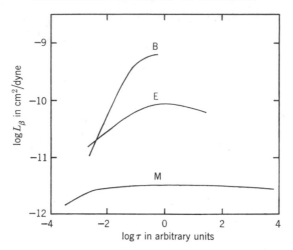

FIG. 14–3. Retardation spectrum of the β mechanism in three methacrylate polymers.[18] B, n-butyl; E, ethyl; M, methyl.

erning the temperature dependence of the retardation times in the ethyl and butyl polymers are 31 and 24 kcal., respectively.

A still sharper secondary mechanism is evidenced in dynamic measurements on polycyclohexylmethacrylate by Hoff[11] and Heijboer.[14] For these, it is necessary to revert to the loss tangent as a means of description. In Fig. 14–4, tan δ as measured by Heijboer at several different frequencies and temperatures has been reduced to a reference temperature of $-60°$ by values of a_T calculated from the Arrhenius relation (equation 42 of Chapter 11) with $\Delta H_a = 11.2$ kcal., and plotted against the logarithm of the reduced frequency. Here measurements in both shear (torsion) and extension (flexure) are combined in the same graph; where the reduced values overlap, they coincide as does tan δ in shear and extension in Fig. 14–2. Values for the moduli were not reported.

Although the retardation spectrum cannot be calculated from measurements of the loss tangent alone, the experimental curve can be compared with one predicted for tan δ on the basis of a single retardation time (one Voigt element in series with a spring, the constants adjusted to give the same maximum value of tan δ and the corresponding frequency). The single-valued spectrum gives a peak only moderately sharper than that observed, in contrast to the very broad maximum in polymethyl methacrylate, also drawn in Fig. 14–4 for comparison.

For the cyclohexyl methacrylate, a very specific internal molecular motion has been postulated [14] to account for the secondary viscoelastic mechanism: the flipping of the cyclohexane ring between two isomeric chair forms, differing in their orientation with respect to attachment to the polymer chain, and separated by an intermediate configuration representing an energy barrier. This interpretation appears to be consistent with the magnitude of the apparent activation energy as well as the fact that the position on the frequency scale is the same for other polymers and copolymers containing the cyclohexyl group and even for a plasticized polymer in which the cyclohexyl is in the plasticizer.

For the other methacrylates, the molecular motion responsible for the β mechanism is less precisely envisioned. It is generally considered [11,14] to involve rotation of the CH_3—O—$\overset{|}{C}$=O groups between positions of relative stability over an energy barrier representing steric restrictions imposed by the methyl groups on the same chain atoms.

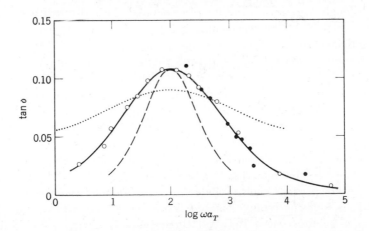

FIG. 14–4. Loss tangent for secondary relaxation mechanism in polycyclohexylmethacrylate, reduced to −60°C. from data of Heijboer [14] measured from −90° to −42°. Open circles, from torsion (G''/G'); closed circles, from flexure (E''/E'). Dashed line is prediction from a single-line retardation spectrum with constants adjusted to make the maximum coincide; dotted line, loss tangent of polymethyl methacrylate from Fig. 14–2 adjusted to same location of maximum on frequency scale.

Studies with copolymers of varying composition [14] show that removal of the steric hindrance by substituting acrylate for methacrylate causes the loss mechanism to disappear; so does substitution of a bulky rigid ester group for the methyl ester, by preventing rotation (such as the cyclohexyl ester, whose own special mechanism attributed to ring flipping occurs at much lower temperatures and/or higher frequencies). On the other hand, substitution of a larger *flexible* ester group causes the mechanism to shift to higher frequencies with the sharpening apparent in Fig. 14–3.

Rotation of the carboxyl unit must involve some local cooperation of surrounding chain backbones in the immediate neighborhood, small adjustments being possible even though the chains are immobilized with respect to convolutional rearrangements. It is probably this cooperation which causes the spectra and the tan δ maximum of polymethyl methacrylate to be so flat. Longer flexible ester groups, such as *n*-butyl, would shield the carboxyl unit from getting enmeshed with neighboring chains, and facilitate its rotation, thus both sharpening the response and shifting it to higher frequencies as observed. Obviously this discussion must remain quite vague, however, until the details of the packing geometry can be specified.

Although the steric hindrance associated with disubstituted chain atoms appears to be responsible for the β mechanism characteristic of methacrylates, secondary loss mechanisms are observed in polymers with monosubstituted chains as well, though usually at higher frequencies and/or lower temperatures, and with somewhat smaller maxima in tan δ, not exceeding perhaps 0.03. These presumably also represent some kind of local motion involving adjustments of the side groups, but its nature is even more vaguely postulated.

Beyond the β mechanism, at still lower temperatures and/or higher frequencies, many polymers reveal additional loss mechanisms represented by shallow maxima in tan δ, sometimes designated by successive letters of the Greek alphabet.[11,13,20] None of these mechanisms has been sufficiently investigated, however, to determine isothermal viscoelastic functions. Between them there is always some residual background loss (tan δ, H, and L never vanish).

In some cases identification of secondary viscoelastic mechanisms and their interpretation in terms of molecular motion can be facilitated by analysis of dielectric dispersion, when the dipole motion responsible for the latter involves rotation of side groups [21–24] (*not* primarily rearrangements of the chain backbone, as in the cases where the temperature dependence of dielectric relaxation times can be described by the WLF equation, mentioned in

Chapter 11). For example, in several members of the methacrylate series, the apparent activation energies for dielectric relaxation times and for the mechanical relaxation times in the β mechanism are approximately the same.[25] The shapes of the respective spectra also change somewhat similarly with increasing side group length, though the dielectric relaxation spectrum always lies at shorter times than the mechanical retardation spectrum. Parallels between time-dependent mechanical and dielectric properties must be drawn with caution, however.[25, 26] The same is true for parallels with nuclear magnetic resonance data; these measure a sort of molecular mobility [27] which may not necessarily be the same as that reflected in mechanical properties.

2. Isochronal or Quasi-Isochronal Viscoelastic Measurements

Because of the greater ease of experimental measurements, there have been far more studies of dynamic viscoelastic properties of glassy polymers where the temperature has been varied at approximately constant frequency, as discussed for polymers in the transition zone in Chapter 12, Section A. For example, Fig. 12–3 with data of Schmieder and Wolf [13] on certain polyvinyl ethers includes measurements of G' and tan δ in shear below the glass transition temperature, and secondary mechanisms are apparent in the small maxima in tan δ near $-150°$ as well as the corresponding negative slopes of G' in this region. Some other examples are given in Fig. 14–5 from data of Hoff [11] in extension (flexure) on many methacrylates and α-chloroacrylates. Here the loss is represented by the relative response width $\Delta\omega/\omega_0$, approximately proportional to tan δ (equation 13 of Chapter 6).

The inflections in the modulus and the maxima in tan δ are much less sharp than those occurring in the transition region as exemplified in Fig. 12–3, because both the dependence of modulus on reduced frequency and the dependence of reduced frequency on temperature (*cf.* equation 43 of Chapter 11) are considerably less. However, an approximate specification of the temperature corresponding to the location of the secondary mechanism at a given frequency can be made. A compilation of such temperatures has been made by Woodward and Sauer,[20] and from them some generalizations can be drawn.

In the methacrylate and α-chloroacrylate series,[11] the β mechanism (*cf.* Figs. 14–2 and 14–3) shifts to lower temperatures with increasing side group length, but is overtaken by the still more rapidly shifting α mechanism or primary transition zone, so that it is submerged and can only be identified by an analysis such as described in Chapter 11, Section D. For example, it cannot be seen in Fig. 14–5a. The temperature location is somewhat higher for the α-chloroacrylates than for the corresponding methacrylates. Certain members of these series have an additional mechanism (identified by Hoff [11] as γ) at about $-150°$ for frequencies of the order of 1 to 5×10^2 cycles/sec., the location being independent of structure. It apparently occurs only when the ester group has at least 3 carbon atoms in a flexible chain; e.g., it appears in each of the examples in Fig. 14–5 except (b), in which the isopropyl group does not meet the requirements. It is

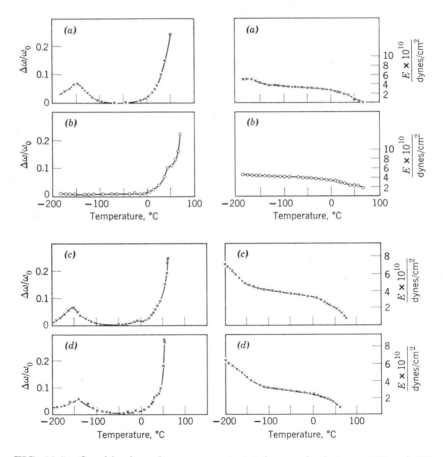

FIG. 14–5. Quasi-isochronal measurements (at frequencies between 100 and 500 cycles/sec.) of the storage modulus and relative response curve width in extension. (a) poly-n-propyl methacrylate; (b) polyisopropyl methacrylate; (c) poly-n-propyl α-chloroacrylate; (d) poly-n-butyl α-chloroacrylate. (After Hoff, Robinson, and Willbourn.[11])

attributed to some kind of internal rearrangement of the hydrocarbon chain.

In the acrylate series, secondary maxima appear at 213°, 223°, and 193°K. respectively for the methyl, ethyl, and n-butyl polymers near 1 cycle/sec.[13] In the polyvinyl ether series, maxima appear at 113° and 123° for the propyl and n-butyl polymers near 5 cycles/sec., with suggestions of additional maxima at 200°K. for these and the ethyl polymer.[13] There seems to be no obvious correlation with the side group length. Secondary mechanisms also appear in polyvinyl acetate,[22] and accurate measurements reveal them in polystyrene [28, 29] and its p-bromo and p-chloro derivatives.[29] The conditions for presence of the γ mechanism have led Illers and Jenckel [29] to postulate that it involves a rearrangement of two or more adjacent CH_2 groups in either backbone or side chain. The presence of a γ mechanism in polystyrene and its derivatives (with an extremely small magnitude) is attributed to occasional juxtaposition of CH_2 groups by head-to-head orientation during polymerization.

C. NON-LINEAR BEHAVIOR OF GLASSY POLYMERS

The preceding sections have of course dealt with deformations under small stresses, where the viscoelastic behavior is linear. For glassy polymers, which with their high moduli can support substantial stresses, non-linear phenomena can be encountered even when the strains are relatively small. The subject of non-linearity requires an entirely different treatment, therefore, from that in the rubbery zone (Chapter 13, Section D), where deviations from Hooke's law are associated with high strains rather than high stresses. Experimental measurements are, unfortunately, rather sparse.

1. Stress Dependence of Viscoelastic Properties

In tensile creep of glassy polystyrene under high stresses, of the order of 10^8 dynes/cm², the rate of deformation at a given time after loading increases with something like the fourth power of the applied stress, instead of being directly proportional.[30] Similar non-linear stress dependence for shear creep of polymethyl methacrylate below T_g was found by Lethersich,[31] and the creep and creep recovery functions were very different in shape, even though the total deformation (of the order of 5%) was fully recoverable.

In dynamic longitudinal deformations in a similar range of applied stresses, at low audio frequencies, polystyrene was found by Sauer and collaborators [30] to exhibit an energy dissipation per cycle which increased rapidly with the amplitude of vibration.

Non-linear phenomena such as these have been discussed in terms of transition-state kinetics by Schwarzl.[32] A substantial asymmetry of a potential barrier to molecular motions, imposed by high external stress, leads to a shift of the viscoelastic time scale to shorter times as well as a broadening of the retardation spectrum. The non-linear behavior of fibers in transient loading experiments has been interpreted in this way by Eyring and collaborators.[33] It may be noted that high tensile stresses, unlike high shear stresses, may invoke an additional effect: the volume expansion under tension, occasioned by a Poisson's ratio substantially smaller than $\frac{1}{2}$, can increase the free volume and thus shorten all retardation and relaxation times by analogy with equation 31 or equation 38 of Chapter 11. If this effect predominated, it would shift the logarithmic time scale of the spectra *without* changing their shapes.[34] Some examples of such behavior have been described, but usually for crystalline polymers (Chapter 15, Section E).

2. Anisotropic Systems

Time-dependent mechanical deformations at small amplitudes can easily be superimposed on large static deformations in glassy polymers without maintaining static stresses, since the static deformations are frozen in after orienting or drawing. However, there appear to be very few direct measurements of time-dependent mechanical properties of highly oriented amorphous polymers in the glassy state.[35] Högberg [36] has studied periodic flexural deformations of polymers oriented by injection molding, and found somewhat higher moduli when the orientation was in the longitudinal direction (parallel to the bar length). That secondary loss mechanisms are affected by orientation is indicated by dielectric loss measurements on polystyrene and polyvinyl chloride.[37]

REFERENCES

1. W. P. Mason, W. O. Baker, H. J. McSkimin, and J. H. Heiss, *Phys. Rev.,* **75**, 936 (1949).

THE GLASSY STATE 319

2. T. A. Litovitz and R. A. Piccirelli, *J. Acoust. Soc. Amer.*, **29**, 1009 (1957).
3. A. J. Barlow and J. Lamb, *Proc. Roy. Soc.*, **A253**, 52 (1959).
4. J. J. Benbow, *Proc. Phys. Soc.*, **B67**, 120 (1954).
5. J. J. Benbow and D. J. C. Wood, *Trans. Faraday Soc.*, **54**, 1581 (1958).
6. C. P. Smyth, *J. Phys. Chem.*, **58**, 580 (1954).
7. J. R. McLoughlin and A. V. Tobolsky, *J. Colloid Sci.*, **7**, 555 (1952).
8. J. R. McLoughlin and A. V. Tobolsky, *J. Polymer Sci.*, **7**, 658 (1951).
9. A. Kovacs, Sc.D. Thesis, University of Paris, 1955.
10. J. Koppelmann, *Rheol. Acta*, **1**, 20 (1958).
11. E. A. W. Hoff, D. W. Robinson, and A. H. Willbourn, *J. Polymer Sci.*, **18**, 161 (1955).
12. S. Iwayanagi and T. Hideshima, *J. Phys. Soc. Japan*, **8**, 368 (1953).
13. K. Schmieder and K. Wolf, *Kolloid-Z.*, **134**, 149 (1953).
14. J. Heijboer, *Kolloid-Z.*, **148**, 36 (1956).
15. K. Sato, H. Nakane, T. Hideshima, and S. Iwayanagi, *J. Phys. Soc. Japan*, **9**, 413 (1954).
16. W. Lethersich, *Brit. J. Applied Phys.*, **1**, 294 (1950).
17. J. D. Ferry, W. C. Child, Jr., R. Zand, D. M. Stern, M. L. Williams, and R. F. Landel, *J. Colloid Sci.*, **12**, 53 (1957).
18. W. C. Child, Jr., and J. D. Ferry, *J. Colloid Sci.*, **12**, 327 (1957).
19. T. Hideshima, *Repts. Prog. Polymer Phys. Japan*, **2**, 53 (1959).
20. A. E. Woodward and J. A. Sauer, *Fortschr. Hochpolym. Forschung*, **1**, 114 (1958).
21. K. Deutsch, E. A. W. Hoff, and W. Reddish, *J. Polymer Sci.*, **13**, 565 (1954).
22. H. Thurn and K. Wolf, *Kolloid-Z.*, **148**, 16 (1956).
23. H. Thurn and F. Würstlin, *Kolloid-Z.*, **156**, 21 (1958).
24. H. Hendus, G. Schnell, H. Thurn, and K. Wolf, *Erg. d. exakt. Naturwiss.*, **31**, 220 (1959).
25. J. D. Ferry and S. Strella, *J. Colloid Sci.*, **13**, 459 (1958).
26. J. D. Ferry and E. R. Fitzgerald, *J. Colloid Sci.*, **8**, 224 (1953).
27. W. P. Slichter, *Fortschr. Hochpolym. Forschung*, **1**, 1 (1958).
28. K. Yamamoto and Y. Wada, *J. Phys. Soc. Japan*, **12**, 374 (1957).
29. K. H. Illers and E. Jenckel, *J. Polymer Sci.*, **41**, 528 (1959).
30. J. A. Sauer, J. Marin, and C. C. Hsiao, *J. Applied Phys.*, **20**, 507 (1949).
31. W. Lethersich, *Proc. XI Congr. Pure and Applied Chem.*, London, **5**, 591 (1947).
32. F. Schwarzl, *Kolloid-Z.*, **165**, 88 (1959).
33. G. Halsey, H. J. White, Jr., and H. Eyring, *Text. Res. J.*, **15**, 295 (1945); C. H. Reichardt and H. Eyring, *ibid.*, **16**, 635 (1946).
34. J. D. Ferry and R. A. Stratton, *Kolloid-Z.*, **171**, 107 (1960).
35. H. Thurn, *Kolloid-Z.*, **165**, 57 (1959).
36. H. Högberg, *Symposium on Plastics Testing and Standardization*, Am. Soc. Testing Matls. Special Technical Publication, No. 247, 1958, p. 95.
37. K. Huff and F. H. Müller, *Kolloid-Z.*, **153**, 5 (1957).

CHAPTER 15

Crystalline and Filled Polymers

When the local structure along a polymer chain has enough regularity and symmetry to permit ordering in a crystal lattice, a decrease in temperature results in a partially crystallized system instead of an amorphous glass such as those described in the preceding chapter. The imperfect character of the crystallinity has usually been described[1] in terms of perfectly ordered regions (crystallites) which are small compared with the molecular contour length, so each molecule may thread itself in and out of several crystallites, with segments in between where its configuration resembles that in the amorphous state. Recent evidence, however,[2,3] indicates the presence of a lattice which is continuous over much larger distances but contains regions of substantial imperfection and disorder occasioned by the difficulty of articulation and packing of the polymer chains. In some lattices, chains appear to be folded back and forth to form lamellae of the order of 100 Å in thickness.

When the temperature is lowered, the crystalline order becomes more nearly perfect, usually described as an increase in the degree of crystallinity, but it can hardly be expected that complete order can be achieved, since the steric restraints imposed on the remaining segments prevent the necessary alignment. Even before the degree of crystallinity attains anything like perfection, the amorphous or disordered regions may undergo a glass transition (often at about $\frac{2}{3}$ the melting point of the most stable crystallites, on the absolute scale[4]) so that below that point the entire structure is immobilized. Besides the structural features of the order of 100 Å in dimensions represented by lamellae (or, in the older interpretation, by the crystallites), there are features discernible with a microscope or even visually: patterns (spherulites) which reflect the mechanism of their nucleation and growth. The subject of micro- and macrostructure of crystalline polymers, which is beyond the scope of this book, is treated in detail in various monographs.[1-5]

A crystalline polymer was included among the characteristic types whose viscoelastic properties were surveyed in Chapter 2, but little was said about the interpretation of its behavior, which is more obscure than that of any of the others. A polymer with a substantial degree of crystallinity differs from those discussed in previous chapters in two important respects. First, the "amorphous" or disordered segments are much too short to conform to the assumption of a Gaussian distribution of chain configurations, on which the flexible chain theories of viscoelastic behavior are based. Second, a large proportion of the volume is occupied by masses which are relatively rigid and immobile.

It is difficult to investigate the effects of these characteristic features directly, since the degree of crystallinity and the length of the strands of the densely netted cross-linked network which the system comprises cannot be controlled independently of temperature and chemical composition; they are consequences of the thermodynamics and kinetics of the crystallization process.[5] However, the short network strands are also present in certain artificially cross-linked polymers whose cross-linking density is much higher than in the vulcanized rubbers mentioned in Chapters 12 and 13. Also, rigid, immobile particulate masses are present in polymers which have been filled (mixed with solid particles) for technological reasons. Hence examination of these latter types of systems can potentially aid in interpreting the properties of crystalline polymers, as pointed out by Landel.[6] All three types are discussed together in the present chapter.

A. THE TRANSITION ZONE FROM FLEXIBLE TO GLASSLIKE CONSISTENCY AND THE PSEUDO-EQUILIBRIUM ZONE

In a sense, most of the systems treated in this chapter do not possess a zone of rubberlike behavior, because the minimum shear modulus is of the order of 10^8 dynes/cm^2 or more, representing a flexible, leathery rather than a rubbery consistency. Nevertheless, there is a transition from that rather high level up to the magnitude of 10^{10} or more characteristic of a glass as the frequency is increased or the time decreased, which is analogous to the rubberlike to glasslike transition in ordinary amorphous polymers. This transition represents the disappearance of mobility, within the experimental time scale, of the short strands of a densely netted system.

1. Densely Cross-Linked Polymers

There have been several investigations of the isothermal viscoelastic functions of polymers highly cross-linked by chemical means, such as hard rubber [7,8] and polyesters,[7,9] where the pseudo-equilibrium shear modulus is in the range of 4×10^7 at sufficiently high temperatures and low frequencies. This level is hardly high enough to represent an extreme departure from the more loosely cross-linked vulcanized rubbers mentioned in previous chapters. However, much higher degrees of cross-linking can be obtained by high-energy radiation.[10]

In polyethylene thus treated, the pseudo-equilibrium shear modulus can have a value [11] as high as 5×10^8 and still show the approximate proportionality to T which is required by the statistical theory of rubberlike elasticity. This would correspond, according to the statistical theory, to an average molecular weight between cross-links of the order of 60, or only about 4 chain atoms. With such short strands, there can certainly be no Gaussian distribution of chain configurations, so the calculation of strand length is meaningless; yet the proportionality of modulus to absolute temperature indicates that the elasticity is nevertheless of the nature of an entropy spring. Measurements on such systems appear to have been limited to isochronal studies, and the viscoelastic functions have not been determined. But it cannot be expected that the relaxation spectrum, for example, would conform anywhere to the theoretical slope of $-\frac{1}{2}$ specified by the usual flexible chain theories, nor that the local mobility could be described by the usual monomeric friction coefficient. At still higher degrees of cross-linking by radiation, the modulus is of the order of 10^{10} even at temperatures as high as 500°K. and relatively low frequencies.[11]

In these measurements on such densely cross-linked polyethylenes, there is no complication from crystalline structure; the measurements are made well above the maximum crystallite melting point, and in any case the steric restrictions of the cross-linking presumably interfere with crystallization.

2. Filled or Loaded Polymers

For a particulate filler which does not interact strongly with the polymer, the principal effects arise from the partial occupancy of volume by rigid and immobile masses. Extensive studies by Landel [6,12] on polyisobutylene loaded with glass beads of the order of 0.004 cm in diameter have revealed the changes in the isothermal viscoelastic functions. In this case the particles are large enough so that the average distances between them even at the highest loading considered are large compared with the root-mean-square end-to-end separation of the polymer molecules; the latter maintain their Gaussian distributions. Moreover, the particles are too far apart to be bridged by single molecules.

The temperature dependence of relaxation and retardation times in these loaded systems could be described by the WLF equation in the form of equation 36 of Chapter 11, with the value of T_s elevated slightly over that of pure polyisobutylene. Here, T_s varied roughly linearly with the volume fraction (ϕ) occupied by filler; for $\phi = 0.37$, T_s was $7°$ higher than for the unloaded polymer. For each individual filled sample, the method of reduced variables could be applied to obtain single composite curves for the viscoelastic functions plotted against reduced frequency or time. The applicability of reduced variables was also apparent in earlier work on filled rubberlike polymers by Becker and Oberst [7] and Blatz.[13]

When the samples with different degrees of loading are compared in corresponding temperature states (*i.e.*, 298°K. for the unloaded polymer, $298° + \Delta T_s$ for each of the loaded samples), the retardation and relaxation spectra fall rather closely together at short times up to a filler volume fraction of 0.2, as illustrated in Fig. 15–1. At higher loading, H is elevated and L is depressed throughout; and at longer times the maximum in L is depressed progressively with increasing volume fraction of filler. The last effect does not correspond to a change in entanglement coupling as pictured in Fig. 13–4 (*cf.* also Fig. 16–9), because the position of the maximum does not shift correspondingly along the time scale. However, the level of L_{max} is approximately proportional to the pseudo-equilibrium compliance obtained from the inflection in a creep curve, this ratio being about 0.20 for all the compositions.

The pseudo-equilibrium compliance, in turn, can be described rather well by an equation similar to one proposed by Eilers: [14]

$$J_0/J = 1 + k\phi/(1 - S'\phi)^2 \qquad (1)$$

where J is the compliance of a composition with volume fraction of filler ϕ, and J_0 that of the unfilled polymer; $k = 5/4$ and $1/S' = 0.80$. The latter parameter has the significance of the volume fraction occupied by the filler particles when close packed; it is greater than that for close-packed spheres (0.74) presumably because of some degree of size heterogeneity.   Equation 1 appears to hold for data

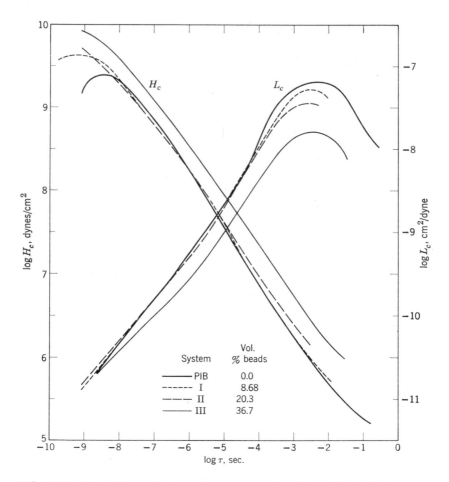

FIG. 15-1.   Relaxation and retardation spectra plotted logarithmically for polyisobutylene and 3 compositions loaded with glass beads, with volume fractions as indicated, reduced to corresponding temperature states (equal values of $T - T_s$).   (Landel.[6])

on several filled polymer systems,[13] including polyurethane rubbers.[15] The drop in compliance (increase in modulus) is analogous to the increase in viscosity caused by suspending rigid spherical particles in a liquid medium.[14, 16]

In a rubber loaded with finely divided carbon black, the behavior is somewhat different. There is good evidence that the polymer molecules are attached to the filler particles by strong forces approaching the nature of chemical bonds.[17, 18] Moreover, in a compound containing 50% by weight of particles of the order of 300 Å in diameter, the interparticle separations are of the order of 100 Å, which is similar to the average vector distance between cross-links in a lightly crosslinked rubber vulcanizate. Hence each filler particle may be bridged to others by many polymer chains, and it acts as a multiple cross-link as well as a rigid occupier of space. (Agglomeration of the particles may also complicate the picture.) The effect on the transition from rubberlike to glasslike consistency is illustrated by data of Payne[8] on a carbon-filled rubber vulcanizate in Fig. 15–2, compared with those for an unfilled vulcanizate which appeared in Figs. 12–7 and 13–2. The filler flattens both relaxation and retardation spectra. The former does not attain a slope of $-\frac{1}{2}$ on the doubly logarithmic plot in the lower region of the transition zone where friction coefficients are usually estimated. Although this slope is reached just to the right of the maximum, the Rouse theory cannot be applied at such short times. At very short times, the relaxation spectrum is essentially unaffected by the filler. The maximum in L is depressed, but almost in proportion to the pseudo-equilibrium modulus J_e; the ratio L_{max}/J_e is 0.115 and 0.10 for the unfilled and filled systems respectively.

In the systems of Fig. 15–2, the level of the pseudo-equilibrium shear modulus was raised by the filler from $10^{6.8}$ to $10^{8.0}$ dynes/cm^2. The subject of the dependence of modulus on the proportion, particle size, and chemical nature of the filler has been widely discussed [17–19] and is beyond the scope of this book. It is evident, however, that it cannot be described in terms of the volume-filling properties alone. The level of the loss modulus in the pseudo-equilibrium zone was raised in Fig. 15–2 from $10^{5.2}$ to $10^{7.0}$ dynes/cm^2, representing a proportionally greater increase; the higher values of tan δ in loaded rubbers in the rubbery zone are well known. The effect of the filler on the temperature dependence of relaxation and retardation times could be described[8] in terms of an increase in T_s of 3° to 5°C. This change, very mild in comparison with the other effects of the filler, is com-

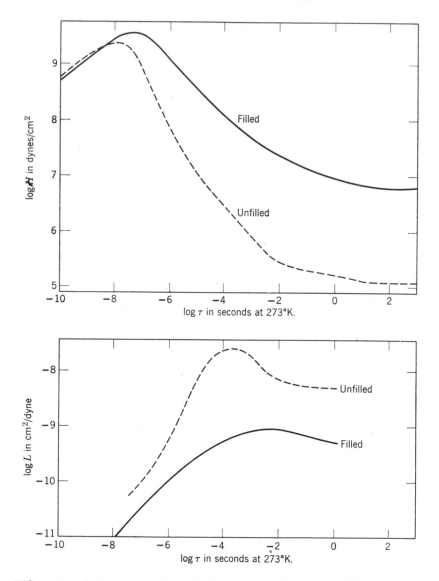

FIG. 15–2. Relaxation and retardation spectra of vulcanized Hevea rubber filled with 50 parts by weight of high-abrasion furnace-type carbon black, calculated from data of Payne,[8] and compared with similar spectra for an unfilled vulcanizate (*cf.* Figs. 12–7 and 13–2), all reduced to 273°K.

parable with that produced by the glass beads in polyisobutylene as discussed above.

If the mid-point of the transition is roughly characterized by the inflection in G' or the maximum in tan δ (the latter corresponding to the characterizations in Table 12–I), the effect of the filler appears as a shift to lower frequencies by about 1.2 logarithmic units. For an isochronal description as in Table 12–II, this would correspond to elevating T_M by about 25°. Since T_s, and presumably T_g, is increased by only 5°, the separation between T_g and T_M is enhanced by the filler.

Similar data for GR-S rubbers with different degrees of loading have been recently reported by Payne.[20]

3. Highly Crystalline Polymers: Viscoelastic Functions

For a highly crystallized polymer, there may be an interval between the glass transition temperature of the amorphous regions and the minimum temperature at which the weakest crystallites begin to melt, within which the structure is relatively stable and measurements of viscoelastic properties can outline the transition from flexible to glasslike consistency. Depending on the degree of crystallinity (which in turn depends on the structural regularity [21] and/or tacticity [22] along the polymer chain—the effects of short-chain branching in polyethylene being a familiar example of the former [21]—as well as the history of quenching and annealing), the level of the shear modulus in the flexible state may be from 10^8 to 10^9 dynes/cm^2, so the transition to a glasslike modulus of the order of 10^{10} is less dramatic than in the soft amorphous polymers treated in Chapter 12.

A useful example is polychlorotrifluoroethylene, since its glass transition temperature has been determined [23] as 52°C. and the temperature at which its degree of crystallinity begins to change [23] as in the neighborhood of 130°. From the latter temperature up to the final melting point of 216°, there is a progressive change in structure. But from 52° to 130° the polymer might be considered as a fairly stable, densely cross-linked, loaded system. Its stress relaxation has been studied by Tobolsky and McLoughlin [24] and Nagamatsu and Yoshitomi.[25]

The relaxation modulus in shear, from measurements of torsion,[25] is plotted logarithmically at various temperatures in Fig. 15–3. At temperatures above T_g, the modulus relaxes with time from $10^{9.5}$ to $10^{8.9}$ dynes/cm^2, and the curves can be accurately superposed by the

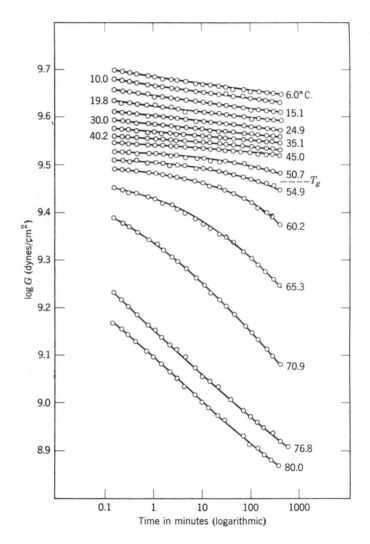

FIG. 15–3. Relaxation modulus in shear plotted logarithmically against time at various temperatures for polychlorotrifluoroethylene (Nagamatsu and Yoshitomi [25]). The glass transition temperature is near 52°C.

method of reduced variables. The temperature dependence of the factor a_T in this region is approximately represented by the Arrhenius form with an apparent activation energy of the order of 180 kcal. Although the temperature range is too small to attempt to distinguish between the merits of the Arrhenius and WLF equations here, it is significant that ΔH_a at $T_g = 325°K$. is predicted by equation 30 of Chapter 11 to be 165 kcal. Thus, as in the filled or loaded systems, the WLF equation appears to be applicable. At temperatures below T_g, at the top of Fig. 15–3, there is much less relaxation (*cf.* Section B below).

Even above T_g, the changes in modulus are of course far less than those occurring in the transition zone in amorphous polymers. When the relaxation spectrum is calculated from the composite curve for $G(t)$ reduced to 80°C., a very broad maximum is obtained, and the level of the spectrum is of the order of 10^8 dynes/cm² (Fig. 15–4).

Similar results have been obtained for polytetrafluoroethylene [26] and polyethylene [27,28] with different degrees of crystallinity. For the latter, the temperature dependence of the factor a_T follows the Arrhenius form over the temperature range where the degree of crystallinity changes very little from its maximum value. The apparent activation energy is about 37 kcal./mole in both "Marlex 50" with a maximum crystallinity of about 80% and "DYNH" with a maximum of about 40%. The relaxation spectra calculated from such measurements are all very broad and flat, revealing little structure unless the scale of ordinates is greatly expanded. It is, of course, im-

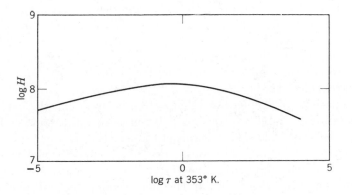

FIG. 15–4. Relaxation spectrum of polychlorotrifluoroethylene from the data of Fig. 15–3 above T_g, reduced to 353°K.

possible to calculate any friction coefficients to compare with those characterizing the rubberlike to glasslike transition in amorphous polymers, and it is difficult to find any basis for comparisons of the position of the transition on the time or frequency scale.

4. Highly Crystalline Polymers: Isochronal Viscoelastic Measurements

As usual, more data are available for the temperature dependence of mechanical properties measured at approximately constant frequency than for the isothermal frequency or time dependence from which viscoelastic functions can be calculated. The transition in polychlorotrifluoroethylene which is portrayed on the time scale in Fig. 15–3 appears on the temperature scale in Fig. 15–5, where G' and tan δ are plotted from measurements at approximately 3 cycles/sec. by Schmieder and Wolf.[29] The temperature of the mid-point of the transition can be roughly specified by the inflection in G' (not the point where $G' = 10^8$ dynes/cm^2 as in Chapter 12) or the maximum in tan δ, as about 104°C.—*viz.*, 52° above T_g. The secondary dispersions will be discussed in the following section. The figure also includes a similar transition for polyvinyl fluoride, at 41°C. at about 2 cycles/sec.

Such transition mid-point temperatures have been reported for numerous crystalline polymers,[29-34] and some are summarized in Table 15–I, many taken from a review by Woodward and Sauer.[30] The distinction between this primary transition and secondary loss mechanisms such as those discussed in Chapter 14 and in Section B below is much less obvious, however, than in amorphous polymers, and the identification may not always be certain. If the temperature happens to fall in the region where the degree of crystallinity is sensitive to temperature, complications will appear. In any case, the results are likely to be profoundly influenced by traces of diluent [33] and thermal and mechanical history.[35]

Comparison of Tables 12–II and 13–I shows that the mid-point temperatures for the crystalline polymers are quite high. (It will be recalled that in loaded vulcanized rubber also, the filler raises T_M.) In a very rough qualitative way, this may reflect a relatively high local frictional resistance in crystalline polymers compared to amorphous polymers of similar chemical composition. Probably the mobilities of the segments in amorphous regions are severely affected by the presence of the almost motionless crystalline regions and the

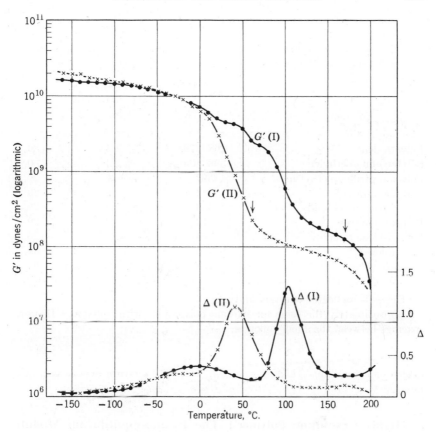

FIG. 15–5. Storage shear modulus and logarithmic decrement (approximately proportional to loss tangent) of polychlorotrifluoroethylene (I) and polyvinyl fluoride (II), plotted against temperature at approximately 3 cycles/sec. (Schmieder and Wolf [29].)

shortness of the strands—some of which are no doubt stretched nearly taut in the process of crystallization—which thread between them; and the local mobilities probably vary widely with degree of disorder.

Polytetrafluoroethylene is unusual in possessing a transition in crystal form near 20°C. and another transition near 30° attributed to random chain motions. These structural modifications are accompanied by marked changes in viscoelastic properties.[26, 30]

Polyethylene with extensive short-chain branching also appears to be a special case because the side groups interfere with crystalline order and the

Table 15–I

TEMPERATURES IDENTIFIED WITH MID-POINTS OF TRANSITION FROM
FLEXIBLE TO GLASSLIKE CONSISTENCY IN CRYSTALLINE POLYMERS

Polymer	T_M, °K.	Freq. of Measurement, cycles/sec.	Ref.
Polyethylene	268–273 [a]	1	30
Polytetrafluoroethylene	393–403 [a]	1	30, 31
Polychlorotrifluoroethylene	397	3	29, 30
Polyvinyl fluoride	314	2	29
Polyvinylidene chloride	353	5	29
Polyacrylonitrile	413	4	29
Polyethylene terephthalate	370	1–6	29, 32
Polyamides [b]	~330	1	30, 33
Polypropylene	253		34

[a] Depends on degree of crystallinity.

[b] Approximately the same for various polyamides with different CH_2-group spacings between the amide linkages.

degree of crystallinity changes gradually with temperature over a very wide range.[36, 37]

5. Highly Crystalline Polymers: The Pseudo-Equilibrium Modulus

The magnitude of the pseudo-equilibrium modulus, reached at long times as in Fig. 15–3, presumably depends on the average molecular weight in the amorphous strands or disordered regions. Since the dimensions of the crystallites or lamellae are of the order of 100 to 200 Å and the crystallites make up a large proportion of the volume, the strands are too short to apply the statistical theory of rubberlike elasticity strictly. However, the results on highly cross-linked (non-crystalline) polyethylene quoted above [11] show that even here the modulus can be proportional to T and has the character of rubberlike elasticity.

Unfortunately, there is no easy way to determine an average strand molecular weight M_c in a crystalline polymer; the magnitude of the modulus can be readily compared only with the degree of crystallinity as gauged by the density.

Experimental information is practically confined to polyethylene, where the degree of crystallinity can be varied by changing either the temperature or the extent of short-chain branching. The effects of these two variables on a quantity similar to the pseudo-equilibrium modulus are shown [36] in Fig. 15–6. Over a considerable range of both variables, the stiffness is a unique function of the density, as previously pointed out by Nielsen.[38]

An approximate theory to relate the modulus to the volume fraction occupied by crystallites has been presented by Bueche.[39] Assuming that the strands threading between the crystallites behave as entropy springs, he evaluates E in terms of the average crystallite length and cross-section area. By applying the theory to data on polyethylene, the latter dimensions can be obtained and turn out to be of the order of 250 Å and 400 Å respectively for samples of high and low short-chain branching respectively—evidently of the correct magnitude.[36]

When viscoelastic measurements are made at different temperatures in a range where the degree of crystallinity is strongly temperature-dependent, the temperature affects the magnitudes of the relaxation

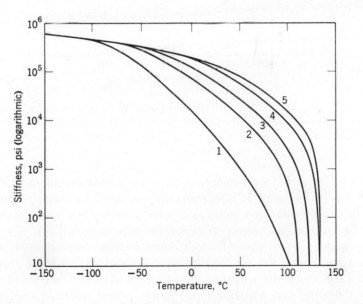

FIG. 15–6. Elastic "stiffness" (100 times stress required to stretch sample 1% at a rate of 10% per min.), plotted against temperature for polyethylenes with the following densities at 25°C.: 1, 0.895; 2, 0.918; 3, 0.935; 4, 0.950; 5, 0.968. The methyl content of sample 1 was 8.7%, that of sample 5 too small to measure.

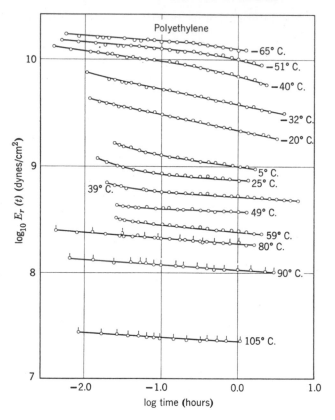

FIG. 15–7. Stress relaxation (in extension) of polyethylene (with high degree of short-chain branching) at various temperatures as indicated (Catsiff, Offenbach, and Tobolsky [40]).

times as usual but even more so the level of the pseudo-equilibrium modulus. The result is illustrated in Fig. 15–7 by measurements of Catsiff, Offenbach, and Tobolsky [40] on polyethylene (presumably of a type with a high degree of short-chain branching). At the lower temperatures, the degree of crystallinity is relatively constant, so the displacements of the curves represent in part at least the shifts of relaxation times and consequent horizontal shift of the transition between flexible and glasslike consistency. Above 5°C., however, the displacements represent primarily vertical shifts due to changes in pseudo-equilibrium modulus, the downward slope reflecting the slow relaxation processes which are discussed in Section D below. Attempts have been made to take the vertical shifts into account with a two-dimensional scheme of reduced variables.[41]

B. THE GLASSY STATE

The effects of crystallites, fillers, or dense cross-links in the glassy state are less obvious than in the flexible and transition zones, but they appear in detailed analyses of secondary viscoelastic mechanisms.

1. Densely Cross-Linked and Filled Polymers

There have been relatively few studies of densely netted [10] and filled [42,43] polymers in the glassy state. The level of the modulus is definitely increased; in polyethylene (at 100° and low audio frequencies) E' is increased from 0.65 to 1.0×10^{11} dynes/cm² by dense radiation-induced cross-linking, and in vulcanized rubber [7] the high-frequency limiting value of G' is increased from 1.0 to 3.0×10^{10} by loading with 50 parts by weight of carbon black. There is little information, however, about the secondary loss mechanisms which are characteristic of the glassy state.

2. Highly Crystalline Polymers

The data in the upper part of Fig. 15–3, corresponding to temperatures below T_g, can also be combined to a single composite curve by the method of reduced variables,[25] using a_T factors whose temperature dependence here follows the Arrhenius form with an apparent activation energy of the order of 125 kcal./mole. The relaxation spectrum calculated from this region is nearly flat, with a level of about $10^{7.7}$ dynes/cm².

The secondary mechanisms which reflect local readjustments, usually of side groups, in glassy amorphous polymers also appear in highly crystalline polymers, where they are attributed to limited local motions of the amorphous strands.

Although information is usually limited to isochronal measurements, one example of reduced isothermal viscoelastic functions over a wide range of frequencies is shown in Fig. 15–8, where tan δ and G'' are plotted against reduced frequency for a polyamide (hexamethylene diamine–decane dicarboxylic acid) with 19% crystallinity containing 1.6% water, from measurements of Illers and Jenckel.[33] The tem-

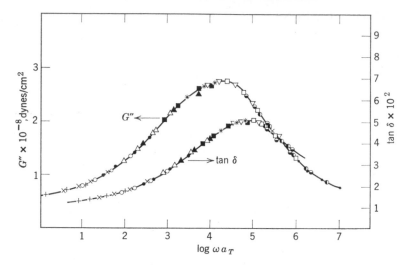

FIG. 15–8. Tan δ and G'' plotted against the logarithm of the frequency reduced to $-40°$C., for the β mechanism of a 6–12 polyamide with 19% crystallinity containing 1.6% water (Illers [33]).

perature and frequency ranges correspond to the first secondary mechanism, accordingly designated as β. The individual temperatures ranged from $-40°$ to $-100°$ and the reduction factor a_T followed the Arrhenius form of temperature dependence with $\Delta H_a = 11$ kcal./mole below $-73°$C. and 22 kcal./mole at higher temperatures. The maximum in G'' is quite broad, being plotted here with a linear scale instead of the usual logarithmic one.

The relaxation spectrum calculated from G'' and G' is plotted logarithmically in Fig. 15–9. Though broad, it is sharper than the spectrum for the β mechanism in polymethyl methacrylate, which is drawn in for comparison. The detailed shape and molecular interpretation of such spectra need much further study.

An isochronal plot of tan δ for the same system, at a frequency of 1 cycle/sec., is shown in Fig. 15–10. Here the maximum of the β mechanism occurs at about $-75°$, as would be predicted from Fig. 15–8 by applying the appropriate temperature reduction. It is notable that the β mechanism can be almost completely eliminated by removing the water, as shown by Curve I in Fig. 15–10. Illers and Jenckel have postulated that it arises from water molecules strongly attached to amide groups by hydrogen bonds, which then act as side groups on the polymer chain. Thus the β mechanism is attributed to motions of such side groups as it is in amorphous polymers with chemically attached side groups (Chapter 14).

Figure 15–10 reveals also another loss mechanism near $-150°$ whose character is very little altered by removal of water. This γ mechanism may be attributed to some kind of local readjustment of adjacent CH_2 groups in the hydrocarbon sequences of the polymer backbone, just as it is in the side groups of certain methacrylates[44] and in the backbone of polystyrene where juxtaposition of CH_2 groups due to head-to-head junctions is postulated[45] (Chapter 14). Willbourn[46] has concluded that four methylene groups bonded at both ends or three if bonded at one end are required for this transition to appear.

Secondary β and γ mechanisms have been observed in many other crystalline polymers by isochronal measurements.[29, 30, 47] For example, in Fig. 15–5, a secondary dispersion for polychlorotrifluoroethylene is seen in both G' and tan δ at about $0°$, and a suggestion of one in polyvinyl fluoride at $-20°$. The former has been studied by several investigators,[23, 48, 49] but no specific interpretation in terms of molecular motions has been proposed.

Polyethylene is an unusually complicated case because of the varying crystallinity associated with different degrees of short-chain branching. Pseudo-isochronal plots of tan δ for three different types[50]

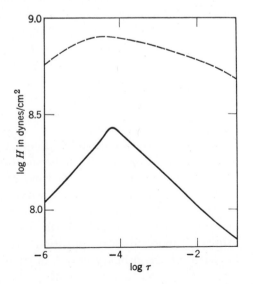

FIG. 15–9. Relaxation spectrum calculated from G'' in Fig. 15–8 and from associated measurements of G' (solid line). Dotted line is the relaxation spectrum of the β mechanism in polymethyl methacrylate, from the data of Fig. 3–3 with an enlarged scale of ordinates, and an arbitrary location on the time scale.

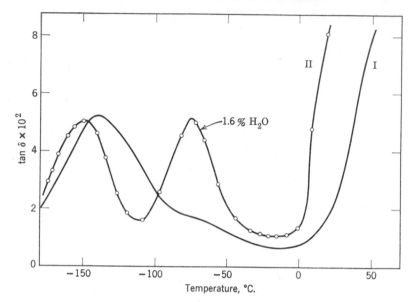

FIG. 15–10. Tan δ at 1 cycle/sec. plotted against temperature for the polymer of Fig. 15–8 (Curve II) and for the same polymer with water removed by melting and slow cooling in vacuum (Curve I). The degree of crystallinity in I was somewhat higher (28%).

are shown in Fig. 15–11. The maximum near 270°K. is believed to be the primary transition from glasslike to rubberlike consistency, because of its close correlation with the branching and consequent degree of crystallinity, and it was so assigned in Table 15–I. The maximum near 160°K. is usually labeled γ because of its similarity in position to the γ mechanism in polyamides (*e.g.*, Fig. 15–10), certain methacrylates (Chapter 14) and other polymers containing CH_2 sequences. It is attributed as usual to rearrangements of adjacent CH_2 groups. The changes in the shape of tan δ in the γ mechanism with crystallinity are obscure. It must be remembered that the magnitude of tan δ, or the area under a peak in tan δ, cannot be taken as a direct measure of the contributions of a certain mechanism to elastic loss; rather, the area under G'' would provide this measure. Figure 15–11 shows that polyethylene also exhibits a loss mechanism at temperatures near 350°K., *above* the one which has been assigned to the primary rubber-to-glass transition. Although this was originally believed to be the primary or α transition,[30] there is evidence that it in-

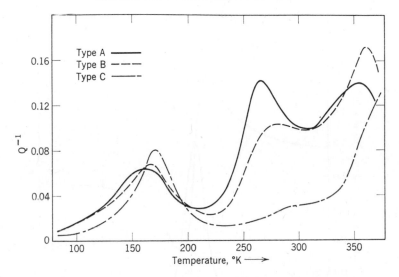

FIG. 15–11. Tan δ at frequencies in the range from about 1200 (at low temperatures) to 200 cycles/sec. (at high temperatures), plotted against temperature for polyethylenes with three degrees of short-chain branching: A, CH_3/CH_2 = 0.032; B, 0.016; C, < 0.001 (Kline, Sauer, and Woodward [50]).

volves motion within the crystallites,[51] or at the crystallite boundaries.[52] The behavior in this region is especially sensitive to thermal and mechanical history.[46,52]

C. RESONANCE DISPERSION

Crystalline polymers,[53,54] as well as polycrystalline solids [55] including metals [56] and some single crystals,[57] have been found by Fitzgerald to exhibit an unusual response to periodic mechanical stress under certain conditions. The frequency dependence of the components of the complex compliance has the characteristics of a resonance dispersion, formally equivalent to resonance absorption in optics.[58] Mechanically, the sample behaves as though the molecular elements possessed inertia as well as elasticity and viscous resistance; its response resembles that of the entire apparatus of a resonance system such as Fig. 6–5. The loss compliance goes through a very sharp maximum on the frequency scale which is much narrower than would be given even by a single retardation time in ordinary viscoelastic

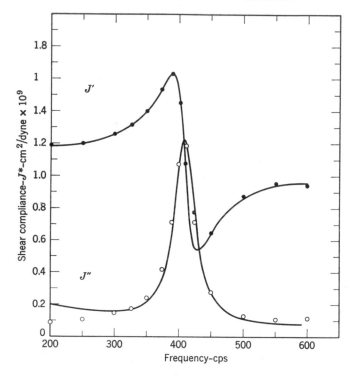

FIG. 15–12. Frequency dependence of the components of the complex compliance of polytetrafluoroethylene at 22.6° near 400 cycles/sec. (After Fitzgerald.[53]) The curves are calculated in accordance with the model of Fig. 15–13.

behavior. At the same time, the storage compliance goes through a maximum and minimum and may even become negative.

The most complete investigation has been made on polytetrafluoroethylene;[53] an example is given in Fig. 15–12. The experimental points are rather well matched by curves calculated from the simple model of Fig. 15–13 with suitable values of the four parameters and an added constant background loss of 0.1×10^{-9} for J''. This model differs from those of the usual phenomenological theory of viscoelasticity by the inclusion of the inertial unit m/l, with dimensions of mass per unit length. It falls completely outside the scope of Chapter 3. The values of G_0 and G are determined by the limiting levels of J' on the two sides of the dispersion; m/l by the resonance frequency; and η by the breadth of the dispersion. The magnitude of

η is reasonable, 10^6 poises. However, that of m/l is too large to be identifiable physically as a real mass per unit length. This result corresponds to the elementary calculation that to produce an audio-frequency resonance with an elastic member of the shape and modulus of the sample, an inertial member with mass considerably greater than that of the sample would be required.

Several resonances of this type have been found in polytetrafluoro-ethylene, as well as in polyethylene (of both low and high degrees of short-chain branching) and polyvinyl stearate.[54] They require measurements at very closely spaced frequencies for recognition. Their locations and magnitudes depend somewhat on temperature and thermal history but much more on stress history, being apparently most prominent after static compression perpendicular to the direction of shear and subsequent release of stress. In addition to the extensive measurements by Fitzgerald, similar phenomena have been reported by other investigators.[59, 60] Illers and Jenckel,[31] employing measurements in torsion, failed to find a resonance reported by Fitzgerald in polytetrafluoroethylene when the conditions of temperature and frequency were duplicated. However, the stress history was undoubtedly different and no static compression was employed. Fitzgerald and Woodward[61] found resonance dispersion in this polymer by the method of flexural vibrations of bars (Chapter 7, Section C), which, like that found in shear deformation, was profoundly affected by additional static stress (in this case tension).

The origin of these resonance dispersion phenomena is at present uncertain. They cannot be accounted for by any of the aspects of molecular behavior discussed in preceding chapters, and they presumably reflect structural features of larger dimensions.

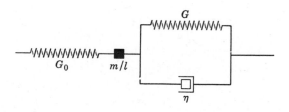

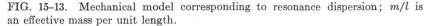

FIG. 15-13. Mechanical model corresponding to resonance dispersion; m/l is an effective mass per unit length.

D. BEHAVIOR AT VERY LONG TIMES

The polycrystalline systems described in this chapter experience relaxation processes extending to indefinitely long times, just as do the more open rubbery networks described in Chapter 13, and strict elastic equilibrium under stress is never attained. In fact, the pseudo-equilibrium modulus is less easily specified in the polycrystalline systems than in rubbery cross-linked systems. In the former, the slow deformation under constant stress (for example) may actually exceed the relatively rapid response attributable to the deformation of the flexible amorphous regions, while in the latter the slow deformation never exceeds a few per cent of the total.

1. Andrade Creep

An example of such slow creep, carried to 12 days, is shown in Fig. 15–14 for a nitrocellulose (essentially trinitrocellulose) at 30°, from measurements of Van Holde.[62] The time dependence of deformation

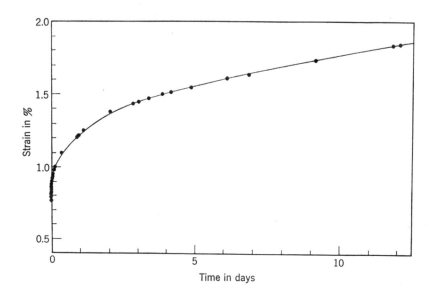

FIG. 15–14. Strain in extension plotted against time for partially crystalline trinitrocellulose at 30°C., under stress of 3.14×10^8 dynes/cm^2.

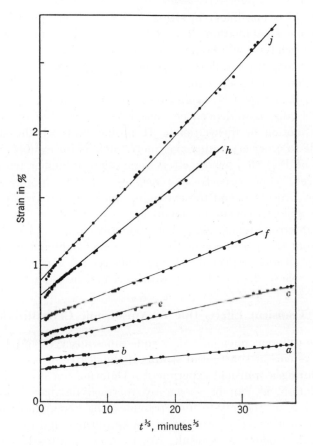

FIG. 15–15.   Andrade plots for creep of nitrocellulose at 30°C. under different tensile stresses, ranging from 0.985×10^8 dynes/cm² (a) to 3.82×10^8 dynes/cm² (j).

in this and many other experiments follows closely the Andrade cube root relation, of the form of equation 10 of Chapter 13, as demonstrated in Fig. 15–15.   Since the viscoelastic behavior is not linear, the creep cannot be formulated in terms of $J(t)$ (or $D(t)$) as in the above-quoted equation, but rather in terms of the tensile strain, $\epsilon(t)$:

$$\epsilon(t) = \epsilon_A + \beta' t^{1/3} \qquad (2)$$

It is found that ϵ_A is directly proportional to stress, so that the "Andrade intercept" compliance is a viscoelastic constant independent of stress, in this case equal to 2.4×10^{-11} dynes/cm². However, the coefficient β' is non-linear in stress, σ, being given approximately by a hyperbolic sine relation, $\beta' = \beta'_0 \sinh \alpha\sigma$. Further comments on non-linear behavior will be made in Section E below.

Creep at long times following the form of equation 2 was found long ago by Filon and Jessop [63] for nitrocellulose plasticized with camphor, and it has been widely recognized in polycrystalline metals.[64] For the latter, the cube root dependence has been interpreted by Mott [65] in terms of motion of dislocations. It is uncertain whether it is also applicable to other crystalline polymers, such as for example the polyethylene of Fig. 15–7 whose stress relaxation at higher temperatures reflects very slow viscoelastic processes. The molecular origin of these slow processes, and the extent of similarity between crystalline polymers and polycrystalline metals, is also uncertain. In polymers, creep and stress relaxation might possibly involve detachment of chains from the periphery of crystallites and subsequent reordering in other positions—especially at temperatures not far below the melting point, where the smaller crystallites would be close to instability.

2. Transient Effects Due to Anisotropic Crystallization

A quite different phenomenon is sometimes observed in partly crystallized systems at substantial strains if the degree of crystallinity increases during a transient experiment. Deformation favors increasing crystallization, as can be shown by thermodynamics,[66] because the prolongation of the crystallites provides the remaining amorphous strands with a wider assortment of configurations and diminishes the forces on their ends. As a result, growth of crystallites during a stress relaxation experiment causes an abnormal decrease of stress whose rate is governed by the crystallization kinetics rather than by viscoelastic properties and can be quite rapid. In fact, after stress relaxation in extension, the sample may elongate spontaneously beyond its initial unstretched length. This process has been investigated in both unvulcanized [67] and vulcanized [68-70] rubbers.

E. ORIENTATION EFFECTS AND NON-LINEAR BEHAVIOR

Departures from linear viscoelastic behavior in crystalline and loaded polymers are more severe, and enter at smaller stresses and strains, than for the amorphous systems described in previous chapters. They have already been encountered in the preceding section in connection with Fig. 15–15. As in Chapter 13, it is convenient to consider first the effects of small time-dependent strains superimposed on large static strains, and then those of finite time-dependent strains.

1. Effects of Orientation

When a polycrystalline polymer is subjected to large strains, as in the drawing of fibers, permanent orientations are produced which persist after removal of the stress. These involve rearrangements of the positions of the crystallites as well as non-random configurations of the strands between the crystallites; a complete description of the anisotropy requires separate specification of the orientations of crystallites and amorphous regions.[71]

The viscoelastic properties of an oriented, anisotropic sample are of course different in different directions. The usual shape chosen for study is a thin strip or fiber oriented by elongation and then subjected to deformations of small amplitude, either by extension (strain in the same direction as the original elongation) or torsion (shear at right angles to the original elongation). In the present discussion, as in Chapter 9, the moduli corresponding to these two deformations will be denoted by E and G respectively, but it must be remembered that these do not have the unique character of the corresponding symbols for isotropic bodies; lateral extension, or shear parallel to the stretch direction, would correspond to quite different moduli.

In the first place, such orientation increases the level of the pseudo-equilibrium modulus in elongation in the stretch direction without greatly affecting the shear modulus at right angles. This effect is illustrated in Fig. 15–16 by dynamic measurements on fibers of polyethylene terephthalate at frequencies in the general range from 100 to 1000 cycles/sec. at 21°C., by Wakelin and associates.[72] For the undrawn fiber, $E'/G' = 2.5$, corresponding to a reasonable value of Poisson's ratio. At high orientation, E' increases by a factor of 7, and E'/G' becomes very large. Equation 2 of Chapter 1, which would give meaningless values of Poisson's ratio, is of course not applicable to these anisotropic systems. Similar increases of E' with orientation have been found in polyamides (e.g.,[72] Nylon 6–6) and polyethylene.[73] They may be due in part to increased degree of crystallinity and in part to the stretching of many of the intercrystalline strands nearly taut in the direction of elongation.

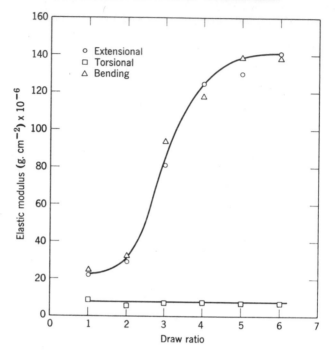

FIG. 15–16. Storage components of Young's modulus in direction of stretch (extensional and bending) and shear modulus perpendicular to that direction (torsional), for polyethylene terephthalate fibers at 21° and at frequencies in the range from 100 to 1000 cycles/sec., plotted against draw ratio.[72]

In Fig. 15–16, the frequency dependence of E', which within a decade of logarithmic time scale is relatively slight, has been ignored. To obtain the effect of orientation on the viscoelastic functions, measurements over a wide range of frequencies are required. An example is provided by the experiments of Tokita [74] on the polyamide Nylon-6 with about 25% crystallinity. Here, by combining a variety of dynamic methods (Chapter 9), E' and E'' were obtained over six logarithmic decades of frequency at a single temperature, 20°C. From the position of the observed maximum in tan δ (about 100 cycles/sec.), bearing in mind that the fibers were equilibrated at 66% relative humidity with a consequent plasticizing effect, it may be inferred that the dispersion reflected primarily the transition from flexible to glass-like consistency; it could not have been the β or γ mechanism seen in Fig. 15–10. The relaxation spectra obtained from these measurements on undrawn fibers and after drawing to 100% elongation are shown in Fig. 15–17. The level of the spectrum is raised somewhat by the orientation, and it is shifted considerably toward longer times. The latter change seems reasonable for rearrangements to give stress release in a direction in which many strands may be already stretched approaching their maximum extensions.

There appear to be no data available on the effect of orientation on the relaxation spectrum in shear at right angles to the direction of stretch. It is conceivable that in this case the relaxation times would be diminished.

An isochronal plot which shows the same type of influence as the isothermal plot of Fig. 15–17 is shown by plotting tan δ as determined for extension by Thompson and Woods [32] for polyethylene terephthalate, undrawn and stretched by drawing (Fig. 15–18). The orientation broadens the maximum and displaces it to higher temperatures, corresponding to the shift to longer times in the preceding figure.

Analogous effects of orientation are sometimes observed in dielectric properties,[75] and can aid in identification and interpretation of the time-dependent mechanical properties, especially where the available information concerning the latter is limited.[35]

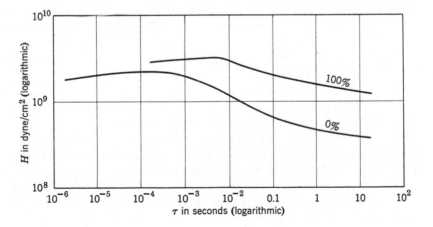

FIG. 15–17. Relaxation spectra in extension of Nylon-6 with about 25% crystallinity at 20°C., undrawn (0%) and drawn (100%). (Data of Tokita.[74])

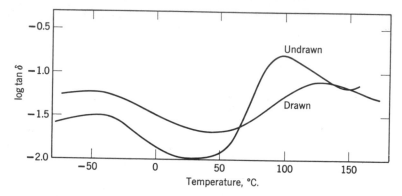

FIG. 15–18. Loss tangent in extension plotted against temperature at about 0.7 cycle/sec. for polyethylene glycol terephthalic acid, undrawn and drawn (conditions of draw not specified). (Thompson and Woods.[32])

2. Finite Dynamic Strains

Whereas in unloaded amorphous polymers, cross-linked or not, dynamic strains of 1% ordinarily fall well within the range of linear viscoelasticity (and the experimental methods described in Chapter 6 provide sensitive tests of such linearity), rubbers loaded with carbon black have viscoelastic properties dependent on amplitude even at much lower strains. For example,[76, 77] G' falls substantially with increasing amplitude, while G'' passes through a slight minimum at very low amplitudes and then rises slightly; as a result, tan δ increases markedly with amplitude.

The results of an investigation carried to extremely low strain,[78] though with measurement only of the absolute Young's modulus $|\mathbf{E}^*|$ rather than its individual components, is shown in Fig. 15–19. Linear viscoelastic behavior is achieved below a strain of 0.1%, and the modulus falls off with increasing amplitude beyond a sort of yield-point strain whose magnitude decreases with increasing proportion of filler. At high strains, the drop in modulus is enormous, and all the compounds appear to approach the unfilled (pure gum) vulcanizate whose modulus is low throughout the amplitude scale.

Strictly, the components E' and E'' cannot be defined in the simple manner outlined in Chapter 1 for a material with non-linear viscoelastic behavior, since the stress and strain cannot both be exactly sinusoidal functions of time. However, $|\mathbf{E}^*|$ is readily defined as the ratio of peak stress to peak strain.

Investigations of the effect of strain history in the systems of Fig. 15–19 showed [78] that the decrease in modulus was of the nature of a thixotropic change; immediately after measurements at high amplitude, low amplitude measurements gave abnormally small values which gradually recovered over a period of time and eventually regained their initial magnitude. This behavior implies the breaking of certain linkages, strained beyond their elastic limits, which can however form again if sufficient time elapses. Contacts between polymer and filler may be involved.[79]

3. Finite Transient Strains

Substantial non-linearity in creep is obvious in Fig. 15–15, and in many other experiments on crystalline polymers and fibers where the

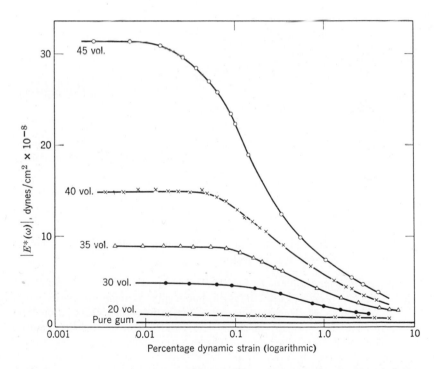

FIG. 15–19. Absolute Young's modulus |E*| plotted against amplitude of sinusoidal strain (with logarithmic scale) at 0.5 cycle/sec., presumably at room temperature, for natural rubber loaded with carbon black at various volumes (per 100 volumes of rubber) as indicated. (After Payne.[78])

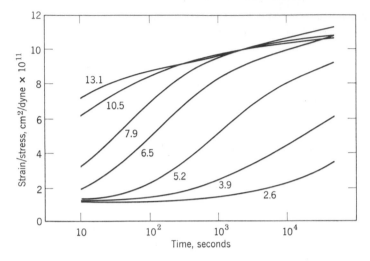

FIG. 15–20. Extensional creep of viscose rayon at 60% relative humidity and 21°C., at various stresses in 10^8 dynes/cm^2 as indicated (O'Shaugnessy,[80] calculated in terms of cgs units by Meredith [81]).

strain/stress ratio as a function of time (which for a linear material in extension would be $D(t)$) depends markedly on the stress. Another example is given in Fig. 15–20, for creep of viscose rayon.[80, 81] The relative disposition of the curves at different stresses could be interpreted as a strong decrease in the magnitude of retardation times with increasing stress. If this occurred without a change in the shape of the relaxation spectrum, the individual curves could be "reduced" to vanishing stress by suitable horizontal adjustments on the logarithmic time scale. This sort of reduced variable treatment has been applied by Catsiff, Alfrey, and O'Shaughnessy,[82] to obtain a single composite curve for creep of nylon.

In the analysis of the data of Fig. 15–15 by equation 2, it is evident that a plot of $(\epsilon(t) - \epsilon_A)/\sigma$ against $(t/a_s)^{1/3}$ should give a single composite curve if $a_s = (\alpha\sigma/\sinh \alpha\sigma)^3$. Here a_s represents the ratio of any retardation time under stress σ to its value at vanishing stress, and is a monotonically decreasing function with increasing stress. The resulting plot would represent the slow contribution to the creep behavior at small stresses over a widely extended time scale.

Similarly, in stress relaxation the stress/strain ratio (which for a linear material would be $E(t)$) depends strongly on the magnitude of imposed strain as illustrated in Fig. 15–21 for data on cellulose by Passaglia and Koppehele.[83]   Again, the differences can be interpreted as due to a decrease in relaxation times with increasing stress, and the curves can be combined approximately into a composite curve by plotting with reduced variables.   The shift factor a_S decreases very rapidly with increasing strain.

The applicability of reduced variables such as these [84] has been much less thoroughly tested, with respect to scope and accuracy, than the reduced variables for temperature dependence (Chapter 11) or concentration dependence (Chapter 16).   The molecular origin of the dependence of a_S on stress or strain, as mentioned in the previous chapter, is also poorly understood.   If, in extension, it is caused by

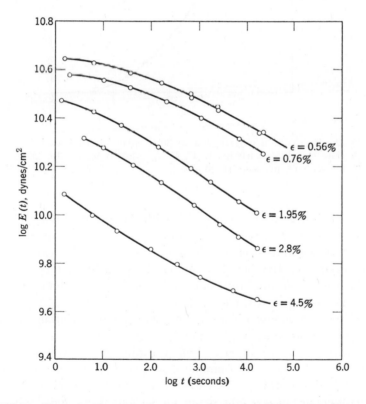

FIG. 15–21.   Extensional stress relaxation in isotropic cellulose monofilaments at 50% relative humidity and 25°C., for various constant strains as indicated (Passaglia and Koppehele [83]).

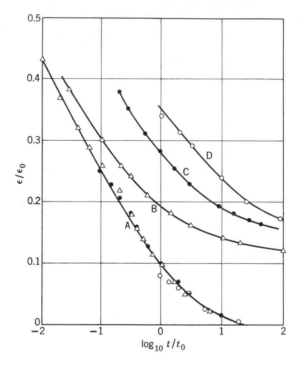

FIG. 15–22. Recovery of polyethylene at 30°C. after having been held at strain ϵ_0 for a time t_0. A, $\epsilon_0 = 0.0012$; B, C, D, $\epsilon_0 = 1.03$. A, $t_0 = 10$, 10^2, and 10^3 sec.; B, 10^3 sec.; C, 10^2 sec.; D, 10 sec.

an increase in free volume associated with the fact that Poisson's ratio differs from $\frac{1}{2}$, the reduced variables have a theoretical foundation.[85, 86] Comparative experiments in extension and shear would be highly desirable. It should be emphasized again that this type of non-linearity is entirely different from that of soft polymers at high strains as discussed in Chapter 13.

Non-linearity in creep is associated with severe deviations from the Boltzmann superposition principle in creep recovery, as noted to a much smaller degree in cross-linked rubberlike polymers at large strains (Fig. 13–13). An example of extreme effects in a crystalline polymer is shown in Fig. 15–22 for recovery of polyethylene[87] following maintenance at constant strain for various times and strain magnitudes. Although this is not exactly a creep recovery experiment, having been preceded by deformation at constant strain rather than at constant stress, it is clear that that recovery is much slower at large strains but is somewhat faster for shorter durations of the initial straining. In general, strains less than 0.01% appear to be required for conformity to the Boltzmann superposition principle in this system.[87]

If the viscoelastic behavior is non-linear, stress-strain curves at constant rate of loading or deformation will be so *a fortiori*, since they can depart from linearity even without this complication (Fig. 13–15). Calculations by Van Holde [62] show that, for the type of non-linearity given by equation 2 and the associated formulation of β', a stress-strain curve at constant rate of loading exhibits a sharp change in slope at strains of about 5% which resembles the apparent yield points observed in such experiments on many textile fibers.[88, 89]

Another consequence of non-linearity is that the relaxation modulus can no longer be calculated by differentiation of a stress-strain curve at constant rate of strain; equation 59 of Chapter 3 is not applicable. Examples of the discrepancies between $E(t)$ so calculated and directly measured for polyethylene have been given by Sandiford.[90]

REFERENCES

1. H. A. Stuart, Ed., *Die Physik der Hochpolymeren*, Vol. III, Springer-Verlag, Berlin, 1955.
2. A. Keller, *Makromol. Chem.*, **34**, 1 (1959).
3. H. A. Stuart, *Ann. N. Y. Acad. Sci.*, **83**, 1 (1959).
4. E. Jenckel, *Kolloid-Z.*, **130**, 64 (1953).
5. L. Mandelkern, *Chem. Rev.*, **56**, 903 (1956).
6. R. F. Landel, *Trans. Soc. Rheology*, **2**, 53 (1958).
7. G. W. Becker and H. Oberst, *Kolloid-Z.*, **148**, 6 (1956).
8. A. R. Payne, in *Rheology of Elastomers,* edited by P. Mason and N. Wookey, Pergamon Press, London, 1958.
9. G. W. Becker, *Kolloid-Z.*, **140**, 1 (1955).
10. A. Charlesby and N. H. Hancock, *Proc. Roy. Soc.*, **A218**, 245 (1953).
11. C. W. Deeley, D. E. Kline, J. A. Sauer, and R. B. Woodward, *J. Polymer Sci.*, **28**, 109 (1958).
12. R. F. Landel, unpublished experiments.
13. P. J. Blatz, *Ind. Eng. Chem.*, **48**, 727 (1956).
14. H. Eilers, *Kolloid-Z.*, **97**, 313 (1941).
15. R. F. Landel and T. L. Smith, unpublished experiments.
16. J. V. Robinson, *Trans. Soc. Rheology*, **1**, 18 (1957).
17. D. Parkinson, *Reinforcement of Rubbers,* Lakeman and Company, London, 1957.
18. A. M. Bueche, *J. Polymer Sci.*, **25**, 139 (1957).

19. R. Houwink and H. J. J. Janssen, *Kautschuk und Gummi*, **7**, 82 (1954); *Rubber Chem. Tech.*, **29**, 409 (1956).
20. A. R. Payne, in *Physical Properties of Polymers*, Macmillan Company, New York, 1959, p. 273.
21. F. J. Ritter, *The Improvement of the Low-Temperature Behaviour of Natural Rubber Vulvanizates by Chemical Modification with Thiol Acids*, Rubber-Stichting, Delft, 1956.
22. G. Natta, *Chim. et ind.*, **77**, 1009 (1957).
23. J. D. Hoffman and J. J. Weeks, *J. Res. Nat. Bur. Standards*, **60**, 465 (1958).
24. A. V. Tobolsky and J. R. McLoughlin, *J. Phys. Chem.*, **59**, 989 (1955).
25. K. Nagamatsu and T. Yoshitomi, *J. Colloid Sci.*, **14**, 377 (1959).
26. K. Nagamatsu, T. Yoshitomi, and T. Takemoto, *J. Colloid Sci.*, **13**, 257 (1958).
27. E. Catsiff, J. Offenbach, and A. V. Tobolsky, *J. Colloid Sci.*, **11**, 48 (1956).
28. J. A. Faucher, *Trans. Soc. Rheology*, **3**, 81 (1959).
29. K. Schmieder and K. Wolf, *Kolloid-Z.*, **134**, 149 (1953).
30. A. E. Woodward and J. A. Sauer, *Fortschr. Hochpolym. Forschung*, **1**, 114 (1958).
31. K. H. Illers and E. Jenckel, *Kolloid-Z.*, **160**, 97 (1958).
32. A. B. Thompson and D. W. Woods, *Trans. Faraday Soc.*, **52**, 1383 (1956).
33. K. H. Illers, *Makromol. Chem.*, **38**, 168 (1960).
34. A. E. Woodward, *J. Applied Phys.*, **25**, 1209 (1954).
35. H. Thurn, *Kolloid-Z.*, **165**, 57 (1959).
36. F. P. Reding, *J. Polymer Sci.*, **32**, 487 (1958).
37. A. Kovacs, Thesis, Paris, 1955.
38. L. E. Nielsen, *J. Applied Phys.*, **25**, 1209 (1954).
39. F. Bueche, *J. Polymer Sci.*, **22**, 113 (1956).
40. E. Catsiff, J. Offenbach, and A. V. Tobolsky, *J. Colloid Sci.*, **11**, 48 (1956).
41. K. Nagamatsu, T. Takemura, T. Yoshitomi, and T. Takemoto, *J. Polymer Sci.*, **33**, 515 (1958); T. Takemura, *ibid.*, **38**, 471 (1959).
42. L. E. Nielsen, R. A. Wall, and P. G. Richmond, *Soc. Plastics Eng. J.*, **11**, 22 (1955).
43. G. W. Becker and H. Oberst, *Kolloid-Z.*, **148**, 6 (1956).
44. E. A. W. Hoff, D. W. Robinson, and A. H. Willbourn, *J. Polymer Sci.*, **18**, 161 (1955).
45. K. H. Illers and E. Jenckel, *Kolloid-Z.*, **165**, 73 (1959).
46. A. H. Willbourn, *Trans. Faraday Soc.*, **54**, 717 (1958).
47. G. W. Becker and H. Oberst, *Kolloid-Z.*, **152**, 1 (1957).
48. A. K. Schulz, *J. Chim. Phys.*, **53**, 933 (1956).
49. K. H. Illers and E. Jenckel, *Kolloid-Z.*, **165**, 84 (1959).
50. D. E. Kline, J. A. Sauer, and A. E. Woodward, *J. Polymer Sci.*, **22**, 455 (1956).
51. K. Wolf, private communication.
52. E. A. W. Hoff, private communication.
53. E. R. Fitzgerald, *J. Chem. Phys.*, **27**, 1180 (1957).
54. E. R. Fitzgerald, *J. Applied Phys.*, **29**, 1442 (1958).
55. E. R. Fitzgerald, *J. Chem. Phys.*, **32**, 771 (1960).
56. E. R. Fitzgerald, *Phys. Rev.*, **108**, 690 (1957).
57. E. R. Fitzgerald, *Phys. Rev.*, **112**, 765, 1063 (1958).
58. G. Joos, *Theoretical Physics*, Third Edition, Hafner Publishing Company, New York, p. 452.

59. C. S. Stearns, quoted by E. R. Fitzgerald, reference 56.
60. S. R. Bodner, *Trans. Soc. Rheology,* **4,** 141 (1960).
61. E. R. Fitzgerald and A. E. Woodward, *Kolloid-Z.,* to be published.
62. K. E. Van Holde, *J. Polymer Sci.,* **24,** 417 (1957).
63. L. N. G. Filon and H. T. Jessop, *Phil. Trans. Roy. Soc.,* **A223,** 89 (1928).
64. A. J. Kennedy, *J. Mech. Phys. Solids,* **1,** 172 (1953).
65. N. F. Mott, *Phil. Mag.,* **44,** 742 (1953).
66. P. J. Flory, *Principles of Polymer Chemistry,* Cornell University Press, Ithaca, 1953, p. 453.
67. A. V. Tobolsky and G. M. Brown, *J. Polymer Sci.,* **17,** 547 (1955).
68. R. D. Andrews, Ph.D. Thesis, Princeton University, 1948.
69. M. Mooney and W. E. Wolstenhome, *Ind. Eng. Chem.,* **44,** 335 (1952).
70. A. N. Gent, *Trans. Faraday Soc.,* **50,** 521 (1954).
71. R. S. Stein, *J. Polymer Sci.,* **34,** 709 (1959).
72. J. H. Wakelin, E. T. L. Voong, D. J. Montgomery, and J. H. Dusenbury, *J. Applied Phys.,* **26,** 786 (1955).
73. K. W. Hillier and H. Kolsky, *Proc. Phys. Soc.,* **B62,** 111 (1949).
74. N. Tokita, *J. Polymer Sci.,* **20,** 515 (1956).
75. K. Huff and F. H. Müller, *Kolloid-Z.,* **153,** 5 (1957).
76. S. D. Gehman, D. E. Woodford, and R. B. Stambaugh, *Ind. Eng. Chem.,* **33,** 1032 (1941).
77. W. P. Fletcher and A. N. Gent, *Trans. Inst. Rubber Ind.,* **29,** 266 (1953).
78. A. R. Payne, *J. Applied Polymer Sci.,* **3,** 127 (1960).
79. K. C. Bryant and D. C. Bisset, *Proc. Third Rubber Technology Conference,* London, 1954, p. 655.
80. M. T. O'Shaugnessy, *Textile Res. J.,* **18,** 263 (1948).
81. R. Meredith, in F. R. Eirich, *Rheology,* Vol. II, p. 261, Academic Press, New York, 1958.
82. F. Catsiff, T. Alfrey, and M. T. O'Shaugnessy, *Textile Res. J.,* **23,** 808 (1953).
83. E. Passaglia and H. P. Koppehele, *J. Polymer Sci.,* **33,** 281 (1958).
84. I. L. Gruntfest, E. M. Young, Jr., and W. Kooch, *J. Applied Phys.,* **28,** 1106 (1957).
85. J. D. Ferry and R. A. Stratton, *Kolloid-Z.,* **171,** 107 (1960).
86. G. M. Bryant, to be published.
87. J. J. Benbow, in *Rheology of Elastomers,* edited by P. Mason and N. Wookey, Pergamon Press, London, 1958.
88. R. Meredith, editor, *Mechanical Properties of Textile Fibers,* North Holland Publishing Co., Amsterdam, 1956.
89. A. K. Van der Vegt, in H. A. Stuart, *Die Physik der Hochpolymeren,* Vol. IV, p. 460, Springer-Verlag, Berlin, 1956.
90. D. J. H. Sandiford, in *Physical Properties of Polymers,* Macmillan Company, New York, 1959, p. 213.

CHAPTER 16

Concentrated Solutions
and Plasticized Polymers

When a polymer is diluted with a solvent of low molecular weight, with which it forms a true solution in the sense that the solvent is molecularly dispersed, the local friction coefficient is sharply reduced. Each polymeric chain unit has in its vicinity diluent molecules as well as other polymeric segments, and the former can be displaced in translatory motion much more easily, thus lowering the effective local viscosity. The resulting reduction in all relaxation times is the most striking effect on viscoelastic properties. However, the detailed shapes of the viscoelastic spectra may also be altered in the transition zone. Furthermore, when the molecular weight is high enough for entanglement coupling to be present, the effective spacing between coupling points is increased by the introduction of diluent, to an extent which appears to depend on the nature of the polymer. This profoundly affects viscoelastic properties in the plateau zone. The effect of diluent on the terminal zone of time scale in uncross-linked polymers is closely associated with its effect on the steady-flow viscosity. Even in the glassy state far below T_g, viscoelastic properties are affected to some extent by the presence of small molecules.

The present chapter deals only with concentrated solutions, which might be defined for convenience as those whose relative viscosities (with respect to the pure solvent) are at least of the order of 100. The corresponding lower limit of polymer concentration might be anywhere from a fraction of a per cent for an unusually long stiff molecule (such as desoxyribonucleic acid [1]) to 10% for a flexible polymer of rather low molecular weight; the upper limit is simply the undiluted polymer, and we shall consider plasticized systems in which the proportion of polymer is 90% or more. As for truly dilute solutions, in which the polymer molecules are largely isolated and the steady-flow viscosities are of the same order of magnitude as those of the solvents, the fragmentary existing knowledge of such systems has already been mentioned in Section A of Chapter 10.

A. THE TRANSITION ZONE FROM RUBBERLIKE TO GLASSLIKE CONSISTENCY

The effects of a diluent or plasticizer on viscoelastic properties in the transition zone can be analyzed in terms of its influence on the temperature dependence function, $a_T(T)$, and, separately, on the absolute values of friction coefficients and the shapes of viscoelastic spectra.

1. The Temperature Dependence of Relaxation and Retardation Times

The function a_T follows the WLF equation for diluted as for undiluted systems, and several concentrated solutions were included in the summaries of Table 11–II and 11–III. To the approximation of equation 36 of Chapter 11, in which the only variable parameter is T_s, a diluent influences the temperature dependence of relaxation times in accordance with its effect on T_s, and this in turn parallels approximately its effect on T_g.

Addition of diluents of low molecular weight depresses T_g sharply, linearly at first in accordance with the equation [2]

$$T_g = T_g{}^0 - kw_1 \tag{1}$$

where w_1 is the weight fraction of diluent and the coefficient k ranges from 200° to 500° for various solvents in polystyrene, for example. The departure from linearity at higher dilution, as illustrated in Fig. 16–1, can be described by various empirical equations.[2,3] It is implicit, of course, that the glass transition of the diluent lies far below that of the polymer, and that the diluent does not crystallize out of the solutions.

If the view is adopted that the glass transition is an iso-free-volume state in the solutions as in the undiluted polymers (Chapter 11, Section C), then the depression of T_g can be attributed to creation of additional free volume

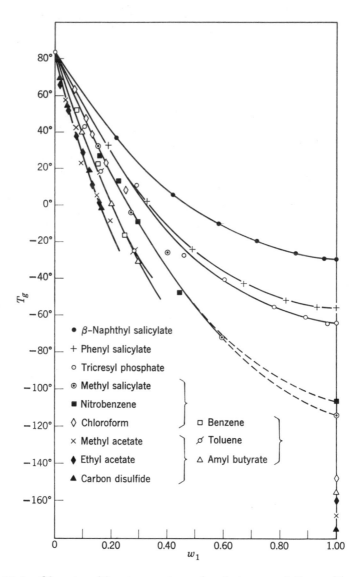

FIG. 16–1. Glass transition temperature of polystyrene solutions with various diluents of low molecular weight, plotted against weight fraction of diluent. The T_g for the undiluted sample appears to be somewhat lower than that usually accepted (Table 11–III). (Jenckel and Heusch.[2])

by introduction of the diluent; in the region where equation 1 holds, we should have [4] at a constant temperature T somewhat above T_g:

$$f(T,w_1) = f_2(T) + \beta w_1 \tag{2}$$

with $\beta = k\alpha_f$. Here f and f_2 are the fractional free volumes of the solution and pure polymer respectively, k is the coefficient in equation 1, and α_f is the thermal expansion coefficient of the free volume, usually identified with the difference $\Delta\alpha$ between the macroscopic expansion coefficients above and below T_g, as in Chapter 11. Thus the depression of T_g expressed in equation 1 makes up by thermal contraction for the increase in f given by equation 2.

It is true that the addition of small amounts of diluent to a polymer often results in a *contraction* of total volume, the latter being slightly less than the sum of the volumes of the components. Thus, Jenckel and Heusch [2] found that the specific volumes of mixtures could be approximately represented by the equation

$$v = w_1v_1 + w_2v_2 + k_vw_1w_2 \tag{3}$$

where v_1 and v_2 are the specific volumes of the pure components and k_v is usually negative. But the fractional free volume of the solution is nevertheless greater than that of the polymer because that of diluent (f_1) is so large. If the *occupied* volumes ($v_o = v[1 - f]$) are strictly additive by weight fraction, then it can be shown [5] that for $w_2 \to 1$ (small amounts of diluent):

$$\beta = f_1(v_1/v_2) - f_2 + k_v/v_2 \tag{4}$$

In accordance with Table 11–II, f_2 is about 0.025, and k_v/v_2 is [2] of the order of -0.01. Hence as a first approximation the last two terms are negligible and β should be roughly equal to f_1—of the order of 0.2 for simple liquids far above their glass transitions.[6] Values of β calculated from the product $k\alpha_f$ do indeed [4] range from 0.1 to 0.3.

Equation 2 can also be expressed in terms of the volume fraction of diluent, ϕ_1, in the form

$$f(T,\phi_1) = f_2(T) + \beta'\phi_1 \tag{4a}$$

leading to the following analog of equation 4:

$$\beta' = f_1 - f_2(v_2/v_1) + k_v/v_1 \tag{4b}$$

Here, $\beta' = \beta v_2/v_1$.

Thus a plasticized polymer whose T_g has been depressed 50°, for example, will have a lower T_s by approximately the same amount, and the temperature dependence of its relaxation times as calculated by equation 36 of Chapter 11 will be less steep than for the pure polymer when the two systems are compared at a given temperature which is above the glass transitions of both. This statement is of course concerned only with the degree of shift of relaxation times with temperature, and not with their absolute magnitudes, which will be taken up below.

For a more precise evaluation of the effects of diluent on the function a_T, equation 26 of Chapter 11 may be used with the coefficients c_1^g and c_2^g related to the parameters f_g and α_f by equations 34 and 35. In this case, the concentration dependence of three quantities— T_g, f_g, and α_f—must be known. The first has been discussed above; information on the other two is very fragmentary. From the data of Table 11–II, there is really no evidence that they change significantly with dilution.

2. Location of the Transition on the Time or Frequency Scale; the Monomeric Friction Coefficient

Since the shapes of the viscoelastic functions in the transition zone are not grossly altered by moderate amounts of diluent (specific differences in shape will be considered subsequently), the primary effect of plasticization at a given constant temperature is the shift of the transition to shorter times or higher frequencies. Quantitatively, this can be expressed by a change in the monomeric friction coefficient ζ_0.

An illustration of the very rapid shift along the frequency scale was provided in an earlier chapter by Fig. 11–16, in which the loss compliance was plotted for four solutions of poly-n-butyl methacrylate in diethyl phthalate,[7] all reduced to a reference temperature of 273°K. The relaxation spectra calculated from these and associated dynamic measurements are shown in Fig. 16–2, revealing a shift of more than 3 logarithmic decades for a concentration change from 30% to 60% by weight.

Values of log ζ_0 calculated by equation 1 of Chapter 12, using the tangents drawn in Fig. 16–2 with the theoretical slope of $\frac{1}{2}$, are (in the usual units of dyne-sec/cm) -6.28, -5.30, -4.05, and -2.90 corresponding to concentrations c in g. polymer per cc. of solution of 0.334, 0.445, 0.549, and 0.654. A plot of log ζ_0 against c is found to be approximately linear, as shown in Fig. 16–3, corresponding to the relation

$$\zeta_0 = 5.8 \times 10^{-10} e^{24c} \tag{5}$$

It is of some interest to calculate the effective local viscosity by a rough Stokes' law approximation as in Chapter 12. For the 30% solution, the re-

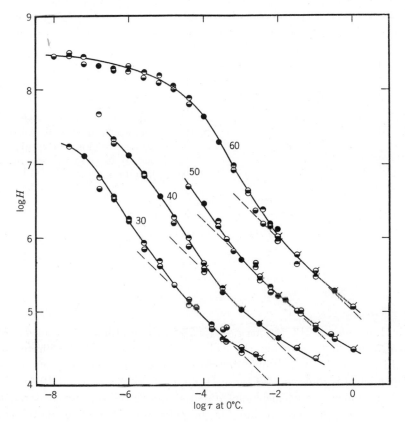

FIG. 16–2. Relaxation spectra of four solutions of poly-n-butyl methacrylate in diethyl phthalate,[6] reduced to 100°C. Dashed lines are tangents drawn with theoretical slope of $-\frac{1}{2}$. Points with top black, calculated from G'; bottom black, from G''.

sult is 0.7 poise, only slightly larger than the viscosity of the pure solvent, which is 0.33 poise.

The values of log ζ_0 extrapolated to T_g are 3.60 and 1.90 for the 50% and 60% poly-n-butyl methacrylate solutions respectively. These represent rather long extrapolations; since the corresponding value for the pure polymer is 3.81, there is no evidence of any consistent trend with concentration.

Figure 16–3 cannot be extended to the pure polymer ($c = \rho = 1.06$), because 273° is below its glass transition temperature. In fact, iso-thermal comparisons of undiluted and substantially plasticized poly-mers above T_g are rare, and only one example is cited here. For poly-

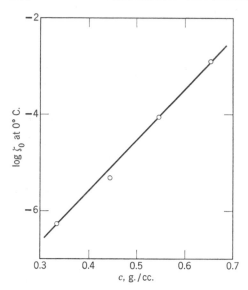

FIG. 16–3. Monomeric friction coefficients of the four solutions of Fig. 16–2, plotted against the polymer concentration in g./cc.

vinyl acetate at 313°K., log ζ_0 is [8] 1.75 in the undiluted polymer [9] and -5.25 in a 50% solution (by volume) in tri-m-cresyl phosphate [10]— a difference of 7 logarithmic decades. If an exponential concentration dependence is assumed for these two data, taking $c = \rho = 1.19$ for the pure polymer, the coefficient of c in the analog of equation 5 is found to be 27, rather close to that for the poly-n-butyl methacrylate solutions. It will be seen below that this is an unwarranted simplification, however.

It is of interest that the concentration dependence of diffusion coefficients of solvent molecules in very concentrated polymer solutions is also exponential [11,12] with a coefficient of the order of 20 to 25. The similarity between the monomeric friction coefficient and the translational friction coefficient of a small foreign molecule has already been pointed out (Table 12–V and accompanying discussion).

But for quite small amounts of diluent (polymer concentrations > 95%), the dependence of ζ_0 on c is not simply exponential, as shown by stress relaxation experiments of Fujita and Kishimoto [4] on polyvinyl acetate and polymethyl acrylate containing a few per cent of water and of methyl alcohol. Although ζ_0 was not calculated specifically, the ratio a_c of relaxation times in the presence and absence of diluent was obtained by shifting stress relaxation curves at different diluent concentrations by a method of reduced variables to be described below; since these measurements were made in the transition zone where the behavior is governed by ζ_0, $a_c = \zeta_0(c)/\zeta_0(c = \rho)$. (To avoid confusion, we continue to use c for the weight of polymer per cc. of solution, which has a maximum value of ρ, the density of pure polymer.) In Fig. 16–4, a_c is plotted logarithmically against the volume fraction of polymer, $\phi_2(=c/\rho)$, for methyl alcohol in the two polymers. Its terminal slope (*i.e.*, at the right) is very high, corresponding to coefficients of c in equation 5 of 100 to 200, but it flattens with decreasing c. By analogy with Fig. 16–3 it might be expected to approach a constant slope corresponding to a coefficient of the order of 25 in more dilute systems.

The dependence of a_c on ϕ_2 in Fig. 16–4 was quite satisfactorily explained by Fujita and Kishimoto on the basis of free volume, as already invoked for the influence of temperature (equation 32 of Chapter 11), pressure (equation 38 of Chapter 11), and side group length (equation 2 of Chapter 12). The analog of these equations for the case of concentration dependence is

$$\log a_c = (1/2.303)(1/f - 1/f_2) \tag{6}$$

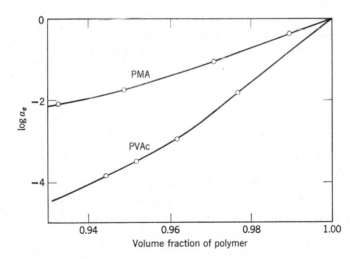

FIG. 16–4. Shift factor a_c (ratio of ζ_0 with and without diluent), derived from stress relaxation measurements by Fujita and Kishimoto [4] on polyvinyl acetate and polymethyl acrylate slightly plasticized with methyl alcohol, plotted logarithmically against volume fraction of polymer.

where the symbols have the same significance as in equation 2. Since $\phi_1 = 1 - c/\rho_2$, equations 4a and 6 can be combined to give

$$\log a_c = -\frac{1}{2.303 f_2} \frac{\beta'(1 - c/\rho_2)}{[f_2 + \beta'(1 - c/\rho_2)]} \tag{7}$$

which contains the one adjustable parameter, β'. This equation fitted the data of Fig. 16–4 and similar data for water-plasticized polymers very well with values of β' in the correct range in the light of equation 4b—namely, 0.23 to 0.37.

When $c \to \rho_2$, equation 7 reduces to a limiting terminal slope

$$d \ln a_c/dc = \beta'/\rho_2 f_2{}^2 \tag{8}$$

which, if the first term on the right side of equation 4b is substituted for β', becomes approximately $f_1 v_2/f_2{}^2$. The presence of $f_2{}^2$ in the denominator is analogous to that in equation 40 of Chapter 11. It shows that the effect of traces of diluent in shifting relaxation times will be much greater near T_g where f_2 is small than at higher temperatures. In particular, the steep terminal slopes in Fig. 16–4 are readily explained by equation 8; that for polyvinyl acetate is greater because 40°C. is closer to its T_g (32°) than to that of polymethyl acrylate (3°), and f_2 for polyvinyl acetate is correspondingly smaller. The ratio of $f_2{}^2$ for the two polymers, from the data of Table 11–II, is 1.8, as compared with the ratio of 2.1 for the two slopes in the figure.

At intermediate concentrations, on the other hand, if the term in k_v in equation 4b is neglected, differentiation of equation 7 yields for the slope and for the coefficient of c in equation 5:

$$d \ln a_c/dc = (f_1\rho_2 - f_2\rho_1)/[f_2 + (f_1\rho_2 - f_2\rho_1)(\rho - c)]^2 \tag{9}$$

where ρ is the density of the solution. For $f_1 = 0.3$, $f_2 = 0.03$, all ρ's near unity, and $c = 0.6$, this gives a value of 14, which is the correct order of magnitude. However, the presence of $(\rho - c)^2$ in the denominator does not correspond to the constant slope which is observed. Actually, it can hardly be expected that the simple free volume interpretation can hold when the plasticization has increased f above a value of about 0.08; the WLF equation in Chapter 11 may also fail at temperatures higher than $T_g + 100°$, corresponding to $f > 0.08$, where it has been postulated that specific effects of molecular structure become more prominent. For $f_1 = 0.3$ and $f_2 = 0.03$, this limiting value of f would restrict the applicability of equation 7 to polymer concentrations above 80%. (Very recent work of Fujita [13] suggests that this restriction is unnecessarily pessimistic, however.)

It would follow then that in the range from 80% to 100% polymer the most important feature of a plasticizing liquid is its coefficient β or β' and therefore, from equation 4 or 4a, its fractional free volume, f_1. For most effective plasticization, f_1 should be as large as possible. However, other properties such as molecular volume, flexibility, cohesive energy density relative to that of the polymer, and local packing geometry will all affect the non-linear coefficient k_v and thereby influence a_c to some extent. At higher proportions of diluent, with $w_2 < 0.8$, the mobility may have to be formulated in other terms. Neither the form of equation 5 nor the plasticizing effectiveness of various diluents has been satisfactorily explained, although there have been many empirical correlations of the latter with various physical properties.[11]

3. Shapes of the Viscoelastic Functions

To show the effect of diluent on the detailed shapes of viscoelastic functions, it is convenient to employ corresponding-state plots as in Section C of Chapter 12. For the relaxation spectrum, we plot $\log H - \log Tc/M_0$ against $\log \tau - \log (a^2 \zeta_0/kT)$. Of course, for a single polymer and its solutions the only variables are ζ_0 and c (which in the pure polymer becomes ρ). In Fig. 16–5, polyvinyl acetate [9] is compared in this manner with its 50% solution [10] in tri-m-cresyl phosphate. They coincide of course at the bottom of the transition zone because this is fixed by the corresponding-state conditions. The diluent causes the spectrum to rise somewhat more sharply from the theoretical slope of $-\frac{1}{2}$ at short times; but at still shorter times it crosses the spectrum of the pure polymer, and its entrance into the glassy zone involves a broader maximum than the latter.

In Fig. 16–6, poly-n-butyl methacrylate [14] is similarly compared with two of the solutions in diethyl phthalate [7] whose relaxation spectra appear in Fig. 16–2. The other two solutions with intermediate concentrations would fall very near the curves drawn. The differences in shape between the spectra of the pure polymer and its solutions are similar in nature to those for the polyvinyl acetate, but less prominent. It is not possible at present to give them molecular interpretations, since the molecular basis for shape of the relaxation spectrum at short times is poorly understood (Chapter 10, Section D).

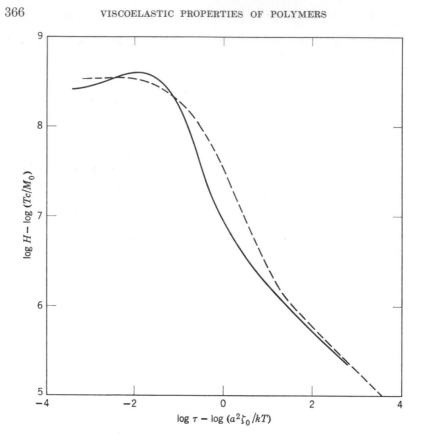

FIG. 16–5. Corresponding-state plot of the relaxation spectra of polyvinyl acetate (solid line) and a 50% solution (by weight) of this polymer (dashed line) in tri-*m*-cresyl phosphate.

The differences in spectral shape are of course reflected in the other viscoelastic functions, especially the loss tangent, which is always the most sensitive. The loss tangents for poly-*n*-butyl methacrylate and three of its solutions are plotted in Fig. 16–7 with the frequency scale reduced in the same way as the abscissa in Fig. 16–6. They show some degree of broadening with increasing dilution, but their maxima remain considerably above the theoretical value of 1.0 which would be predicted throughout the transition zone by the flexible chain theory in its simple form.

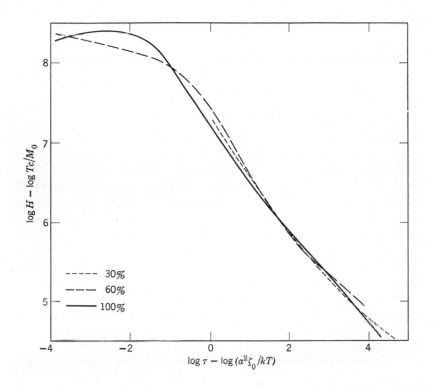

FIG. 16–6. Corresponding-state plots of the relaxation spectra of poly-n-butyl methacrylate and of two solutions in diethyl phthalate, with polymer concentration by weight as indicated.

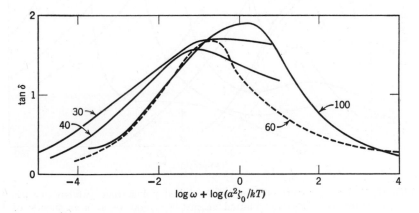

FIG. 16–7. Loss tangents of poly-n-butyl methacrylate and of three solutions in diethyl phthalate, plotted against the logarithm of the frequency reduced as in the abscissa of Fig. 16–6. Figures denote polymer concentration in weight per cent.

4. Isochronal or Quasi-Isochronal Viscoelastic Measurements

When measurements are made at approximately constant frequency on plasticized polymers over a range of temperatures, the location of the transition zone naturally shifts to lower temperatures with increasing dilution. It is difficult to find examples for uncross-linked polymers, because most experimental methods are not adapted to the fluid systems obtained at higher dilutions. However, the pattern can be illustrated by lightly cross-linked polystyrene swollen in dibutyl phthalate to various extents, as shown in Fig. 16–8 where measurements of tan δ at 1 cycle/sec. by Illers and Jenckel [15] are plotted against temperature at various polymer concentrations. (As mentioned in the following chapter, swelling after cross-linking distorts the polymer chains from their most probable configuration distributions, but this probably does not greatly change the behavior illustrated, and the cross-linked systems have of course the advantage of maintaining rigidity so that they can be studied with equipment de-

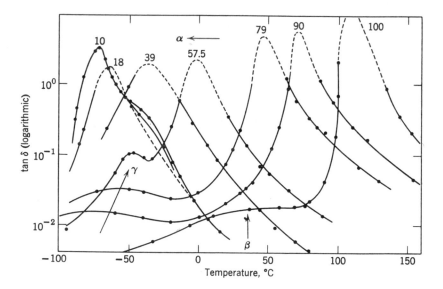

FIG. 16–8. Loss tangents of lightly cross-linked polystyrene swollen to various extents in dibutyl phthalate, plotted against temperature at a frequency of 1 cycle/sec. Figures denote polymer concentration in weight per cent (Illers and Jenckel [15]).

signed for solid samples.)   The shift to lower temperatures is accompanied by minor changes in the height of the maximum and the peak breadth.   Such changes reflect a combination of the effect of diluent on the a_T function *and* its effect on the shapes of the isothermal viscoelastic functions.

5. Reduced Variables for Concentration Dependence

The corresponding-state plot of Fig. 16–6 implies, insofar as the curves coincide in the transition region, that all relaxation times are proportional to ζ_0 and that the magnitudes of contributions to H are all proportional to c as well as to T.   This is, of course, exactly what the flexible chain theories predict, as discussed at the end of Section A, Chapter 10.   On this basis, a scheme of reduced variables can be devised to combine measurements at different concentrations as well as temperatures, without actually calculating ζ_0 and without requiring that the detailed shapes of the viscoelastic functions conform to the simple theories.

Any composition may be chosen as a reference state.   If the undiluted polymer is selected, and a_c denotes as above the ratio of relaxation times at concentration c to those in the pure polymer at concentration ρ_2, the analogs of the coordinates numbered 5, 6, 9, and 10 in Chapter 11 are: [16]

$$G_c(t) = (\rho_2/c)G(t), \qquad vs. \qquad t/a_c \qquad (10)$$

$$G'_c = (\rho_2/c)G', \qquad vs. \qquad \omega a_c \qquad (11)$$

$$J_c(t) = (c/\rho_2)J(t), \qquad vs. \qquad t/a_c \qquad (12)$$

$$J'_c = (c/\rho_2)J', \qquad vs. \qquad \omega a_c \qquad (13)$$

in which the subscript c denotes reduction concentrationwise to the pure polymer.   Extension to the other viscoelastic functions is obvious.   This method has been applied to obtain composite functions for a number of polymers in the range of small amounts of added diluent,[4, 17–20] with a_c determined empirically.   It cannot in general be expected, however, that the values of a_c applicable in the transition zone will also be successful in the plateau and terminal zones for polymers of high molecular weight, because of the marked effects of dilution on entanglement coupling.

B. THE RUBBERY (PLATEAU) AND TERMINAL ZONES

In the plateau and terminal zones, the viscoelastic properties are dominated by the presence of an entanglement network in concentrated polymer solutions as in the undiluted uncross-linked polymers, although the lower the concentration the higher is the molecular weight required for establishment of a network by entanglement coupling.

1. The Maxima in Loss Compliance and Retardation Spectrum

As pointed out in Chapter 13, the maximum in loss compliance is one of the most characteristic features of the plateau zone, and it provides information about the degree of entanglement coupling in uncross-linked polymers. The related maximum in the retardation spectrum gives a comparative picture of the degree of entanglement when reduced to corresponding states as in Figs. 13–4 and 13–5.

The spectrum L is plotted in corresponding states in Fig. 16–9 for the four poly-n-butyl methacrylate solutions whose relaxation spectra appeared in Fig. 16–2. While they coincide throughout the transition zone, the shifts of the maxima in a direction along approximately a slope of $\frac{1}{2}$ with increasing dilution indicate that the average degree of polymerization of a strand in the entanglement network is increasing correspondingly. The value of Z_e can be estimated from the maximum in J'' as in Chapter 13, by the equations derived from the Marvin theory (Chapter 10, Section F). For solutions, equations 3 and 4 of Chapter 13 take the form:

$$J''_m = 0.32 Z_e M_0 / cRT \qquad (14)$$

$$\omega_m = 48kT/a^2 \zeta_0 Z_e^2 \qquad (15)$$

Values of Z_e obtained in this manner for the poly-n-butyl methacrylate solutions are listed in Table 16–I. As in Table 13–II, a somewhat smaller estimate is obtained from J''_m than from ω_m. Those calculated from J''_m, which are the least ambiguous, are plotted logarithmically against c in Fig. 16–10 together with the corresponding value for the pure polymer.

The values for the solutions, reduced to 273°K., cannot be compared with those for the pure polymer unless the latter are reduced to 273°K. from the original reference temperature of 373°K. to take into account the factor f discussed in Section D, Chapter 11. This reduction—a factor of 0.48 in going from

373° to 273°, based on an apparent heat of dissociation of coupling points of 2.27 kcal.[21]—brings the pure polymer to a reference state which is hypothetical because 273° is below its T_g. The comparison of Z_e should still be valid, however.

The slope of the line in Fig. 16–10 corresponds to Z_e being proportional to $c^{-2.6}$. (An earlier estimate was $c^{-2.3}$, probably within the uncertainty of the analysis.) This rather high exponent, representing a very rapid increase in strand length with dilution, may be peculiar to polymers of the methacrylate type, possibly associated with the unusual temperature dependence of Z_e in these polymers referred to

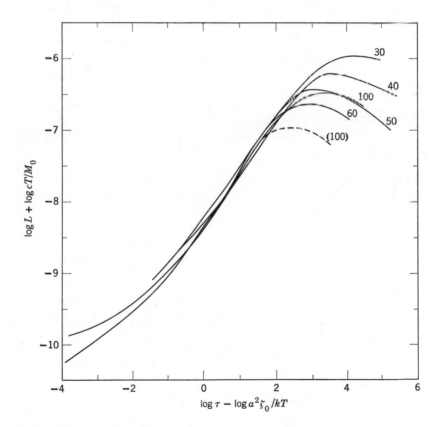

FIG. 16–9. Corresponding-state plots of the retardation spectra of four solutions of poly-n-butyl methacrylate in diethyl phthalate, identified by polymer concentrations in weight per cent. Dashed line is reduced for temperature dependence of Z_e (see Table 16–I).

Table 16–I

AVERAGE DEGREE OF POLYMERIZATION PER ENTANGLEMENT
NETWORK STRAND IN SOLUTIONS OF POLY-n-BUTYL
METHACRYLATE IN DIETHYL PHTHALATE AT 273°K

Concn., wt. %	Z_e from J''_m	Z_e from ω_m
30	429	820
40	260	390
50	147	235
60	92	175
100	92 [a]	162 [a]
	30 [b]	53 [b]

[a] Calculated at 373°K. (*cf.* Table 13–II).

[b] Reduced to 273°K. for dependence of Z_e on temperature given in Chapter 11, Section D.

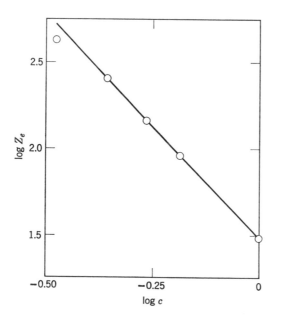

FIG. 16–10. Average degree of polymerization per strand of the entanglement network, plotted logarithmically against concentration for poly-n-butyl methacrylate and four solutions in diethyl phthalate.

above.[22]   If the probability of entanglement at any point on a polymer chain were a constant independent of position, the number of entanglements per chain should be directly proportional to concentration—*i.e.*, Z_e proportional to c^{-1}.   Data on solutions of polyisobutylene,[23, 24] to be discussed below, are consistent with the latter relation.

If the values of Z_e previously given for several pure methacrylate polymers in Table 13–II and those for the poly-*n*-butyl methacrylate solutions in Table 16–I are all reduced to a common temperature of 62° to allow for the temperature variation of Z_e, they turn out to be approximately a function of c/M_0 alone, as shown in Fig. 16–11. Here $\log Z_e = -3.10 - 2.31 \log (c/M_0)$.   The ratio c/M_0 (for the pure polymers, ρ/M_0) is the moles of monomer units per cc., and may be regarded as a measure of the density of polymer backbones.   Thus the average length of entanglement network strands depends on the

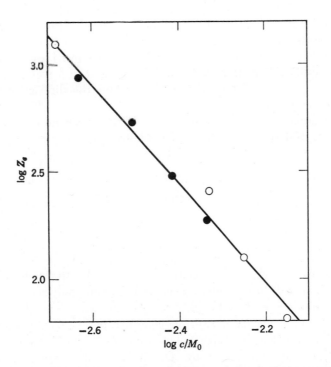

FIG. 16–11.   Average degree of polymerization per strand of the entanglement network, plotted logarithmically against the moles of monomer units per cc., for four methacrylate polymers (open circles) and the four solutions of Fig. 16–10 (black circles).

latter density alone, and not on whether the backbones are "diluted" by solvent molecules or by side groups.[22] This reinforces the view that the entanglement coupling phenomenon involves the long-range contour of chains as portrayed in Fig. 10–17, even though coupling in the methacrylate series may be somewhat atypical.

It should not be thought, of course, that all the viscoelastic properties of the polymethacrylate systems are determined solely by the concentration of chain backbones. For example, the monomeric friction coefficients of un-diluted poly-n-octyl and dodecyl methacrylates at 0°C. are larger by a factor of 200 than the corresponding values for solutions of the n-butyl polymer with the same concentration of monomoles per cc.

2. Reduced Variables in the Plateau and Terminal Zones

If the degree of entanglement changes with concentration, this effect can be taken into account in modifying the scheme of reduced variables with coordinates numbered 10 to 13 above in a manner exactly analogous to that of allowing for the temperature dependence of Z_e by the so-called ſ-shift of Section D, Chapter 11 (*cf.* Figs. 11–15 and 11–16). This will only be applicable if $M \gg 2M_e$ ($Z \gg 2Z_e$), and in a region of time or frequency scale near the maximum in J'' where the slippage of coupling points is slight. If Z_e is proportional to c^{-n}, and the undiluted polymer is the reference state, then the analog of ſ in concentration dependence is $(c/\rho_2)^n$, and reduction should be achieved in the plateau region by plotting

$$(\rho_2/c)^n G_c(t) = (\rho_2/c)^{n+1} G(t), \qquad vs. \qquad (\rho_2/c)^{2n} t/a_c \qquad (16)$$

$$(\rho_2/c)^n G'_c = (\rho_2/c)^{n+1} G', \qquad vs. \qquad (\rho_2/c)^{2n} \omega a_c \qquad (17)$$

$$(c/\rho_2)^n J_c(t) = (c/\rho_2)^{n+1} J(t), \qquad vs. \qquad (c/\rho_2)^{2n} t/a_c \qquad (18)$$

$$(c/\rho_2)^n J'_c = (c/\rho_2)^{n+1} J', \qquad vs. \qquad (c/\rho_2)^{2n} \omega a_c \qquad (19)$$

The use of a scheme such as this with $n = 2.3$ to 2.6 would cause the maxima in L to coincide, for example, for the poly-n-butyl metha-crylate solutions of Fig. 11–16.

For dynamic measurements on concentrated polyisobutylene solu-tions of high molecular weight in Decalin, in the range from 8 to 100% polymer,[23, 24] it was found by De Witt[23] that reduction required dividing G' by c^2, as in scheme 17 above with $n = 1$. A similar con-clusion had been reached by Hatfield and Rathmann[25] for creep meas-urements on polyisobutylene plasticized by oil (77 to 100% polymer).

However, it is not possible to confirm the applicability of $a_c c^{-2n}$ in the abscissas of coordinates 10 to 13 from these investigations, since they did not extend into the transition zone and the factor a_c representing the concentration dependence of the friction coefficient is not available.

At lower polymer concentrations and/or lower molecular weights, the qualification that $M \gg 2M_e$ is not fulfilled and the concentration dependence must be very complicated to describe, as slippage of coupling points is profoundly influenced by the loose ends in the entanglement network. Even at moderately high molecular weights, the coupling will disappear when the dilution reaches the point where $Z_e \cong Z/2$, depending on the value of n. For solutions more dilute than this, the scheme of reduced variables can be based on the concentration dependence predicted by the simple flexible chain theory in Chapter 10, Section A, where equations 20 and 21 become

$$H = (cRT/M)\Sigma\tau_p\delta(\tau - \tau_p) \tag{20}$$

$$\tau_p = 6\eta M/\pi^2 p^2 cRT \tag{21}$$

From 21, it follows that $a_c = \eta\rho_2/\eta_p c$, where η_p is the viscosity of the undiluted polymer. Thus the steady-flow viscosity, if it is available, fixes the time shift of the reduction without any arbitrary choice.

For reductions of data in moderately dilute solution, it has been convenient to use a hypothetical reference state of unit viscosity and unit concentration, rather than the pure polymer, which usually lies outside the range of conditions wherein equations 20 and 21 are applicable. The fact that this state is physically non-existent does not detract from its usefulness. Then, reducing for both temperature and concentration, we plot: [16]

$$G_r(t) = G(t)T_0/Tc, \quad vs. \quad tTc/\eta T_0 \tag{22}$$

$$J_r(t) = J(t)Tc/T_0, \quad vs. \quad tTc/\eta T_0 \tag{23}$$

$$G'_r = G'T_0/Tc, \quad vs. \quad \omega\eta T_0/Tc \tag{24}$$

$$\eta'_r = \eta'/\eta, \quad vs. \quad \omega\eta T_0/Tc \tag{25}$$

where the subscript r refers to the hypothetical reference state. The direct proportionality of the moduli contributions to c is the same as that appearing in the reduction scheme for the plateau zone, 10 to 13.

The reduction scheme embodied in 24 and 25 appears to provide satisfactory composite curves even at concentrations and/or molecular weights high enough to cause substantial entanglement coupling as

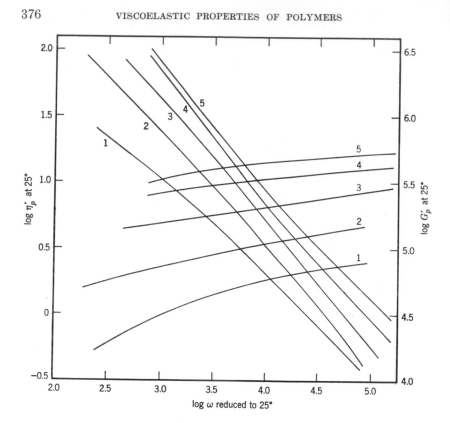

FIG. 16–12. Dynamic storage modulus G' (ascending curves) and dynamic viscosity η' (descending curves), plotted logarithmically against frequency, after reduction of data at various temperatures to 25°C., for cellulose tributyrate ($M = 300,000$) in 1,2,3-trichloropropane at the following weight fractions of polymer: 1, 0.072; 2, 0.104; 3, 0.156; 4, 0.210; 5, 0.256.

judged by the shape of the spectra, so long as the degree of coupling is not so tight that the network resembles a cross-linked one. An example of its application is shown in Figs. 16–12 and 16–13, where dynamic data on solutions of cellulose tributyrate in 1,2,3-trichloropropane [26] are reduced first for temperature alone as in Chapter 11 (coordinates 14 and 16, which require no empirical choice of parameters) and then for concentration as well. The individual curves match quite well in the composite plots. Many other examples have been given [16, 24, 27–29] for solutions in which the concentration may range up to the order of 25% for molecular weights of the order of 10^5 or up to 10% for M of the order of 10^6.

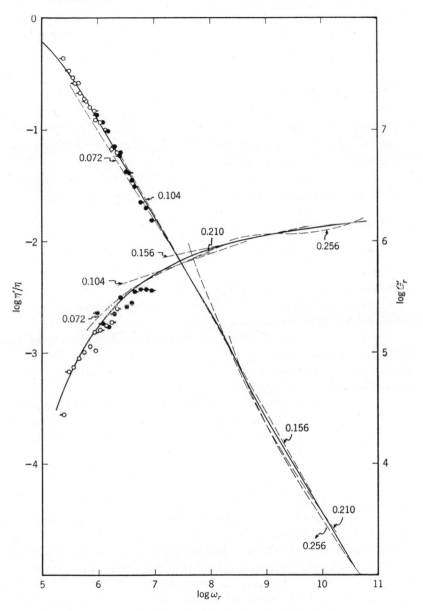

FIG. 16–13. Data of Fig. 16–12, and some additional data represented by individual points, reduced to unit viscosity and unit concentration by coordinates 24 and 25. Numbers denote weight fraction of polymer corresponding to dashed lines reproduced from Fig. 16–12.

For high molecular weights and intermediate concentrations near the terminal zone, De Witt [23] has successfully used a reduction scheme equivalent to

$$G'_r = G'T_0/Tc^2, \qquad vs. \qquad \omega\eta T_0/Tc^2 \qquad (26)$$

$$\eta'_r = \eta'/\eta, \qquad vs. \qquad \omega\eta T_0/Tc^2 \qquad (27)$$

which is in a sense intermediate between 16–19 and 22–25. The problem of the transition between the free and entangled conditions has been discussed by Takemura.[30]

3. Concentration Dependence of Steady-Flow Viscosity

In reduction schemes such as 14 and 16 of Chapter 11 and 24 and 25 or 26 and 27 of the present chapter, where a_T and a_c have been eliminated in terms of η, the effects of temperature and concentration on relaxation times have been absorbed into their respective effects on the steady-flow viscosity. For the temperature dependence, this is a convenient situation, because the viscosity can be adequately described by the WLF equation over wide ranges of temperature or by the Arrhenius equation over narrower ranges, especially when far above T_g. For the concentration dependence, the scheme is very useful if steady-flow viscosity data are available, but there is no simple way of describing the latter by an analytical expression.

Many empirical expressions have been proposed [31] to describe the dependence of viscosity on concentration and molecular weight in polymer solutions over various ranges of these variables. In several studies,[32, 33] it has been found that the relative viscosity η/η_s (where η_s is the viscosity of the solvent) is approximately a single function of $cM^{0.68}$ when data on one polymer for different solvents, concentrations, and molecular weights are assembled. This is illustrated in Fig. 16–14 for solutions of polyisobutylene in xylene, Decalin, and a mixture of Decalin and cyclohexanol in which the polymer was on the verge of phase separation; [32] and with different coordinates in Fig. 16–15 for solutions of cellulose tributyrate in 1,2,3-trichloropropane,[33] including also curves for several other polymers.[1, 27, 32]

In a more restricted range of conditions, η has been found to be proportional to the 3.4 power of M when different samples are compared at the same concentration in solution,[32, 34–36] thus following the same molecular weight dependence as in the pure polymer (Fig. 10–15 and associated discussion). This corresponds to a slope of unity in

Fig. 16–15, which is approximated over several decades, and therefore to a proportionality of η to c^5 at constant M. There is probably no direct theoretical significance in the exponent of 5. If Z_e is proportional to c^{-1} ($n = 1$ in the reduction schemes 16 to 19), the exponent implies [33] that ζ_0 is proportional to the 1.6 power of concentration. Such a relation could be compatible with the exponential

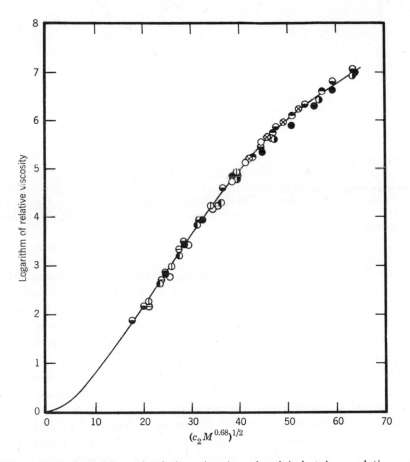

FIG. 16–14. Logarithm of relative viscosity of polyisobutylene solutions at 25°C. plotted against $(cM^{0.68})^{1/2}$. Black circles refer to a fraction of molecular weight 2.5×10^6 in a mixture of 69.9% Decalin and 30.1% cyclohexanol (in which the polymer was on the verge of precipitation); other points refer to 5 samples of molecular weights from 0.32 to 4.0×10^6 in xylene and 3 samples from 1 to 2.5×10^6 in Decalin. The concentrations ranged from 5 to 40% polymer by weight.

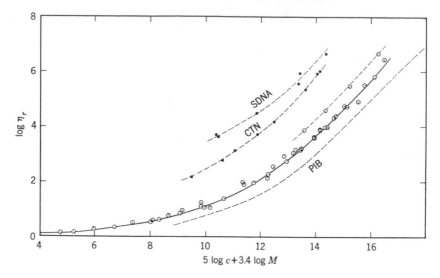

FIG. 16–15. Relative viscosity of cellulose tributyrate solutions in 1,2,3-tri-chloropropane at 25° plotted logarithmically against $c^5M^{3.4}$. The molecular weights range from 55 to 300×10^3 and concentrations from 7 to 36% polymer by weight. Other polymers: PIB, polyisobutylene, from data of Fig. 16–14; SDNA, sodium desoxyribonucleate[1] in water; CTN, cellulose trinitrate in iso-phorone.[27]

dependence in equation 5 only within a very limited concentration range. The chief value of plots such as Figs. 16–14 and 16–15 is, there-fore, for approximate prediction of viscosities when limited experi-mental data for different concentrations and molecular weights are available. In particular, the concentration dependence can be esti-mated from the molecular weight dependence or vice versa. Viscosity estimates obtained in this way can then be used to predict viscoelastic properties by the reduction schemes outlined above if master curves for G' and η', for example, are available.

The single function of $cM^{0.68}$ illustrated in Figs. 16–14 and 16–15 must fail as the concentration approaches the density of the pure poly-mer, because with vanishing diluent the relative viscosity η/η_s cannot of course remain the same for different solvents; all systems must approach the same η.

The above comparisons are all isothermal. The temperature de-pendence of viscosity is also a function of concentration, of course, and the apparent activation energy for viscous flow increases with c.

Data of the type portrayed here are usually obtained so far above T_g that the effect of diluent on temperature dependence cannot be described by the WLF equation with a changing T_s as discussed for data in the transition zone in Section A above. If it is described by an apparent activation energy ΔH_η over a limited temperature range, then for several polymers $\Delta H_\eta - \Delta H_{\eta_s} = kc$, roughly,[32, 37, 38] where ΔH_{η_s} is the apparent activation energy for the solvent. In several cases, k is of the order of 15 kcal./mole. If the data refer to a temperature range below T_g of the pure polymer, this linear relation must fail as the concentration approaches the density of the pure polymer and T_g of the mixture approaches the temperature of measurement. For a poor solvent, the departure from linearity apparently occurs at lower concentrations.[37]

For cellulose tributyrate solutions,[33] the above linear relation does *not* hold; there is an additional contribution to ΔH_η which depends on the molecular weight. It has been attributed to a change in the average spacing between entanglement coupling points with temperature, occasioned by the change in root-mean-square end-to-end distance which is characteristic of cellulose derivatives.[39]

From the dependence of viscosity on molecular weight at constant concentration, it should be possible in principle to calculate the average molecular weight of a strand of the entanglement network as done for undiluted polymers in Fig. 10–15, and thus to determine the value of n in the proposed relation $Z_e \propto c^{-n}$ introduced above. Unfortunately, the break in a plot of log η against log M is often difficult to specify in diluted systems. However, it has been concluded that $n = 1$ for polyisobutylene, polystyrene, and cellulose tributyrate.[33, 40] In view of the evidence given above that $n = 2.3$ to 2.6 for poly-*n*-butyl methacrylate, however, it appears to be impossible to draw any generalizations about this relationship at present.

4. Shapes of the Viscoelastic Functions

In the plateau and terminal zones in moderately concentrated polymer solutions, one of the most instructive functions is the dynamic viscosity η', which approaches the steady-flow viscosity η with decreasing frequency. This has already been illustrated for some solutions of polyisobutylene and cellulose tributyrate in Fig. 10–9, where it was pointed out that the differences between the observed behavior and the prediction of the Rouse theory in the terminal zone could be attributed to molecular weight heterogeneity.

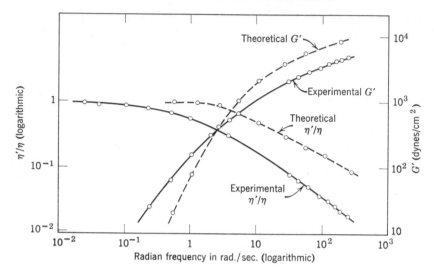

FIG. 16–16. Ratio η'/η and G' plotted logarithmically against frequency for an 8% solution of polyisobutylene, $\overline{M}_w = 1.1 \times 10^6$, in Decalin, with the theoretical curves from the Rouse theory.[23]

Another example for both η' and the storage modulus G' is given in Fig. 16–16 for an 8% solution of polyisobutylene in Decalin, weight-average molecular weight 1.1×10^6 (data of De Witt and associates [23]), together with the predictions of the Rouse theory. The latter require no adjustable parameters since in equation 21 the relaxation times are completely specified by knowledge of the molecular weight (the weight average being used here) and steady-flow viscosity. For η', the difference between theory and experiment appears largely as a shift in frequency scale by about a factor of six, although as expected for this sample of very broad molecular weight distribution the experimental curve changes slope more gradually. For G' the differences in slope and curvature, also attributable to the molecular weight heterogeneity, are much more apparent. Very similar comparisons have been made for concentrated aqueous polyvinyl alcohol solutions by Onogi and associates.[36] The agreement with the calculated values for both G' and η' would be better if a higher average such as the $z + 1$ were used for the molecular weight. As the plateau zone is entered at higher frequencies, η' falls much more steeply, as seen in Fig. 16–13, attaining a slope of -1 on a logarithmic plot instead of the $-\frac{1}{2}$ predicted by the Rouse theory.

Alternatively, the detailed viscoelastic behavior may be represented by the relaxation spectrum. An example in the terminal zone is shown in Fig. 16–17 for aqueous solutions of four polyvinyl alcohol samples of different molecular weights, compared at the same temperature and concentration.[36] The terminal zone shifts to longer times with something like the 4.5 power of M. This is in agreement with the expected behavior of the Rouse terminal relaxation time (proportional to ηM, and hence to $M^{4.4}$). However, the terminal zone is spread over several decades of time scale on account of the molecular weight heterogeneity in these samples.

If H is plotted logarithmically against τ/η, the proportionality of longest relaxation times to η is thereby reduced out, only the proportionality to M remaining. In practice the molecular weight distribution is more important than the magnitude of any average of M, as illustrated by terminal zone plots for 35% solutions of polymethyl methacrylate in dibutyl phthalate in Fig. 16–18. In these data of Watkins, Spangler, and McKannan,[41] the terminal zone of the spectrum is increasingly broadened and extended to longer times by increasing molecular weight heterogeneity. The relation of the shape

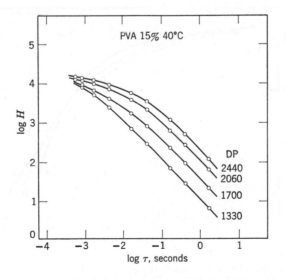

FIG. 16–17. Relaxation spectra in the terminal zone of four aqueous polyvinyl alcohol solutions, all at a concentration of 15% at 40°C., with different degrees of polymerization as indicated. (After Onogi, Hamana, and Hirai.[36])

of the spectrum in the terminal zone to molecular weight distribution
has been discussed in Section C of Chapter 10.

When the relaxation spectrum is reduced to a reference state of
unit concentration and viscosity, the proportionality of the terminal
relaxation times to η has again been reduced out, leaving only proportionality to M. In Fig. 16–19, spectra calculated from the data
of Fig. 16–13 and similarly for two other cellulose tributyrate fractions [26] are compared after reduction in this manner, and there is a
tendency for the terminal zone to shift to longer times with increasing
M as expected. Moreover, the level of H in the plateau zone drops
somewhat with increasing M, just as it does in undiluted polymers
(Fig. 13–6).

The plateau zone of H in cellulose tributyrate solutions appears to
be quite flat, rather than having the complicated curvature found in
many undiluted polymers (Figs. 3–3 and 13–6). In polyisobutylene
solutions,[24] it is flat for M of the order of 10^6, but for a smaller M it
is a monotonically decreasing function with a minimum negative slope
on a doubly logarithmic scale of about -0.25. The latter shape is
exhibited by several vinyl polymers of comparable molecular weights,

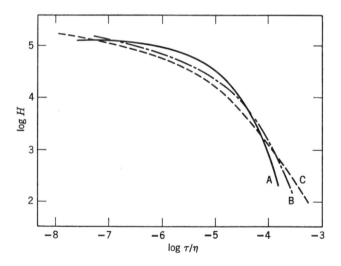

FIG. 16–18. Relaxation spectra plotted logarithmically against τ/η for 35% solutions of polymethyl methacrylate in dibutyl phthalate at 25°C. A, fraction with
$\bar{M}_n = 59,000$, $\bar{M}_w = 106,000$; B, unfractionated polymer with $\bar{M}_n = 42,000$, $\bar{M}_w =$
105,000; C, blend with $\bar{M}_w = 238,000$, $\bar{M}_z/\bar{M}_w = 2.3$ (calculated). (Data of Watkins, Spangler, and McKannan.[41])

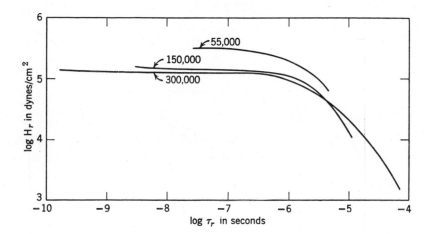

FIG. 16–19. Relaxation spectra in solution, reduced to unit viscosity and concentration, for the cellulose tributyrate of Fig. 16–13 ($M = 300,000$) and two other cellulose tributyrate fractions with molecular weights as indicated.[26]

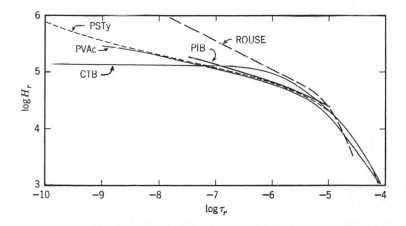

FIG. 16–20. Relaxation spectra in solution for several polymers of comparable molecular weight reduced to unit viscosity and concentration. CTB, cellulose tributyrate, $\bar{M}_\eta = 340,000$ (Fraction H of Fig. 16–19); PVAc, polyvinyl acetate in 1,2,3-trichloropropane,[40] $\bar{M}_w = 420,000$; PSTy, polystyrene in Decalin,[27] $\bar{M}_w = 370,000$; PIB, polyisobutylene in Decalin,[22] $\bar{M}_\eta = 320,000$. Rouse, Rouse theory for $M = 340,000$.

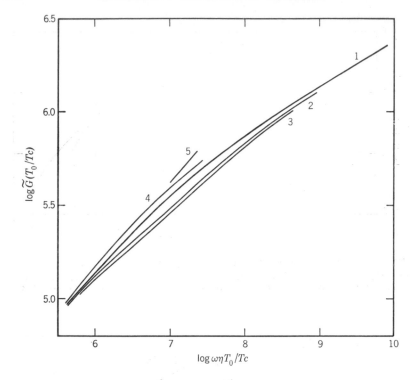

FIG. 16–21. Wave rigidity $\widetilde{G}$ reduced to unit viscosity and concentration, for concentrated solutions of polyvinyl acetate in 5 different solvents: 1, 1,2,3-trichloropropane; 2, methyl isobutyl ketone; 3, methyl ethyl ketone; 4, cyclohexanone; 5, diisobutyl ketone.[42]

as illustrated in Fig. 16–20 where the contrast between them and the cellulose tributyrate is evident. (For cellulose trinitrate in isophorone, molecular weight 145,000, the slope is of intermediate character,[27] about −0.15.) The relaxation spectrum calculated from the Rouse theory for a molecular weight of 340,000 is also indicated; for these moderately sharp fractions, it defines the position of the terminal zone reasonably well.

In a few cases where solutions in different solvents have been compared,[24, 42] the viscoelastic properties reduced to unit concentration and viscosity are almost independent of the nature of the solvent, even when the latter is so poor that the polymer is on the verge of phase separation. This is illustrated in Fig. 16–21 by the "wave-rigidity"

$\tilde{G}$ (approximately equal to G', as explained in Chapter 5, Section E) for concentrated solutions of polyvinyl acetate in five different solvents.[42] The solution in diisobutyl ketone was near the critical mixing point.

As a final example of a polymer with a very different molecular structure, Fig. 16–22 shows the relaxation spectrum of a 1.2% solution of aqueous sodium desoxyribonucleate,[43] weight-average molecular weight 5.8×10^6. This very stiff molecule, even at such a low concentration, exhibits the symptoms of extensive entanglement coupling in the form of a broad plateau in H. Nevertheless, the terminal relaxation time is given by the Rouse theory as $10^{1.95}$ sec., calculated by equation 21 with $p = 1$ and the measured viscosity of $10^{3.91}$ poises, in approximately the correct location. The plateau zone comprises a maximum and minimum as seen in many undiluted polymers of high molecular weights.

There are evidently no marked differences in the shapes of the viscoelastic functions for solutions which can be attributed to detailed chemical structure or polymer-solvent interaction. The most important features appear to be the stiffness of the chain backbone and the molecular weight heterogeneity. But it is not possible yet to specify their influence clearly.

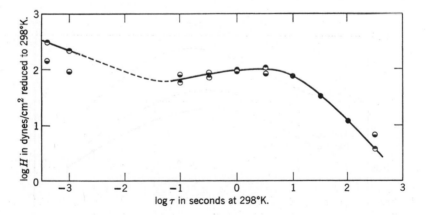

FIG. 16–22. Relaxation spectrum of aqueous sodium desoxyribonucleate, 0.012 g. polymer per cc., reduced to 25°C. (After Helders, Ferry, Markovitz, and Zapas.[43]) Points top black, calculated from G'; bottom black, from η'.

C. THE GLASSY STATE

There have been very few studies of viscoelastic properties of polymer solutions below T_g, partly perhaps because they are of little technical interest; plasticizers are generally introduced for the benefit of their influence above T_g.

Isothermal plots of tan δ against the logarithm of the frequency are given in Fig. 16–23 for polymethyl methacrylate and two plasticized compositions with dibutyl phthalate, encompassing the so-called β mechanism which, it will be recalled, occurs near a frequency of 1 cycle/sec. at room temperature (Chapter 14). In these results of Heijboer,[44] the shape of the maximum (which has been seen before in Fig. 14–3) is not much changed by the addition of diluent, but its height is increased; and the position of the maximum on the frequency scale is shifted slightly to higher frequencies. The latter displacement is much more moderate than that observed for the α mechanism (the primary transition between glasslike and rubberlike consistency) for small amounts of diluent as illustrated by Fig. 16–4. It undoubtedly represents a slight loosening of the local structure which facilitates the side group motions to which the β mechanism is attributed.

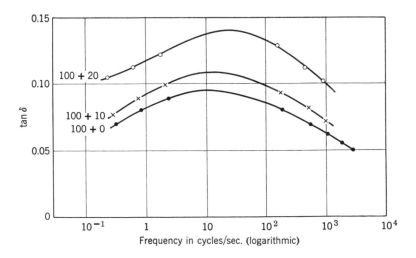

FIG. 16–23. Loss tangent plotted against logarithm of frequency at 40°C. for polymethyl methacrylate and two solutions containing dibutyl phthalate with weight compositions as indicated. (After Heijboer.[44])

In another investigation by Yamamoto and Wada [45] on polymethyl methacrylate containing very small amounts of water, up to 0.25%, isochronal plots of tan δ against temperature revealed a shift to *higher* temperatures with increasing moisture content. The reduction in local mobility which this implies was attributed to the ability of the small water molecules to fill voids in the polymer structure and thus diminish the fractional free volume. Such an interpretation would necessitate a very large negative value of k_v in equation 3 within the very limited concentration range where the polymer and diluent are compatible.

In lightly cross-linked polystyrene swollen with diethyl phthalate, the dispersion region identified by Illers and Jenckel [15] as the β mechanism shifts to lower temperatures, and that identified as the γ mechanism shifts to higher temperatures with increasing proportion of diluent. The γ maximum also becomes narrower on the frequency scale.

Some other examples involving longitudinal bulk wave propagation, which is dominated by compressibility rather than shear effects, will be mentioned in Chapter 18.

REFERENCES

1. F. E. Helders and J. D. Ferry, *J. Phys. Chem.* **60**, 1536 (1956).
2. E. Jenckel and R. Heusch, *Kolloid-Z.*, **130**, 89 (1953).
3. T. G. Fox, *Bull. Amer. Phys. Soc.*, [2], **1**, 123 (1956).
4. H. Fujita and A. Kishimoto, *J. Polymer Sci.*, **28**, 547 (1958).
5. J. D. Ferry and R. A. Stratton, *Kolloid-Z.*, **171**, 107 (1960).
6. A. K. Doolittle, *J. Applied Phys.*, **23**, 236 (1952).
7. P. R. Saunders, D. M. Stern, S. F. Kurath, C. Sakoonkim, and J. D. Ferry, *J. Colloid Sci.*, **14**, 222 (1959).
8. M. L. Williams and J. D. Ferry, *J. Colloid Sci.*, **10**, 474 (1955).
9. M. L. Williams and J. D. Ferry, *J. Colloid Sci.*, **9**, 479 (1954).
10. M. L. Williams and J. D. Ferry, *J. Colloid Sci.*, **10**, 1 (1955).
11. E. Jenckel, in H. A. Stuart, *Die Physik der Hochpolymeren*, Vol. IV, p. 566, Springer-Verlag, Berlin, 1956.
12. S. Prager and F. A. Long, *J. Amer. Chem. Soc.*, **73**, 4072 (1951).
13. H. Fujita and A. Kishimoto, *Bull. Chem. Soc. Japan*, **33**, 274 (1960); *J. Polymer Sci.*, (in press).
14. W. C. Child, Jr., and J. D. Ferry, *J. Colloid Sci.*, **12**, 327 (1957).
15. K. H. Illers and E. Jenckel, *Rheol. Acta*, **1**, 322 (1958).
16. J. D. Ferry, *J. Amer. Chem. Soc.*, **72**, 3746 (1950).
17. A. W. Nolle and J. F. Mifsud, *J. Applied Phys.*, **24**, 5 (1953).

18. E. Catsiff, T. Alfrey, Jr., and M. T. O'Shaugnessy, *Textile Research J.*, **23**, 808 (1953).
19. T. Yoshitomi, K. Nagamatsu, and K. Kosiyama, *J. Polymer Sci.*, **27**, 335 (1958).
20. B. A. Dunell and J. M. R. Quistwater, *J. Chem. Phys.*, **29**, 450 (1958).
21. J. W. Berge, P. R. Saunders, and J. D. Ferry, *J. Colloid Sci.*, **14**, 135 (1959).
22. P. R. Saunders and J. D. Ferry, *J. Colloid Sci.*, **14**, 239 (1959).
23. T. W. De Witt, H. Markovitz, F. J. Padden, Jr., and L. J. Zapas, *J. Colloid Sci.*, **10**, 174 (1955).
24. J. D. Ferry, L. Jordan, W. W. Evans, and M. F. Johnson, *J. Polymer Sci.*, **14**, 261 (1954).
25. M. R. Hatfield and G. B. Rathmann, *J. Applied Phys.*, **25**, 1082 (1954).
26. R. F. Landel and J. D. Ferry, *J. Phys. Chem.*, **59**, 658 (1955).
27. D. J. Plazek and J. D. Ferry, *J. Phys. Chem.*, **60**, 289 (1956).
28. J. D. Ferry, W. M. Sawyer, G. V. Browning, and A. H. Groth, Jr., *J. Applied Phys.*, **21**, 513 (1950).
29. L. D. Grandine, Jr., and J. D. Ferry, *J. Applied Phys.*, **24**, 679 (1953).
30. T. Takemura, *J. Polymer Sci.*, **28**, 185 (1958).
31. A. K. Doolittle, in *Colloid Chemistry,* edited by J. Alexander, Vol. VII, Chapter 8, Reinhold Publishing Corp., 1950.
32. M. F. Johnson, W. W. Evans, I. Jordan, and J. D. Ferry, *J. Colloid Sci.*, **7**, 498 (1952).
33. R. F. Landel, J. W. Berge, and J. D. Ferry, *J. Colloid Sci.*, **12**, 400 (1957).
34. F. Bueche, *J. Applied Phys.*, **24**, 423 (1953).
35. F. Bueche, *J. Applied Phys.*, **26**, 738 (1955).
36. S. Onogi, I. Hamana, and H. Hirai, *J. Applied Phys.*, **29**, 1503 (1958).
37. J. D. Ferry, E. L. Foster, G. V. Browning, and W. M. Sawyer, *J. Colloid Sci.*, **6**, 377 (1951).
38. J. D. Ferry, L. D. Grandine, Jr., and D. C. Udy, *J. Colloid Sci.*, **8**, 529 (1953).
39. L. Mandelkern and P. J. Flory, *J. Amer. Chem. Soc.*, **74**, 2517 (1952).
40. T. G. Fox and S. Loshaek, *J. Applied Phys.*, **26**, 1080 (1955).
41. J. M. Watkins, R. D. Spangler, and E. C. McKannan, *J. Applied Phys.*, **27**, 685 (1956).
42. W. M. Sawyer and J. D. Ferry, *J. Amer. Chem. Soc.*, **72**, 5030 (1950).
43. F. E. Helders, J. D. Ferry, H. Markovitz, and L. J. Zapas, *J. Phys. Chem.*, **60**, 1575 (1956).
44. J. Heijboer, *Kolloid-Z.*, **148**, 36 (1956).
45. K. Yamamoto and Y. Wada, *J. Phys. Soc. Japan*, **12**, 374 (1957).

CHAPTER 17

Gels and Cross-Linked Solutions

Although the term "gel" has been used with varied and imprecise implications in the literature, we shall adopt the definition that it is a substantially diluted system which exhibits no steady-state flow. A polymer gel is then a moderately dilute cross-linked solution, whether linked by chemical bonds or crystallites or some other kind of junction. The present chapter is concerned with cross-linked solutions in general, both those sufficiently dilute to be called gelatinous and more concentrated systems such as plasticized polyvinyl chloride, whose network structure arises from a small degree of crystallinity.

A distinction must be drawn between gels which are diluted first and then cross-linked and those which are cross-linked first and then swollen.[1,2] In the former, the network strands have their average random configurations in the unstrained state (except perhaps for gels linked at quite high dilution, where the polymer coils overlap each others' domains only to a limited extent). In the latter, however, the strands are all extended beyond their normal root-mean-square lengths, in proportion to the cube root of the swelling factor ρ/c. For such systems, the flexible chain theories of viscoelastic behavior may require modification. However, there is very little experimental information about them, most investigations having been concerned with gels of the former type.

As in the preceding chapter, the discussion may be divided into consideration of different characteristic zones.

A. PSEUDO-EQUILIBRIUM MECHANICAL PROPERTIES

Almost all studies of viscoelastic properties have been made on gels whose cross-links can be dissociated by an increase in temperature. This is of course the case when the cross-links are crystallites, as generally inferred for gels of polyvinyl chloride,[3] polyacrylonitrile,[4] and cellulose nitrate;[5] and also in gelatin[6] and pectin[7] where the mechanism of linkage, though still in doubt, may involve some kind of highly specific secondary attractive forces between certain loci on the polymer chains. The fact that crystallites melt or secondary bonds dissociate with rising temperature implies an equilibrium, or quasi-equilibrium, with the consequence that the number of linkages also changes with changing polymer concentration. This feature complicates the effects of concentration on all the viscoelastic properties, and has the disadvantage that the degree of cross-linking cannot be varied independently of the temperature or concentration.

The most direct measure of the density of cross-linking is the average degree of polymerization per network strand, Z_c, calculated in accordance with the statistical theory of rubberlike elasticity by the equation (cf. Chapter 10, Section E)

$$Z_c = cRT/G_e M_0 \tag{1}$$

where c is as usual the concentration in g. polymer per cc., and G_e is the pseudo-equilibrium shear modulus measured under circumstances where the effects of the slow changes to be described in Section C below are small. However, this equation may be subject to a severe correction for loose molecular ends if the molecular weight before gelation is small or the polymer contains species of low molecular weight.[8]

1. Aging Effects

The term "pseudo-equilibrium" in the title of this section refers not only to the impossibility of obtaining a strict stress-strain equilibrium in a network polymer as discussed at the end of Section E of Chapter 10, but also to the frequent failure to obtain thermodynamic equilibrium with respect to the unstressed state of a gel network following a change in temperature. A gel system is usually mixed at a temperature well above the melting points of crystallites, or so high that no links due to secondary bonds are present, and then cooled to a temperature at which the cross-links will form. The pseudo-equilibrium modulus increases rapidly with time as the network is built up, but it does not approach a limiting value; it goes on increasing for long periods of time. An extreme example is shown in Fig. 17–1 for gels of polyacrylonitrile in dimethyl formamide containing 20% polymer, studied by Bisschops.[4] The pseudo-equilibrium modulus increases linearly with time at a rate which increases rapidly with decreasing temperature. The rate is also very strongly dependent on concentration, being proportional to something like c^{22} in a narrow range between 18 and 23% concentration by weight. The temperature and concentration dependence can be interpreted in terms of the rate of nucleation of the crystallites which act as cross-linking points in the network whose elasticity is being measured.

In other cases, the changes with time are slower, as for polyacrylonitrile in dimethyl acetamide,[4] cellulose trinitrate in isophorone,[9] and polyvinyl chloride in di-2-ethylhexyl phthalate.[3] In the latter, and in other polymers with structural irregularity due to lack of tactic

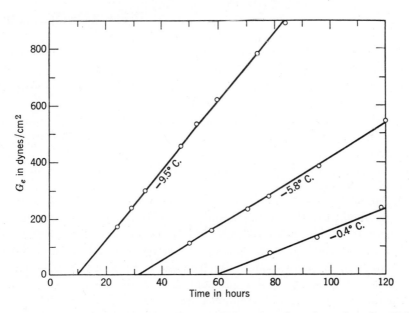

FIG. 17–1. Pseudo-equilibrium shear modulus plotted against time for 20% gels of polyacrylonitrile in dimethyl formamide, aged at the three temperatures indicated. (After Bisschops.[4])

order or copolymerization, the degree of crystallinity is presumably limited [10,11] and the increase in G_e with time eventually becomes sufficiently slow to permit viscoelastic measurements on a reasonably stable sample. In some cases, it is desirable to age a gel for many weeks prior to viscoelastic measurements.

Changes in temperature after the network is established lead to complicated hysteretic effects [3,4] which can be interpreted qualitatively in terms of the relative stabilities of crystallites formed at different temperatures. Those formed at the highest temperatures are most resistant to melting,[12,13] and the resistance to melting also increases with aging.[3] Similar phenomena are evident in gelatin gels [1] although it is not certain whether the linkages here can be described as crystallites. The network (as measured by the magnitude of G_e) is somewhat more stable with respect to time when a gel is aged at a low temperature and then brought to a somewhat higher temperature and kept there until the weaker crystallites have melted.

2. Dependence of Pseudo-Equilibrium Modulus on Temperature and Concentration

In gels as in other cross-linked systems there is a pseudo-equilibrium zone where the modulus changes only slightly with time or frequency (Curves V in Chapter 2), and corresponds approximately to the equilibrium modulus of equation 1. It should accordingly be directly proportional to the absolute temperature. In some gels with permanent chemical cross-linkages, this proportionality has been confirmed.[14] In those with dissociable or fusible cross-links, it can hold only in a temperature range where the network density has attained its maximum value. This is fulfilled,[3] for example, for a 10% gel of polyvinyl chloride in di-2-ethylhexyl phthalate between $-30°$ and $25°C$. Another example is shown in Fig. 17–2 for gels of polyvinyl alcohol with Congo red in water, from measurements of Hirai.[15] From $0°$ to about $40°$ the proportionality to T is followed, but at higher temperatures the modulus drops rapidly as the cross-links (whatever they are—caused by some sort of secondary associative forces) dissociate and Z_c correspondingly increases. In many gels, such as aqueous gelatin, the latter phenomenon dominates over the entire experimentally accessible temperature range, and the modulus is a monotonically decreasing function with increasing temperature, as illustrated [16] in Fig. 17–3. It vanishes above a melting point which

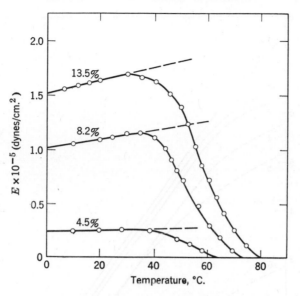

FIG. 17–2. Pseudo-equilibrium modulus (presumably shear) plotted against temperature for three aqueous gels of polyvinyl alcohol with 0.5% Congo Red, at three polymer concentrations as indicated (after Hirai [15]).

represents the melting or dissociation temperature of the strongest linkages present.

The concentration dependence of the pseudo-equilibrium modulus can be expressed by a power relation over a moderate range of concentration, as illustrated for gels of polyvinyl chloride in Fig. 17–4. The slope of the linear portion of this doubly logarithmic plot is 3.47. Slopes between 3 and 4 are obtained for polyvinyl chloride gels in many other solvents. For gelatin gels in water, on the other hand, the slope of this plot is usually [1,6] close to 2.

At very high polymer concentrations the modulus veers sharply upward from the linear power relation, in a range where its magnitude is approaching that of a hard solid. The network is so dense here that the strands are not long enough to execute the configurational changes required for rubberlike elasticity. The viscoelastic properties of such solutions, like those of the densely netted systems briefly referred to in Chapter 15, could not be described in terms of flexible chain theories. At the other end of the concentration scale, the modulus drops sharply as the concentration decreases toward the minimum value

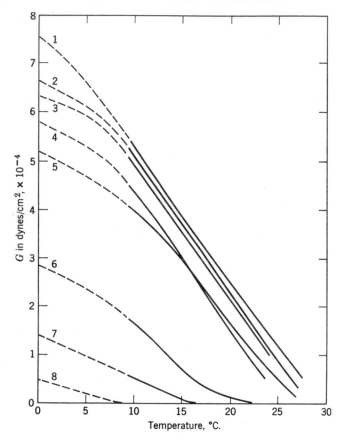

FIG. 17–3. Pseudo-equilibrium shear modulus plotted against temperature for aqueous gels of various gelatins at a concentration of 4 g./100 cc. (The gelatins had undergone different chemical and thermal treatments in their preparation.) The dashed segments refer to a temperature range in which aging processes were too slow to approach an equilibrium structure.[16]

needed for establishment of a network. In accordance with the theory of gel formation,[17] a minimum of two linkages (weight average) per molecule is required for the latter. The minimum concentration for gelation increases of course with increasing temperature and decreasing molecular weight. Below this minimum concentration, there is no pseudo-equilibrium modulus, and the viscoelastic properties are those of an uncross-linked solution as described in Chapter 16 (containing, however, a substantial proportion of branched aggregates

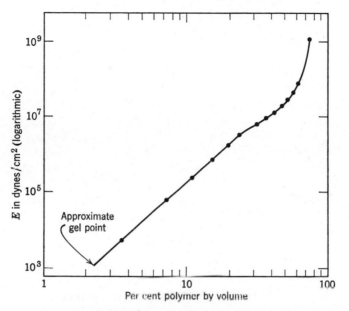

FIG. 17–4. Pseudo-equilibrium Young's modulus plotted logarithmically against polymer concentration by volume for gels of polyvinyl chloride in di-2-ethyl-hexyl phthalate near room temperature, after aging 30 days. (After Walter.[3])

if the concentration is only slightly below the gel point [5,18]—which would influence the relaxation spectrum as discussed in Chapter 10, Section C).

If the cross-links were formed by a binary association equilibrium between loci on the polymer chains, and the fraction of such loci combined were small, Z_c should be proportional to c^{-1} and hence G_e to c^2 as observed for gelatin at moderate concentrations.[1] This calculation, however, implies that the molecular weight is high enough so that $Z \gg Z_c$ and the loose ends of the network can be neglected. Actually, gel networks are often so imperfect, with so many loose ends, that when Z_c is calculated from measured values of G_e by equation 1 with no loose end correction the result [3,14] is higher than Z! The presence of these imperfections, arising from the fact that Z_c is of the same order of magnitude as Z and, usually, from molecular weight heterogeneity, together with the probable feature that in crystallite networks the junctions are multiple with many chains radiating from a linkage, make the concentration dependence of G_e difficult to formulate theoretically.

There are also gels in which G_e decreases rapidly with decreasing temperature (much more rapidly than proportional to T) and vanishes below a sort of inverted melting point.[5, 19] This phenomenon arises from an unusual thermodynamic interaction between polymer and solvent, causing crystallites (or association linkages) to be stable at higher temperatures.[5]

In gels with permanent cross-links formed before dilution, equation 1 does not hold because of the abnormal extensions of the network strands, leading to an additional factor of $(c/\rho)^{-2/3}$ according to the statistical theory.[2] In such gels, there is of course no change in Z_c with concentration, so that the concentration dependence of G_e reflects the change in c alone.

B. THE TRANSITION ZONE FROM RUBBERLIKE TO GLASSLIKE CONSISTENCY

A lightly cross-linked gel resembles in many respects a cross-linked undiluted polymer such as a vulcanized rubber, with the local friction coefficient diminished by the presence of diluent. The transition from rubberlike to glasslike consistency which it manifests at sufficiently short times or high frequencies can be described much as those in Chapter 12.

1. The Temperature Dependence of Relaxation and Retardation Times

The comments in the preceding chapter on the effects of diluent on temperature dependence hold for gels as for concentrated (uncross-linked) solutions essentially without modification. The diluted systems in Tables 11–II and 11–III involving polyvinyl chloride and cellulose tributyrate are gels, and in each the temperature dependence can be described by the WLF equation with a characteristic parameter T_s or with T_g, f_g, and α_f. Thus again the primary effect of the diluent is to depress T_s or T_g. The presence of the cross-linking may be expected to make T_g slightly higher than it would be in an uncrosslinked solution of the same concentration,[20] but this is a minor consideration.

For a gel at a single concentration, reduced variables cannot be used to describe the temperature dependence of viscoelastic properties unless the degree of cross-linking changes negligibly within the temperature range covered or else the frequency or time scale is such that the measurements reflect rearrangements of chain segments short enough to be oblivious of the cross-links. In a number of cases, however, these qualifications have been fulfilled, permitting the construction of composite viscoelastic functions over a wide range of temperatures.[21, 22]

2. Location of the Transition Zone on the Time or Frequency Scale

As in uncross-linked solutions, the monomeric friction coefficient increases very rapidly with increasing polymer concentration. For example, in gels of polyvinyl chloride in dimethyl thianthrene,[21, 23, 24] log ζ_0 is -5.58 and -1.26 at 25°C. for polymer concentrations of 10% and 40% by volume, respectively. If an exponential concentration dependence is assumed as in equation 5 of Chapter 16, the coefficient of c is 24. Thus, the dependence is quite similar in magnitude to that observed in the few uncross-linked systems for which data are available, and the cross-links do not appear to influence the local chain rearrangements as long as they are not too closely spaced.

A similar result is obtained for gels of cellulose tributyrate in dimethyl phthalate,[22] as shown in Fig. 17-5 where the relaxation spectra are plotted for three concentrations reduced to -25°C. The highest two do not achieve a slope of $-\frac{1}{2}$ within the experimental range covered, so log ζ_0 can be calculated only for the 20.4% gel (-2.3 at -25°C.). However, the separation on the logarithmic time scale near log $H = 6.5$ between this and the 42.6% gel corresponds to an exponent of about $22c$ in a relation of the form of equation 5 in Chapter 16.

In Fig. 17-5, the relaxation spectrum for the 42.6% gel is somewhat higher after cooling below -25°; the difference was attributed to additional cross-linking by growth of crystallites as described in the preceding section. For the 57.5% gel, the method of reduced variables was applicable only over a very limited temperature range; it was concluded that there were substantial changes in the degree of cross-linking with temperature.[22]

3. Shapes of the Viscoelastic Functions

It is instructive to examine the frequency dependence of G' and tan δ for the cellulose tributyrate gels described above, as portrayed in Fig. 17-6. The limiting low-frequency or pseudo-equilibrium modulus increases rapidly with concentration, approximately with the 2.6 power, intermediate between the exponents for polyvinyl chloride and for gelatin quoted in the preceding section. But the limiting high-frequency modulus can be expected to depend much less, if at

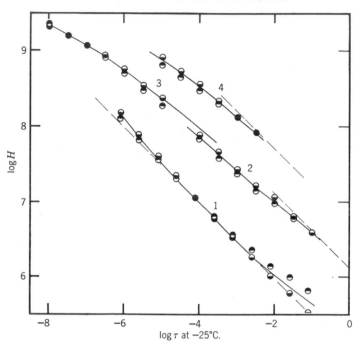

FIG. 17–5. Relaxation spectra for gels of cellulose tributyrate in dimethyl phthalate [22], reduced to −25°C. Polymer concentrations in weight per cent: 1, 20.4; 2, 42.6% before cooling below −25°; 3, 42.6% after cooling below −25°; 4, 57.5%.

all, on concentration, since those for polymers and ordinary vitrifying liquids are similar in magnitude (Chapter 16). The transition from rubberlike to glasslike consistency must in general become more gradual with increasing concentration, not because of the effect of concentration itself but because of the associated change in cross-linking. This feature is reflected in the loss tangent curves, which become increasingly broader with increasing concentration.

In spite of the broadening of the transition, there should always be a region of H at the long-time end of the transition where the theoretical slope of $-\frac{1}{2}$ is followed and accordingly ζ_0 can be calculated by equation 1 of Chapter 12—provided that the spacing between cross-links is long enough to fulfill the criterion of Gaussian statistics assumed in the flexible chain theories. In accordance with Chapter 10, Z_c should be at least of the order of 20. In practice, this restric-

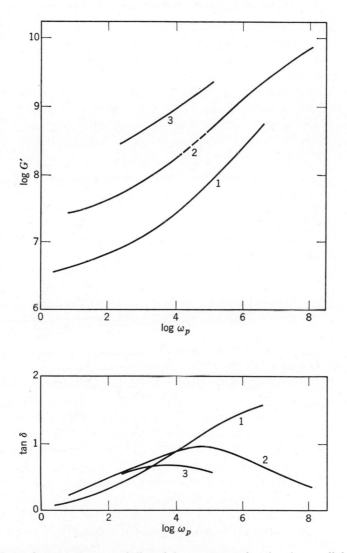

FIG. 17-6. Storage shear moduli and loss tangents for the three cellulose tri-butyrate gels described in Fig. 17-5, similarly identified.

tion appears to be too severe, for Z_c in the 20.4% cellulose tributyrate gel as calculated from equation 1 is 3.5, and for the 42.6% gel it is only a little over unity (*cf.* Table 13–I). The cellobiose monomer unit probably has considerable internal flexibility in this case. But whenever a gel is too densely netted for the strands to rearrange their configurations with a wide latitude of choice, it may be anticipated that the flexible chain theories will not describe its properties; the relaxation spectrum will nowhere achieve a slope as steep as $-\frac{1}{2}$, and no friction coefficient can be calculated (*cf.* Chapter 15).

4. Isochronal Viscoelastic Measurements

When the transition between rubberlike and glasslike consistency is traversed by changing the temperature at approximately constant frequency (or time), the characteristic inflection in modulus is observed, as for undiluted polymers (*cf.* Fig. 12–3). Examples are given in Fig. 17–7, where log G' and tan δ derived from dynamic measurements at about 1 cycle/sec. are plotted against temperature for plasticized compositions of polyvinyl chloride in diethylhexyl succinate ranging from 41% to 100% polymer. (The lower concentrations, at least, could be described as gels.) The effect of changing concentration must include its effects on ζ_0 and the shapes of the viscoelastic functions as well as on the temperature dependence of a_T. The location of the maximum shifts rapidly to higher temperatures with increasing concentration as in Fig. 16–8. With increasing c, the transition first becomes more gradual, evidenced by the decrease in steepness at the inflection of G' and the flattening in tan δ; this corresponds to the same trend in the isothermal viscoelastic functions as in Fig. 17–6. As the composition approaches pure polymer, however, the transition on the temperature scale sharpens again. It is difficult to interpret the latter phenomenon without knowledge of the individual functions $a_T(T)$ and $G'(\omega)$. It may, however, be associated with the melting of some crystallites and consequent loosening of the network in the high-temperature range where the high-concentration data fall. Similar isochronal measurements have been reported by other investigators.[26] An example for gels with permanent cross-links was given in the preceding chapter (Fig. 16–8).

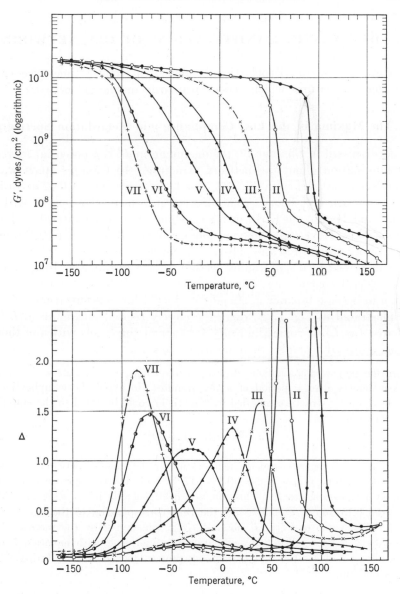

FIG. 17–7. Log G' and Δ plotted against temperature for measurements at approximately 1 cycle/sec. on polyvinyl chloride plasticized with diethylhexyl succinate, with compositions as indicated: I, 100% polymer; II, 91%; III, 79%; IV, 70.5%; V, 60.7%; VI, 51.8%; VII, 40.8%. (After Schmieder and Wolf.[25])

C. VISCOELASTIC MANIFESTATIONS OF GEL NETWORKS

Turning now to viscoelastic phenomena at longer times, we encounter the features which depend primarily on the gel network.

1. The Maxima in the Loss Compliance and Retardation Spectrum

As discussed in Chapter 13, the maximum in J'' is a potential source of information about the network structure. In Chapter 10, it was mentioned that the ratio J''_{max}/J_e should have a value of 0.42 according to the Bueche theory (somewhat lower values according to Kirkwood and Hammerle-Kirkwood); cf. equation 1 of Chapter 13. For cross-linked Hevea and polyurethane rubbers, this ratio is 0.21 and 0.22 respectively. For the polyvinyl chloride and cellulose tributyrate gels described in the preceding section, it is 0.20 to 0.28. In spite of this general concurrence, however, there is a tendency for the maximum to become broader in shape with increasing concentration. This is illustrated in Fig. 17–8 where the closely related maximum in L is plotted (as L/J_e) logarithmically for four of these gels with the time scale adjusted to make their positions coincide.

In the polyacrylonitrile gels studied by Bisschops,[4, 27] creep measurements taken quickly over a period of a few minutes (to avoid the complications of the changing structure revealed by Fig. 17–1) could be fitted to the empirical equation

$$J(t) = J_e At^n/(1 + At^n) \qquad (2)$$

where $n = 0.75$ regardless of the temperature or the stage of network buildup (i.e., the history in the sense of Fig. 17–1) and A was approximately inversely proportional to J_e. This equation held generally in the range of J/J_e between 0.15 and 1, encompassing the time corresponding to the maximum in L. The value of J''_{max}/J_e obtained from equation 2 by the methods of Chapter 4 is $n\pi/8 = 0.29$. Combination of equation 2 with equation 5 of Chapter 13 would imply that ζ_0 increases proportional to $J_e^{-0.67}$ during network buildup.

2. Behavior at Very Long Times

In describing the mechanical response of gel networks at long times, it is necessary to distinguish between conditions where the cross-links are stable and where they may be forming and dissociating during the period of the experiment. In the former case, the behavior resembles that of permanently cross-linked networks as discussed in Section C of Chapter 13. The relaxation of stress beyond the pseudo-equilibrium value, or the additional creep beyond the pseudo-equilibrium compliance, is very slight. Creep measurements have been fitted [28-30] to an equation of the Andrade form, equation 10 of Chapter 13.

If, on the other hand, cross-links are forming and dissociating while the measurements are in progress, phenomena similar to chemical stress relaxation (Section E of Chapter 13) may be encountered. The stress may drop nearly to zero in a stress relaxation process, whereas the shear modulus as measured in a moderately rapid deformation (corresponding to the pseudo-equilibrium zone of time scale) remains nearly unchanged.[31] Such behavior, observed in gelatin gels at temperatures not far below the gel melting point, has been attributed to

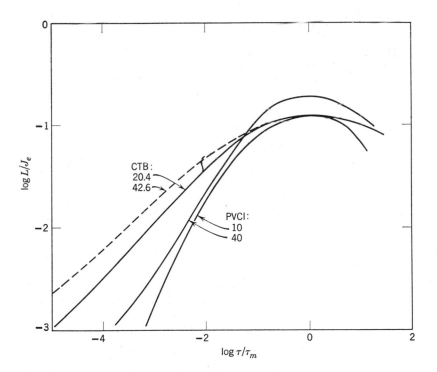

FIG. 17-8. L/J_e in the vicinity of its maximum plotted logarithmically against τ/τ_{max} for two polyvinyl chloride gels in dimethyl thianthrene and two cellulose tributyrate gels in dimethyl phthalate, with concentrations as indicated (volume and weight per cent, respectively).

the dissociation of cross-links and the formation of new ones with the network strands in unstressed configurations.[31] The dissociation of the linkages cannot be described by a single rate constant, however, as in the chemical scission of networks. The relaxation is gradual, corresponding to a broad spectrum. It is slower at lower temperatures and slower in gels which have been aged longer.

Useful information about this complicated phenomenon can be obtained by reverse relaxation experiments, as illustrated in Fig. 17–9. Here [31] a 5.9% aqueous gelatin gel was aged for 12.3 hours at 20.2°C. A small shearing strain was suddenly imposed, and the instantaneous stress corresponded to a shear modulus of 0.73×10^4 dynes/cm^2. After 24 hrs., the stress had relaxed to 0.35 of its initial value. The strain was then returned to zero. The change in stress corresponded to a shear modulus of 0.99×10^4; *i.e.*, the rigidity had increased slightly while the stress was relaxing, indicating that while some links were breaking a somewhat greater number were forming. During the next 24 hrs., the new stress, opposite in direction to the original, relaxed to 0.31 of its initial value. Then the strain was imposed again as in the original deformation, and the change in stress corresponded to a shear modulus of 0.91×10^4.

In such experiments, for a constant period of aging before the initial relaxation, the longer the period of the initial relaxation the slower is the reverse

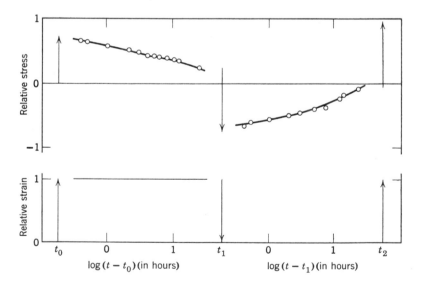

FIG. 17–9. Stress relaxation in a 5.9% aqueous gelatin gel at 20.2°C. (For explanation see text.)

relaxation; the new bonds formed in the strained state have more time to anneal and develop resistance to dissociation. But when the period of initial relaxation is kept constant and the period of aging preceding it is varied, a long aging period is followed by a rapid reverse relaxation. This is the result of the slow initial relaxation in a well-aged gel, which does not allow the new bonds to form until toward the end of the initial relaxation period, leaving them relatively weak.

In general, these results can be interpreted in terms of a complicated steady state of making and breaking of linkages, in which the longer a given linkage lasts without dissociation, the smaller its probability of dissociation becomes.

An alternative interpretation of the stress relaxation in gelatin gels has been proposed by Tobolsky,[32] in terms of prolongation of crystallites in the direction of elongation (or at 45° to the direction of slide, in shear) as mentioned in Chapter 15. It appears to be difficult to reconcile this picture with all the details of the experimental observations, but no definite conclusions can be reached at present.

REFERENCES

1. J. D. Ferry, *Adv. Protein Chem.*, **4**, 1 (1948).
2. P. J. Flory, *J. Amer. Chem. Soc.*, **78**, 5222 (1956).
3. A. T. Walter, *J. Polymer Sci.*, **13**, 207 (1954).
4. J. Bisschops, *J. Polymer Sci.*, **17**, 89 (1955).
5. S. Newman, W. R. Krigbaum, and D. K. Carpenter, *J. Phys. Chem.*, **60**, 648 (1956).
6. G. Stainsby, Ed., *Recent Advances in Gelatin and Glue Research*, Pergamon Press, London, 1958.
7. H. Deuel, J. Solms, and H. Altermatt, *Vierteljahrss. Naturf. Ges. Zürich*, **98**, 49 (1953).
8. P. J. Flory, *Principles of Polymer Chemistry*, Cornell University Press, Ithaca, 1953, Chapter IX and p. 463.
9. D. J. Plazek and J. D. Ferry, *J. Phys. Chem.*, **60**, 289 (1956).
10. B. D. Coleman, *J. Polymer Sci.*, **31**, 155 (1958).
11. F. E. Bailey, Jr., and R. D. Lundberg, *Abstr. American Chemical Society*, Chicago, 1958, p. 2T.
12. L. A. Wood, *Adv. Colloid Sci.*, **2**, 57 (1946).
13. L. Mandelkern, *Chem. Rev.*, **56**, 903 (1956).
14. P. R. Saunders and A. G. Ward, in *Rheology of Elastomers*, edited by P Mason and N. Wookey, Pergamon Press, London, 1958, p. 45.
15. N. Hirai, *Bull. Inst. Chem. Res. Kyoto Univ.*, **33**, 21 (1955).
16. J. D. Ferry, *J. Amer. Chem. Soc.*, **70**, 2244 (1948).
17. P. J. Flory, Reference 8, Chapter IX.
18. H. Boedtker and P. Doty, *J. Phys. Chem.*, **58**, 968 (1954).
19. A. K. Doolittle, *Ind. Eng. Chem.*, **38**, 535 (1946).
20. T. G. Fox and S. Loshaek, *J. Polymer Sci.*, **15**, 371 (1955).

21. J. D. Ferry and E. R. Fitzgerald, *J. Colloid Sci.*, **8,** 224 (1953).
22. R. F. Landel and J. D. Ferry, *J. Phys. Chem.*, **60,** 294 (1956).
23. J. D. Ferry, R. F. Landel, and M. L. Williams, *J. Applied Phys.*, **26,** 359 (1955).
24. J. D. Ferry, D. J. Plazek, and G. E. Heckler, *J. chim. phys.*, **55,** 152 (1958).
25. K. Schmieder and K. Wolf, *Kolloid-Z.*, **127,** 65 (1952).
26. L. E. Nielsen, R. Buchdahl, and R. Levreault, *J. Applied Phys.*, **21,** 607 (1950).
27. J. Bisschops, *J. Polymer Sci.*, **12,** 583 (1954).
28. L. N. G. Filon and H. T. Jessop, *Phil. Trans. Roy. Soc.*, **A223,** 89 (1928).
29. D. J. Plazek, *J. Colloid Sci.*, **15,** 50 (1960).
30. D. J. Plazek, Unpublished experiments.
31. M. Miller, J. D. Ferry, F. W. Schremp, and J. E. Eldridge, *J. Phys. Colloid Chem.*, **55,** 1387 (1951).
32. A. V. Tobolsky, *J. Phys. Chem.*, **59,** 575 (1955).

CHAPTER 18

Viscoelastic Behavior in Bulk (Volume) Deformation

The scarcity of information on viscoelastic behavior in bulk compression of polymers was mentioned in Chapter 2; the survey there of typical polymeric systems, whose more detailed examination has occupied the preceding seven chapters, was limited to behavior in shear and extension. The response to confining pressure may be regarded as primarily a collapse of free volume, as discussed in Chapter 11, together with a smaller contraction due to distortion of molecular domains such as would occur in compression of a hard solid. No long-range configurational rearrangements are of course involved, though local adjustments accompany the collapse of free volume.

In the present chapter we shall discuss a few examples in which the time-dependent bulk behavior has been evaluated, and then some related investigations in which the bulk longitudinal modulus M^* has been measured, reflecting a combination of bulk and shear properties.

A. VISCOELASTIC BEHAVIOR IN BULK COMPRESSION

That the response of a polymer to bulk compression can be time-dependent is illustrated by Fig. 18–1, in which the pressure is plotted against relative volume change for polystyrene (above T_g) subjected to various rates of compression by Matsuoka and Maxwell.[1] This experiment corresponds to taking a stress-strain curve at constant rate of strain in shear or elongation; the more rapid the experiment, the higher the stress at any given strain, and if the behavior is linear the

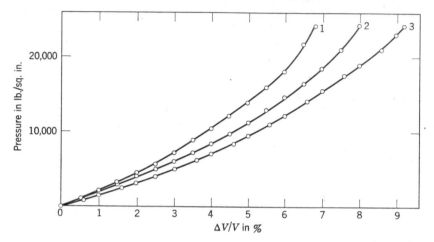

FIG. 18–1. Pressure plotted against proportional volume change for polystyrene compressed at 149°C. The ratios of rates of volume change are 1:0.16:0.012 for Curves 1, 2, and 3. (After Matsuoka and Maxwell.[1])

ordinary viscoelastic functions can be calculated from such curves by differentiation (equation 59 of Chapter 4, for example). Time-dependent behavior in bulk creep has also been investigated by Jenckel and Gehrke.[2]

There is an unusual non-linear feature in such volume changes which is entirely foreign to shear and elongation phenomena.[3,4] Implicit in the dependence of relaxation times on free volume (as reflected in their dependence on temperature, pressure, side group length, and diluent, treated in earlier chapters) is the conclusion that the relaxation times must be progressively lengthened during the experiment as the macroscopic volume decrease is accompanied by collapse of free volume. The previous free volume treatments have of course been concerned with relaxation times in shear, but the temperature dependence of relaxation times appears to be the same in bulk as in shear for polystyrene and polyvinyl acetate (from the isothermal contraction experiments of Kovacs,[4] Fig. 11–9) and for polyisobutylene and natural rubber (from the dynamic measurements of Marvin and collaborators [5,6] to be discussed below). Hence it may be inferred that the relaxation or retardation times characterizing the course of bulk contraction will also increase as the contraction proceeds. As a result, an inherently narrow distribution of relaxation times could give rise to a very gradual relaxation or volume creep process. To avoid this effect it would be necessary that the proportional volume change due to confining pressure be very small compared with the initial fractional free volume f. This condition may be met in dynamic but ordinarily not in transient experiments.

1. Analysis of Isothermal Volume Contraction

When an amorphous polymer is suddenly cooled to a temperature T in the neighborhood of its T_g, the isothermal contraction of volume follows a gradual course [3,4] such as illustrated by Fig. 11–9. Considered as a creep recovery, the region of constant slope on a semilogarithmic plot would correspond to a flat (plateau) distribution of retardation times [7] if it were not for the inherent non-linear feature mentioned above. Actually, a *single* retardation time reproduces the course of contraction when its change during the experiment is taken into account. Thus, Jenckel and Rehage [3] reproduced the linear course of plots similar to those in Fig. 11–9 by assuming a single time parameter whose value increases with elapsed time: $\tau = b + at$. The following treatment, based on that of Kovacs [8] but somewhat differently formulated, introduces the free volume explicitly.

The process may be regarded as creep recovery corresponding to a model for a single-line retardation spectrum (the latter has previously been encountered in discussing secondary relaxation mechanisms in the glassy state in connection with Fig. 14–4). The rate of volume contraction would then be given by the equation [8]

$$dv/dt = -K_p(v - v_\infty)/\eta_p = -(v - v_\infty)/\tau_v \qquad (1)$$

where v is specific volume and the symbols refer to the elements of a model such as portrayed in Fig. 18–2.

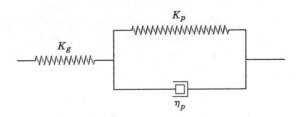

FIG. 18–2. Model corresponding to bulk retardation spectrum with a single retardation time. K_g, bulk modulus at high frequencies or short times; other symbols defined in text.

The modulus K_g in the model may be qualitatively identified with the limiting value of the bulk modulus observed at high frequencies or short times where there are no local structural rearrangements during the experiment, while the reciprocal of K_p is that portion of the equilibrium compressibility (measured at long times or low frequencies) which is associated with local structural rearrangements and collapse of free volume—i.e., β_f in Chapter 11, Section C7. The viscosity η_p is related to the bulk viscosity associated with volume changes at low frequencies. There is of course no "steady-flow" bulk viscosity, but the limiting value of the dynamic bulk viscosity at low frequencies (η_v) is related to η_p according to the model of Fig. 18-2 by the equation $\eta_p = \eta_v (K_g + K_p)^2 / K_g^2$.

In equation 1, η_p and τ_v depend on the free volume and hence on the total specific volume v. If the decrease in v with time is due entirely to collapse of free volume, we have for the relative free volume at any instant

$$f(t) = f_\infty + (v - v_\infty)/v \tag{2}$$

where f_∞ is the equilibrium relative free volume at temperature T after local configurational rearrangements have been accomplished. If the bulk viscosity and volume relaxation time depend on f in the same manner as the corresponding shear quantities (equations 32 and 38 of Chapter 11, for example), we have

$$\ln [\eta_p(t)/\eta_{p\infty}] = \ln [\tau_v(t)/\tau_{v\infty}] = B(1/f(t) - 1/f_\infty) = -s \tag{3}$$

By combining equations 1–3, the course of the isothermal volume contraction is predicted to a close approximation [8] as

$$fe^{-s} - f_i e^{-s_i} - \text{Ei}(-s) + \text{Ei}(-s_i) = (t - t_i)/\tau_{v\infty} \tag{4}$$

where the volume change is measured by s of equation 3, the subscript i refers to the moment after sudden cooling when thermal equilibrium is reached, and Ei is the exponential integral function.

This result fits very closely with experimental data on glucose and polyvinyl acetate, as illustrated by the former [9] in Fig. 18–3. (The fact that glucose is not a polymer is irrelevant, since as mentioned in Chapter 11 the bulk viscoelastic properties are closely similar for all supercooled liquids whether polymeric or not.) Here the dependence of τ_v on both time and temperature has been taken into account by using the WLF equation to predict the temperature dependence of f_∞, and remarkably good coincidence with the experimental curves is obtained for isothermal contractions at different temperatures. The

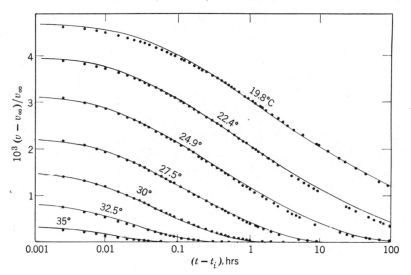

FIG. 18–3. Isothermal volume contraction of glucose measured after sudden cooling to the temperatures indicated. Points, experimental; curves, calculated from equation 4 (Kovacs [9]).

value of f_∞/B was taken as 0.020 at $T = 295.6°K.$, and α_f as 3.54×10^{-4} deg^{-1}. The value of τ_v of course changes rapidly with temperature; at each temperature in Fig. 18–3, τ_v was determined empirically by the best match on the time scale. When extrapolated to a nominal T_g of $308.7°K.$ by the WLF equation, τ_v was 0.015 ± 0.005 hr., $i.e.$, of the order of 1 min., an entirely reasonable magnitude.

Thus the volume contraction appears to be characterized by a single retardation time, or at most a very narrow distribution. The magnitude of η_v at the glass transition temperature can be estimated by taking for K_p and K_g some values found for glycerol,[10] of the order of 5 and 7×10^{10} dynes/cm^2, respectively. Then η_v is approximately 10^{12} poises. Thus the bulk (volume) viscosity at T_g appears to be similar in magnitude to the shear viscosity at the same temperature.

It may be recalled that the shear viscoelastic behavior of glasses of low molecular weight can be described over a considerable range of time scale by a single retardation time (Chapter 14), whereas in polymeric glasses broad spectra are always present. This contrasts with the bulk viscoelastic behavior where, near T_g, a single retardation time appears to suffice for systems of both low and high molecular weight.

The course of isothermal contraction has also been treated theoretically by Hirai and Eyring,[11] following the hole theory of liquids.[12] Here the important parameters are the molar volume of a hole, V_h, and the change in compressibility at the glass transition temperature, $\Delta\beta$ (identifiable with β_f). For the case of quenching well below T_g, they predict an approximately linear pilot of v against log t as evidenced by the central portions of the curves in Figs. 11–9 and 18–3. The slope is given by $2 \times 2.303RT \ \Delta\beta \ v_i/3V_h$, as compared with the value predicted by Kovacs, $2.303f_g{}^2 \ \Delta\alpha \ v_\infty/B\alpha_f$. For a small change in temperature below T_g, however, the theory of Hirai and Eyring predicts an exponential course of volume contraction with $v - v_\infty = (v_i - v_\infty)e^{-t/\tau}$, where τ is a characteristic retardation time; this follows also from equation 4 when s_i approaches zero.[13]

2. Dynamic Bulk Functions from Longitudinal Bulk Wave and Shear Wave Propagation

As mentioned in Chapter 8, the components of the dynamic bulk modulus can be obtained by difference from measurements of the longitudinal bulk modulus $\mathbf{M}^*$ and the shear modulus $\mathbf{G}^*$, afforded by wave propagation at high frequencies:

$$K' = M' - (\tfrac{4}{3})G' \tag{5}$$

$$K'' = M'' - (\tfrac{4}{3})G'' \tag{6}$$

For soft polymers, the negative term in equation 5 is relatively small, but that in equation 6 may be similar in magnitude to M'' so that the subtraction involves great uncertainty.[14,15] A calculation was made by Marvin, Aldrich, and Sack[5] for data on polyisobutylene of high molecular weight reduced to 25°C. Within the rather wide scatter of the data, the same a_T factors used for the shear viscoelastic functions gave single composite curves for the bulk functions, in agreement with the subsequent conclusions from the transient measurements of Kovacs[4] that the respective temperature dependences are identical. The results are plotted in Fig. 18–4; K' goes through a dispersion increasing from about 1.6 to 5×10^{10} dynes/cm², and the corresponding maximum in K'' is 6×10^9 dynes/cm².

The center of the dispersion region lies near 10^7 cycles/sec., and if there were a single retardation time it would be of the order of 1.6×10^{-8} sec. at 25°C. This would correspond, after reduction by the WLF equation to the glass transition temperature of 202°K., to a retardation time in the Kovacs type of experiment of about 0.5 sec.,

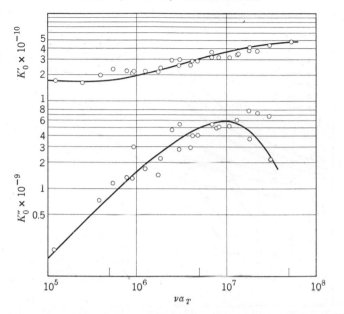

FIG. 18–4. Storage and loss moduli for bulk compression of polyisobutylene, reduced to 25°C. (Marvin, Aldrich, and Sack [5]).

reasonable in magnitude in view of the expected time scale for molecular motions at T_g.

3. Direct Measurements of Dynamic Bulk Functions

Direct measurements of dynamic bulk properties have been made by Marvin and collaborators.[6, 16]   In the most extensive series,[6] a soft vulcanized rubber with 12% combined sulfur was subjected to dynamic compressional deformations between 50 and 1000 cycles/sec. in the temperature range between $-30°$ and 50°C. and under various static confining pressures up to 1000 atm.   Since the deformations (produced by piezoelectric transducers) were very small, the free volume changes involved in the measurement were negligible and the non-linear features of transient experiments such as Kovacs' did not appear.   The dispersion of the components of the complex bulk compliance (dynamic compressibility) is illustrated in Fig. 18–5, which gives isochronal plots of B' and B'' at 1000 cycles/sec. against temperature at various pressures.   Here B' increases by something like

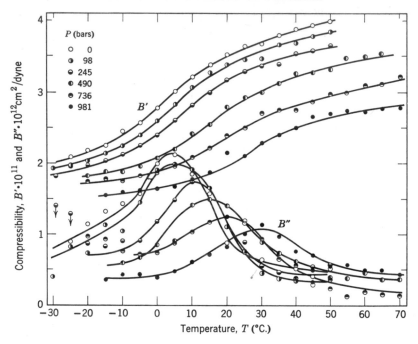

FIG. 18–5. Storage and loss compliances for bulk compression of a lightly vulcanized natural rubber at 1000 cycles/sec., plotted against temperature for several static confining pressures as indicated (McKinney, Belcher, and Marvin [6]).

a factor of two in passing from a limiting value B_g characteristic of glasslike consistency (no local structural adjustments) to a value B_e characteristic of fluidlike consistency (full local structural adjustments). Correspondingly, B'' passes through a maximum. Increasing pressure shifts the dispersion to higher temperatures and also decreases the levels of both B_g and B_e, as evidenced by these isochronal plots.

Although the frequency range of these measurements was limited, the frequency dependence of the storage and loss bulk compliances was successfully represented by expressing the effects of both temperature and frequency with reduced variables. For this purpose, shift factors a_{TP} were calculated essentially by a combination of equations 33 and 39 of Chapter 11, using the "universal" values of 0.025 and 4.8×10^{-4} for f_g and α_f (with Doolittle's $B = 1$). The value of β_f was determined from $(\partial T/\partial P)_\omega$ as 1.15×10^{-11} cm^2/dyne (using equation 41 of Chapter

11). The dependences of B_e and B_g on temperature and pressure were determined empirically to be as follows (for pressure in dynes/cm^2):

$$B_e(T,P) \times 10^{11} = 3.21 + 1.58 \times 10^{-2}T - 1.22 \times 10^{-9}P$$
$$- 5.80 \times 10^{-12}PT + 1.42 \times 10^{-19}P^2 \quad (7)$$

$$B_g(T,P) \times 10^{11} = 2.25 + 0.85 \times 10^{-2}T - 0.57 \times 10^{-9}P \quad (8)$$

Plots of B' and B'' reduced to 1 atm. pressure and 273°K., using these relations, are shown in Fig. 18–6. The superposition appears to be within experimental error, and affords a picture of the dispersion over a very extended frequency range. The total decrease in B' under these conditions is $\Delta B = 0.71 \times 10^{-11}$ cm^2/dyne, while B'' passes through a maximum of about 0.20×10^{-11}.

The form of the dispersion indicates a moderately broad distribution of retardation times. For example, the ratio $B''_{max}/\Delta B$ is 0.28, as compared with the value 0.50 to be expected for a single retardation time in the model of Fig. 18–2. Without more extensive information, it is not clear whether this result is necessarily inconsistent

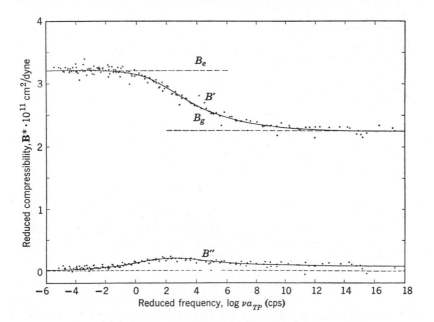

FIG. 18–6. Storage and loss compliances of Fig. 18–5 reduced to 273°K. and 1 atm. pressure, as described in the text (McKinney, Belcher, and Marvin [6]).

with the conclusion drawn from Kovacs' work. The latter is restricted to the vicinity of T_g, of course, where f is only slightly larger than f_g, whereas most of the measurements of Marvin and collaborators were made far above T_g where f is substantially greater than f_g even at the maximum confining pressure used.

Of particular interest is a comparison of ΔB with the value of β_f obtained from the temperature-pressure coefficient $(\partial T/\partial P)_\omega$. The measured values of B' and B'' are all adiabatic, and must be corrected to isothermal values by equation 21 of Chapter 5. The result [6] gives $\Delta B_{iso} = 1.21 \times 10^{-11}$ cm^2/dyne, in excellent agreement with β_f, supporting the interpretation of β_f as that portion of the compressibility which is associated with local structural rearrangements and collapse of free volume. For isothermal compression, the ratio β_f/β is 0.33, indicating that only about a third of the compressibility is of this character.

B. BULK LONGITUDINAL VISCOELASTIC BEHAVIOR

There have been numerous investigations of the bulk longitudinal modulus **M*** as derived from wave propagation measurements in polymers as well as other solids and liquids. Often the velocity of propagation and absorption coefficient for such waves are called simply "velocity of sound" and "sound absorption" (or, depending on the frequency, ultrasonic velocity and absorption) respectively.

In simple liquids, $G' = 0$, so $K' = M'$ in equation 5 and the bulk storage modulus is measured directly. The loss component M'' is frequently expressed in terms of the absorption coefficient for wave propagation, α (cf. Chapter 5, equation 11 and associated discussion). Often the acoustic attenuation is given in decibels/cm ($=8.686\alpha$). When $\alpha\lambda/2\pi \ll 1$, the analog of equation 16 of Chapter 5 for bulk longitudinal waves is

$$M'' = 2\rho v^3 \alpha/\omega$$

or
$$M''/\omega = 2\rho v^3 \alpha/\omega^2 = \eta'_v + (\tfrac{4}{3})\eta' \tag{9}$$

where v is the velocity of propagation. Thus at low frequencies α is proportional to ω^2, and from their ratio the low-frequency limiting value of the right side of equation 9, viz., $\eta_v + (\tfrac{4}{3})\eta$, can be calculated. Since η is known from shear measurements, η_v can be obtained by difference.[17]

For many simple polyatomic liquids, the energy absorption (loss) is far greater than given by the $(\tfrac{4}{3})\eta$ term in equation 9, and **M*** undergoes a dispersion which can be attributed to a lag in the transfer from translational to vibrational energy.[18,19] In such circumstances equation 9 would be inapplicable. This phenomenon is much less apparent in associated and highly viscous liquids, however, and is presumably absent in polymers. For associated liquids, η_v obtained from equation 9 is of the same order as or smaller than η, and their temperature dependences are the same.[20,21] Here the additional absorption besides that represented by the $(\frac{4}{3})\eta$ term is attributed [20,21] to structural rearrangements, as in the case of polymers.

1. Frequency Dependence of Viscoelastic Functions

From the preceding section, it may be inferred that the frequency dependence of M' and M'' would reflect the sum of $\mathbf{K}^*$ with a relatively narrow relaxation spectrum and $(\frac{4}{3})\mathbf{G}^*$ with a broad relaxation spectrum. Because M' and M'' are relatively unfamiliar quantities, experimental data are often left in the form of the propagation velocity v and attenuation or absorption coefficient α, rather than converted to M' and M'' by the analogs of equations 15 and 16 of Chapter 5. For the sake of orientation, it may be noted that v is roughly proportional to $\sqrt{M'}$, while α is related to tan δ by the following equation:

$$\tan \delta = \alpha\lambda/\pi[1 - (\alpha\lambda/2\pi)^2]$$

An example of data from longitudinal bulk wave propagation is shown in Fig. 18–7 with results of Ivey, Mrowca, and Guth [22] on butyl rubber. The velocity increases monotonically with frequency, and the attenuation per wavelength goes through a maximum whose position shifts to higher frequencies with increasing temperature. The maximum in $\alpha\lambda$ at about log $\nu = 6.5$ at 20°C. may be compared with the location of the maximum in tan δ for shear deformation at about log $\nu = 6.7$ at 25°C. (Table 12–I). But the measurement of $\alpha\lambda$ is a combination of shear and bulk properties.

2. Isochronal Measurements

More commonly, measurements are made at a single frequency over a range of temperatures. An example is shown in Fig. 18–8, where v and attenuation $(=8.686\alpha)$ at 2×10^6 cycles/sec. are plotted against temperature for polyvinyl acetate, as reported by Thurn and Wolf.[23] Three zones of dispersion are apparent. The one at 93°C. undoubtedly represents the primary transition from glasslike to rubberlike consistency, in which v drops by about 50% because of the virtual disappearance of the $(\frac{4}{3})G'$ term in equation 5 as it becomes smaller than K' by several orders of magnitude. But a dispersion in K' itself like those of Figs. 18–4 and 18–5 may well be included here also. A retardation time of the Kovacs type of 10 min. at T_g would

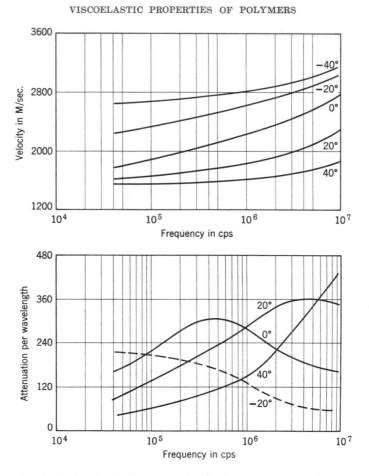

FIG. 18–7. Bulk longitudinal wave velocity (v) and attenuation per wavelength (α) plotted against frequency for butyl rubber, at 5 temperatures as indicated. (After Ivey, Mrowca, and Guth.[22])

at 93° be reduced (with the data of Table 11–II) to about 3×10^{-8} sec., corresponding to a critical frequency of 5×10^{6} cycles/sec., rather near the experimental frequency.

The secondary dispersions, at $-10°$ and $-85°$, presumably can be attributed to side group rearrangements as are the β mechanisms and other secondary effects discussed in Chapter 14. But it is difficult to guess the relative roles of volume and shear deformations in these motions. In shear (torsion) measurements at about 10 cycles/sec., Schmieder and Wolf [24] found secondary maxima in tan δ at $-30°$ and

−100°C. No certain identification of these respective mechanisms can be made, since maxima in α and tan δ are not really equivalent, and the respective frequency ranges are very different. If the secondary maxima in Fig. 18–8 do correspond to the secondary shear maxima, the temperature dependence of the associated relaxation times must be quite high.

The temperature locations of maxima such as those in Fig. 18–8 have been determined for many polymers by Thurn and Wolf,[23] and these and other results have been discussed by Woodward and Sauer.[25] They can tentatively be identified as corresponding to the shear maxima discussed in Chapter 14; at 2×10^6 cycles/sec., the bulk longitudinal maxima in attenuation occur at temperatures 20° to 70° higher than the respective shear maxima in tan δ at much lower frequencies.

Further investigations of plasticized systems [26] have outlined some complex changes in isochronal plots of attenuation against temperature with varying composition. Some examples for the system polyvinyl chloride-di-n-butyl phthalate are given in Fig. 18–9. The pure

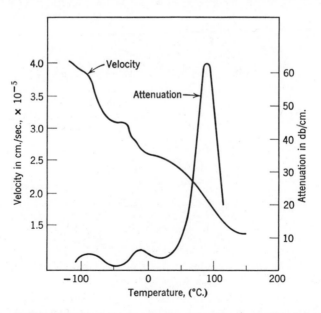

FIG. 18–8. Bulk longitudinal wave velocity (v) and attenuation (α) at 2×10^6 cycles/sec. plotted against temperature for polyvinyl acetate. (After Thurn and Wolf.[23])

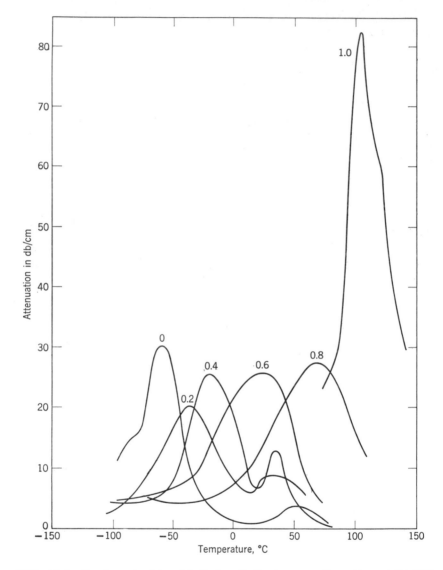

FIG. 18–9. Isochronal plots of bulk longitudinal wave attenuation at 2×10^6 cycles/sec. against temperature for mixtures of polyvinyl chloride and di-*n*-butyl phthalate. Figures denote weight fraction of polymer. (After Thurn and Würstlin.[26])

plasticizer has its own glass transition, reflected in a peak near $-50°$, and another at much higher temperatures which must represent compressional phenomena only. The pure polymer has a peak at about $100°$ which reflects the transition from glasslike to rubberlike consistency (possibly plus a bulk dispersion). At intermediate compositions, there are in some cases single and in others multiple maxima, whose positions on the temperature scale generally (but not always) shift upwards with increasing polymer concentration.

REFERENCES

1. S. Matsuoka and B. Maxwell, *J. Polymer Sci.*, **32**, 131 (1958).
2. E. Jenckel and P. Gehrke, unpublished experiments; P. Gehrke, Ph.D. Dissertation, Aachen, 1960.
3. E. Jenckel, in H. A. Stuart, *Die Physik der Hochpolymeren*, Vol. III, p. 627, Springer-Verlag, Berlin, 1955.
4. A. Kovacs, *J. Polymer Sci.*, **30**, 131 (1958).
5. R. S. Marvin, R. Aldrich, and H. S. Sack, *J. Applied Phys.*, **25**, 1213 (1954).
6. J. E. McKinney, H. V. Belcher, and R. S. Marvin, *Trans. Soc. Rheology*, **4**, 347 (1960).
7. A. Kovacs, Sc.D. Thesis, University of Paris, 1954.
8. A. Kovacs, *Compt. rend.*, **250**, 109 (1960).
9. A. Kovacs, *J. Colloid Sci.* (to be published).
10. T. A. Litovitz and T. Lyon, *J. Acoust. Soc. Amer.*, **30**, 856 (1958).
11. N. Hirai and H. Eyring, *J. Polymer Sci.*, **37**, 51 (1959).
12. H. Eyring and J. O. Hirschfelder, *J. Phys. Chem.*, **41**, 249 (1937).
13. A. Kovacs, Colloque Internationale de Rheologie, Paris, 1960.
14. A. W. Nolle and P. W. Sieck, *J. Applied Phys.*, **23**, 888 (1952).
15. J. R. Cunningham and D. G. Ivey, *J. Applied Phys.*, **27**, 967 (1956).
16. J. S. McKinney, S. Edelman, and R. S. Marvin, *J. Applied Phys.*, **27**, 425 (1956).
17. T. F. Hueter and R. H. Bolt, *Sonics,* John Wiley and Sons, New York, 1955, Appendix.
18. J. Andreae and J. Lamb, *Proc. Phys. Soc.*, **69B**, 814 (1956).
19. T. A. Litovitz, *J. Chem. Phys.*, **26**, 469 (1957).
20. T. A. Litovitz and E. H. Carnevale, *J. Applied Phys.*, **26**, 816 (1955).
21. T. A. Litovitz, E. H. Carnevale, and P. A. Kendall, *J. Chem. Phys.*, **26**, 465 (1957).
22. D. G. Ivey, B. Mrowca, and E. Guth, *J. Applied Phys.*, **20**, 486 (1949).
23. H. Thurn and K. Wolf, *Kolloid-Z.*, **148**, 16 (1956).
24. K. Schmieder and K. Wolf, *Kolloid-Z.*, **134**, 149 (1953).
25. A. E. Woodward and J. A. Sauer, *Adv. Polymer Sci.*, **1**, 114 (1958).
26. H. Thurn and F. Würstlin, *Kolloid-Z.*, **156**, 21 (1958).

Additional References

27. Y. Wada and K. Yamamoto, *J. Phys. Soc. Japan,* **11,** 887 (1956).
28. J. Schuyer, *J. Polymer Sci.,* **36,** 475 (1959).
29. W. W. Brandt, *J. Chem. Phys.,* **26,** 262 (1957).
30. R. E. Nettleton, *J. Acoust. Soc. Amer.,* **31,** 557 (1959).
31. R. N. Work, *J. Applied Phys.,* **27,** 69 (1956).
32. O. Nakada, *Repts. Prog. Polymer Phys. Japan,* **2,** 39 (1959); *J. Polymer Sci.,* **43,** 149 (1960).
33. R. Buvet, Sc.D. Thesis, Paris, 1960.
34. Y. Wada, H. Hirose, T. Asano, and S. Fukutomi, *J. Phys. Soc. Japan,* **14,** 1064 (1959).
35. K. Krebs and J. Lamb, *Proc. Roy. Soc.,* **A244,** 558 (1958).
36. R. Bass and J. Lamb, *Proc. Roy. Soc.,* **A247,** 168 (1958).
37. D. N. Hall and J. Lamb, *Trans. Faraday Soc.,* **55,** 784 (1959).
38. D. N. Hall, *Trans. Faraday Soc.,* **55,** 1319 (1959).

CHAPTER 19

Illustrative Applied
Calculations

The stress patterns prescribed in experimental measurements of the basic viscoelastic functions—creep, stress relaxation, and sinusoidally oscillating deformations—are sufficiently close to those occurring in certain conditions of processing and use of polymeric materials so that the functions are useful directly for prediction and interpretation of technological information. Often reduced variables can be used to make rough estimates of predicted behavior under widely different conditions of temperature, plasticization, and other variables.

There are other situations of processing and use, as well as empirical test procedures employed in technology, which correspond to more complicated experimental patterns of varying deformation and load. Insofar as the viscoelastic behavior is linear, such properties can often be expressed in terms of the basic viscoelastic functions. Some progress is even being made in treating non-linear cases.[1] Finally, the so-called ultimate properties of polymers, which describe the conditions for mechanical rupture, are related in part to the viscoelastic behavior; the dependence of ultimate strength and deformation on temperature, rate of loading, and other variables can be clarified to a considerable extent in terms of viscoelastic functions. Various applied calculations of this sort are briefly illustrated here in the final chapter.

A. PREDICTIONS OF VISCOELASTIC BEHAVIOR UNDER SPECIFIC CONDITIONS

A few numerical calculations have been chosen to illustrate the possibilities for predictions of viscoelastic behavior. The initial data used here are drawn in part from simple measurements on specific systems and in part from theory and generalizations in the preceding chapters.

1. Dynamic Properties and Non-Newtonian Viscosity from Steady-Flow Viscosity

Given that the steady-flow viscosity at 220°C. of a certain sample of polystyrene with average molecular weight 240,000 is 4×10^4, what are the storage modulus and the real part of the dynamic viscosity at a frequency of 1 cycle/sec., and what is the apparent non-Newtonian viscosity at a shear rate of 6 sec.$^{-1}$, all at a temperature of 180°C.?

First the steady-flow viscosity at 180°C. is estimated. From Table 11–III, T_s is taken as 410°K. From equation 36 of Chapter 11, log a_T based on T_s as reference is found to be -3.98 at 493°K. and -2.64 at 453°K. Thus Δ log a_T in going from 220° to 180° is 1.34. In accordance with equation 12 of Chapter 11, we must add Δ log $T\rho$ ($= -0.03$) to obtain Δ log η; the latter is thus 1.31, so $\eta = 8 \times 10^5$ poises at 180°C.

The terminal Rouse relaxation time, neglecting molecular weight heterogeneity, can be estimated from equation 21 of Chapter 10; taking the density as approximately unity, it is 3.1 sec. The dynamic viscoelastic functions predicted by the Rouse theory, equations 4 and 5 of Chapter 10, can be expressed in the form

$$G'/(\rho RT/M) = \Phi_1(\omega\tau_1) \tag{1}$$

$$\eta'/\eta = \Phi_2(\omega\tau_1) \tag{2}$$

The shapes of logarithmic plots of the functions Φ_1 and Φ_2 are illustrated in Figs. 10–5 and 10–9 respectively; tables for constructing them are given in Appendix E. By interpolating at the appropriate value of log $\omega\tau_1 = 1.29$, we obtain log $G'/(\rho RT/M) = 0.64$ and log $(\eta'/\eta) = -0.81$. Thus log G' is 5.83 (units dynes/cm^2) and log η'

is 5.1 (units poises). The experimental values for this system [2] are 5.9 and 5.0 respectively. The agreement is better than expected considering the probable degree of molecular weight heterogeneity. It should be emphasized that the molecular weight is high enough for presence of coupling entanglements, but that these calculations refer to the terminal zone where all the relevant relaxation times are prolonged by the coupling to the same extent (Chapter 10, Section C3).

To estimate the non-Newtonian viscosity, we use the approximation [3] that $\eta_a(\dot{\gamma})$ is similar to $|\eta^*|(\omega)$ at equal values of $\dot{\gamma}$ and ω (here both are 6 sec.$^{-1}$). The absolute dynamic viscosity $|\eta^*|$ is $[\eta'^2 + (G'/\omega)^2]^{1/2}$; its logarithm is 5.22. Thus the apparent viscosity is predicted to be smaller than the steady-flow value by about a factor of 5. No experimental comparison is available.

The applications of reduced variables in predicting the dependence of non-Newtonian viscosity on both temperature and concentration in lubricating oils with polymeric additives have been discussed by Horowitz.[4] Logarithmic plots of η'/η against $\mathfrak{T}/c$, where $\mathfrak{T}$ is the shear stress and c the concentration of additive, gave useful composite curves. Bueche [5] has shown how such a composite curve, determined empirically for solute samples of known molecular weight at a concentration in the neighborhood of 20%, can be used by matching the scales of logarithmic plots to provide a rapid estimate of the molecular weight of an unknown sample. The method of reduced variables has also been applied to the viscoelastic properties of asphalts.[6]

2. Storage Modulus in the Transition Zone

Given the glass transition temperature [7] of polyethyl acrylate as $-23°$C., at what temperature will the storage modulus be about $10^{8.5}$ dynes/cm^2 at a frequency of 1.6 cycles/sec. (10 rad./sec.)?

In this calculation, the molecular weight (if sufficiently high) does not enter, since the required modulus falls in the transition zone where properties are substantially independent of molecular weight. The estimation can be made in terms of the monomeric friction coefficient, using a sequence of approximations by analogy. First, the friction coefficient corresponding to the given mechanical behavior can be estimated. By comparing a series of curves of G' against frequency (like Fig. 12–1) with curves of H against τ (like Fig. 12–4) for various polymers, the conclusion is reached that log $G' = 8.5$ corresponds to log $H = 8.2$ at the equivalent value of τ ($= 1/\omega$). To calculate the friction coefficient, the curvature of H must be taken into account. Assuming that the spectrum for polyethyl acrylate will have about the same shape as those in Panel II of Fig. 12–7, we conclude that log $H = 8.2$ at log $\tau = -1$ (i.e., $1/\omega$ when $\omega = 10$ rad./sec.) corresponds to log $H = 6.0$ at log $\tau = 2.3$. The latter point should be in the region of the Rouse slope and hence the friction coefficient can be calculated by equation 1 of Chapter 12. The result is log $\zeta_0 = 0.0$.

We now estimate from the data in Table 12–III that log ζ_0 at T_g is about 5.0, so that log a_T (from T_g as the reference) is -5.0. Using equation 26 of Chapter 11 in the form

$$-5.0 = -17.44(T - 250)/(51.6 + T - 250)$$

we obtain $T = 271°K$. For experimental verification, the mid-point temperature of the transition region at 1.6 cycles/sec. is given by Schmieder and Wolf[8] as $268°K$. (Table 12–II); this should correspond approximately to log $G' = 8.5$.

3. Effect of Plasticizer on Mechanical Loss

How much butyl acetate must be added to polymethyl acrylate to produce maximum damping (loss tangent or logarithmic decrement of free vibrations) at 60 cycles/sec. at 25°C.?

From Table 12–I, the maximum in tan δ occurs at 0.5 cycle/sec. at 298°K. in the pure polymer; the molecular weight again does not enter, if sufficiently high. Enough diluent must be added to give log $a_c = -2.1$, shifting the frequency from 0.5 to 60. In equation 7 of Chapter 16, β' for butyl acetate may be taken as 0.23; Fujita[9] lists values of 0.22 and 0.24 for this diluent in polystyrene and polymethyl methacrylate respectively. The fractional free volume of the polymer, f_2, is $f_g + \alpha_f(T - T_g)$; taking the values of the coefficients from Table 11–II, we obtain $f_2 = 0.037$. Equation 7 of Chapter 16 then takes the form

$$-2.1 = -\frac{1}{2.303} \frac{0.23\phi_1}{0.037(0.037 + 0.23\phi_1)}$$

from which $\phi_1 = 0.035$. Thus addition of butyl acetate to a concentration of 3.5% by volume should produce the desired result.

4. Discrepancy between Steady-Flow Viscosity and High-Frequency Dynamic Viscosity

If the viscosity of a polymerizing system is monitored by a high-frequency characteristic impedance device (Chapter 5, Section F) operating at 20,000 cycles/sec., at what stage of the polymerization will the measured viscosity deviate from the steady-flow viscosity by as much as a factor of 2?

Although the customary measurement of $\mathcal{R}_M$, the in-phase component of the characteristic impedance, gives a combination of G' and η' in accordance with equation 17 of Chapter 5, we can assume that the contribution of the former will be small and that the measured viscosity is essentially η'; thus we seek the conditions for which η'/η is $\frac{1}{2}$.

(a) *Condensation Polymerization.* Consider the polymerization of decamethylene adipate at 109°C., for which the viscosity is empirically related to the weight-average molecular weight as given by Flory [10] as follows:

$$\log \eta = 1.435 + 0.0117 \bar{M}_w^{\frac{1}{2}} \tag{3}$$

As the polymerization proceeds, both $\bar{M}_w$ and η increase, with a concomitant increase in the terminal relaxation time given by equation 21 of Chapter 10. Since the molecular weights in condensation polymerization follow the "most probable" distribution, it would be most appropriate to integrate the function Φ_2 of equation 2 for varying molecular weight,[11] but an approximate calculation can be made on the basis of a single species of molecular weight $\bar{M}_w$. Then from Φ_2 (Appendix E) we find that $\eta'/\eta = \frac{1}{2}$ corresponds to $\log \omega\tau_1 = 0.26$. Since $\omega = 1.26 \times 10^5$, the critical value of $\log \tau_1$ is -4.84, and from equation 21 of Chapter 10 the critical value of $\log \eta M$ is 5.88. Combination of this with equation 3 gives

$$\log \bar{M}_w = 4.45 - 0.0117 \bar{M}_w^{\frac{1}{2}}$$

and trial-and-error solution gives $\bar{M}_w = 4500$. This represents the required critical stage of polymerization.

(b) *Addition Polymerization.* In addition polymerization, high molecular weights are produced at the very beginning of the reaction, and the critical state must be expressed by an extent of conversion rather than by an average molecular weight. Consider the polymerization of styrene at 25°C. under conditions where the initial product has a weight-average molecular weight of 400,000. The problem can be solved with reasonable simplicity only if the critical extent of conversion corresponds to a high enough polymer concentration so that $\eta \gg \eta_s$ in equation 10 of Chapter 10. In this case, the terminal relaxation time is given by equation 21 of Chapter 10 with $p = 1$ and ρ replaced by c. The critical value of $\log \tau_1$ is still -4.84 as in the preceding example. Assuming $\eta \gg \eta_s$, we then have at the critical moment

$$\log \eta = \log \left(\pi^2 cRT\tau_1/6M\right) = \log c + 0.17 \qquad (4)$$

The viscosity η is that of a solution of polystyrene in styrene. Its concentration dependence can be estimated empirically in various ways, the simplest of which is the fifth power dependence mentioned in Chapter 16, Section B3. From data on polystyrene in xylene and in Decalin,[12] it can be estimated that at moderate concentrations

$$\log \eta = \log \eta_s + 5 \log c + 3.4 \log \left(2M/M_0\right) - 6$$

where M_0 is the monomeric molecular weight. For styrene, $\eta_s = 0.007$ poise. Thus $\log \eta = 5 \log c + 5.09$. Combining this with equation 4, we obtain $c = 0.044$ g. polymer per cc. This is indeed a high enough concentration to ensure that $\eta \gg \eta_s$. Since the density of styrene is about 0.9 g./cc., we can conclude that at about 5% conversion to polymer the measured dynamic viscosity will differ substantially from the steady-flow viscosity. This is an overestimate because the concentration falls a little too low for validity of the fifth power concentration dependence of η.

These numerical examples provide only a few illustrations of a wide variety of possible calculations. In some cases the theoretical relations in Chapters 10 and 11 may have to be modified empirically to suit particular types of systems. With such adjustments, they should have a wide range of applicability.

B. VISCOELASTIC BEHAVIOR UNDER MORE COMPLICATED LOADING PATTERNS

Mechanical testing procedures in common use involve more complicated patterns of stress history than the simple creep and relaxation experiments on which the definitions of the transient viscoelastic functions are based, and the sinusoidally varying stress which is inherent in the definitions of the so-called dynamic properties. Certain relations between the behavior under complicated conditions and the basic viscoelastic functions are presented here together with some related problems. They have the drawback, in some cases severe, of being limited to linear viscoelastic systems and hence small strains.

However, it may be possible to modify them for extension to larger strains by approximate, semi-empirical means.[1]

1. Relation of Stress Relaxation to Deformation at Constant Strain Rate

In the use of devices like the Instron tester (Chapter 6), the question arises as to the relation between the stress observed after a constant rate of elongation to a given strain (A) and that which would be observed after immediate extension to this strain followed by stress relaxation for the same time interval (B). According to the relations in Chapter 3, the respective stresses are (written for extension)

$$\sigma_A = (\epsilon/t) \int_0^t E(z)dz \tag{5}$$

$$\sigma_B = \epsilon E(t) \tag{6}$$

where ϵ is the strain at which stress σ is measured, and $E(z)$ is the relaxation modulus. For specific comparison, a particular form of $E(z)$ must be chosen. If it can be approximated by a linear function of $\ln z$,

$$E = a - b \ln z \tag{7}$$

corresponding approximately (equation 3 of Chapter 4) to a flat relaxation spectrum with $H_l = b$, these equations become

$$\sigma_A = (a + b)\epsilon - b\epsilon \ln t \tag{8}$$

$$\sigma_B = a\epsilon - b\epsilon \ln t \tag{9}$$

Thus the stress in procedure (A) is always larger than in procedure (B). However, if $H_l \ll E(t)$, the two procedures will give almost identical results, and the relaxation modulus, while changing slowly with time, will be close to a pseudo-equilibrium modulus. The "stiffness" measurement referred to in Fig. 15–6 was obtained by procedure A; for polyethylene under these conditions, $H_l/E(t)$ is of the order of 0.1, so the "stiffness" is reasonably close to the nature of a pseudo-equilibrium modulus.

2. Stress Relaxation Following Deformation at Constant Strain Rate

If a sample is stretched at constant strain rate to a strain ϵ at time t_1, and then the stress is allowed to relax at constant strain, the course of relaxation is given by

$$\sigma = (\epsilon/t_1) \int_{-\infty}^{\infty} H_l\tau[e^{-(t-t_1)/\tau} - e^{-t/\tau}]\, d\ln\tau \qquad (10)$$

where t is the total elapsed time, instead of the simple course followed after instantaneous strain,

$$\sigma = \epsilon \int_{-\infty}^{\infty} H_l e^{-t/\tau}\, d\ln\tau = \epsilon E(t) \qquad (11)$$

However, for $t \gg t_1$, equation 10 reduces to equation 11, thus justifying the assumption implicit in experimental procedures that rapid loading is equivalent to instantaneous for practical purposes.

3. Energy Stored, Energy Dissipated, and Work of Deformation in Transient Loading

The total work of deformation in tests such as those described above has two contributions, corresponding to the stored elastic energy and the energy dissipated as heat (assuming isothermal conditions). These can be formulated as follows for deformation in simple extension, the usual geometry for practical test procedures.

For deformation at constant rate of tensile strain, $\dot{\epsilon}$, the total work of deformation per unit volume is

$$W = \int_0^{\epsilon} \sigma\, d\epsilon = \dot{\epsilon}^2 t^2 E_e/2 + \dot{\epsilon}^2 \int_{-\infty}^{\infty} H_l\tau[t - \tau(1 - e^{-t/\tau})]\, d\ln\tau \quad (12)$$

while the stored energy is

$$\mathcal{E}_{st} = \dot{\epsilon}^2 t^2 E_e/2 + (\dot{\epsilon}^2/2) \int_{-\infty}^{\infty} H_l\tau^2(1 - e^{-t/\tau})^2\, d\ln\tau \qquad (13)$$

where E_e is the equilibrium Young's modulus (cross-linked systems only) and t is the time elapsed since the beginning of the deformation. The difference between these two expressions is the energy dissipated. It is evident that the latter depends on H_l but not on E_e. It would be expected that the greater the proportion dissipated, the greater the work that can be put into deformation without occurrence of rupture. However, rupture depends on several different features as briefly discussed in Section E.

4. Energy Stored and Dissipated in Periodic (Sinusoidal) Loading

Qualitatively, it is evident that the ratio of energy dissipated to energy stored per cycle in a sinusoidal deformation is proportional to tan δ, and this statement has appeared many times in the literature. For a quantitative comparison, some arbitrary specifications must be made. The maximum energy per unit volume stored in a cycle is (for shear strain)

$$\mathcal{E}_{st} = \int_0^{\gamma_0} G'\gamma \, d\gamma = G'\gamma_0^2/2 \tag{14}$$

where $\gamma = \gamma_0 \sin \omega t$. The dissipated energy continuously increases; since the maximum energy storage is achieved in a process lasting a quarter of a cycle, it is perhaps most logical to compare it with the energy dissipated in a quarter cycle, which is

$$\mathcal{E}_d = \int_0^{\gamma} (G''\dot{\gamma}/\omega)d\gamma = \pi G''\gamma_0^2/4 \tag{15}$$

Thus the ratio of energy dissipated to energy stored per quarter cycle is

$$\mathcal{E}_d/\mathcal{E}_{st} = (\pi/2) \tan \delta \tag{16}$$

A related problem of interest is the ratio of energy dissipated per second to energy stored during steady-state flow of a viscoelastic liquid. This is readily calculated to be $2/J_e\eta$, where J_e is the steady-state compliance and η the viscosity. It is close in magnitude to the reciprocal of the terminal relaxation time of the system.[14] Thus, for a single Maxwell element, the above ratio is $2/\tau$, while for a concentrated or undiluted polymer (with $\eta \gg \eta_s$) the Rouse theory gives $30/\pi^2\tau_1$, or approximately $3/\tau_1$, where τ_1 is the terminal relaxation time.

5. Cycling Deformations at Constant Strain Rate

When a sample in an extension tester is stretched at a constant rate of elongation ($\dot{\epsilon}$) to an elongation ϵ_1 at time $t_1 = \epsilon_1/\dot{\epsilon}$ and then the direction of travel is reversed to return it to its original length at a rate $-\dot{\epsilon}$, the stress-strain curves trace a hysteresis loop as illustrated [13] in Fig. 19–1. The area within the loop represents the energy dissipated as heat during the cyclic procedure. If the linear viscoelasticity theory can be applied, the forward stress-strain curve is given by equation 5, or by its equivalent, equation 5 of Chapter 3 written for extension:

$$\sigma_F = \dot{\epsilon} \int_{-\infty}^{\infty} H_l \tau (1 - e^{-t_1/\tau}) \, d \ln \tau + E_e \dot{\epsilon} t \tag{17}$$

whereas that for the reverse segment can be shown to be

$$\sigma_R = \dot{\epsilon} \int_{-\infty}^{\infty} H_l \tau [(2 - e^{-t_1/\tau}) e^{-(t-t_1)/\tau} - 1] \, d \ln \tau + E_e \dot{\epsilon} (2t_1 - t) \tag{18}$$

The work of forward deformation is given by equation 12, while the work recovered on the reverse deformation cannot be readily calculated because zero stress on this segment corresponds to a finite strain which depends on the form of H_l in a complicated manner according to equation 18. It may be remarked that the point of zero stress at the end of the cycle does not necessarily correspond to zero stored energy, since (in model language) some spring elements may be stretched and others compressed to balance the stress at zero. The apparent permanent set immediately after removal of the sample from the instrument would then undergo some modification with further creep recovery.

The ratio of the hysteresis area to the work of deformation has been used as a measure of the loss characteristics of a viscoelastic material.[13] However, it is evident that its relation to the fundamental viscoelastic functions is quite complicated.

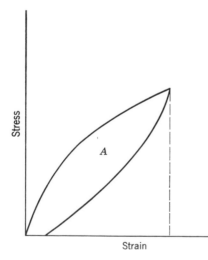

FIG. 19–1. Stress-strain hysteresis loop for constant rate of strain (Reding [13]). The direction of the strain rate is reversed at the upper right.

6. Rebound of Rigid Spheres from Viscoelastic Plates

When a sphere of an essentially perfectly elastic material rebounds from a plane surface of a viscoelastic solid, its velocity is diminished by a factor called the coefficient of restitution,[15] ϑ. The impact can be provided either by dropping a ball vertically or by swinging it horizontally suspended from a string. If the viscoelastic plate is thick enough so that the time required for an elastic wave to be reflected from its other side and return is longer than the time of contact, then ϑ is essentially independent of the thickness and in practice also of the velocity of impact. The experiment is similar physically to an oscillating free vibration measurement (as in a torsion pendulum) at an equivalent frequency which is nearly equal to the reciprocal of twice the time of contact.[15, 16] An effective logarithmic decrement (equivalent to Δ in equation 15 of Chapter 6) can be estimated by the relation $\Delta = 1 - \vartheta^2$. The deformation for a hard viscoelastic solid is of course a combination of shear and compression, but for the usual range of Poisson's ratio the majority of the stored energy is attributable to the shear.[15] Although the utility of this method for obtaining viscoelastic data appears to be rather limited, it is evident that when the basic viscoelastic functions are known the rebound behavior can be predicted.

7. Rolling Friction on a Viscoelastic Surface

When a rigid sphere is pressed against a plane viscoelastic surface with a normal force and is rolled along with a small force parallel to the surface, the viscoelastic material undergoes deformation (combination of shear and compression, but mostly shear) followed by recovery. The parallel force required to maintain a constant velocity is related to the elastic loss in the viscoelastic substratum.[17]

The coefficient of rolling friction, λ, defined as the ratio of the vertical load (W) to the parallel rolling force, depends on the load, the sphere radius, and the viscoelastic properties of the substratum. The rather complicated relationships have been worked out by Tabor[18] and Flom and Bueche.[17, 19] Approximately, $\lambda = K(W/G_e r^2)^{1/2} \tan \delta$, where G_e is the pseudo-equilibrium shear modulus and $\tan \delta$ the loss tangent of the substratum, and r is the radius of the sphere; K is a dimensionless constant of the order of unity. The method has been applied to measurement of losses in rubbers.[19, 20]

Similarly, the coefficient of friction of a rolling cylinder on a viscoelastic surface has been treated by May, Morris, and Atack.[21] Calculations based on a Gaussian distribution of relaxation times indicated that the frictional force as a function of reciprocal velocity resembles in shape the logarithmic distribution function itself. However, the problem has not been solved in terms of a general distribution of arbitrary form.

C. MISCELLANEOUS APPLICATIONS OF VISCOELASTIC PROPERTIES

Some practical aspects of viscoelastic behavior in the terminal zone (Chapter 10, Section C) and the rubbery zone (Chapter 13, Section F) have already been mentioned; others are inherent in Chapters 15 and 16. We now call attention to some additional applications.

1. Generation of Heat in Rapid Oscillating Deformations

From equation 15 above, the energy dissipated *per second* in small oscillating deformations is (per unit volume of material)

$$\dot{\varepsilon} = \omega G'' \gamma_0^2 / 2 = \omega J'' \mathbb{T}_0^2 / 2 \tag{19}$$

where γ_0 and $\mathbb{T}_0$ are the peak strain and peak stress respectively. Thus for deformation with a specified strain the important function is G'', while for a specified stress it is J''.

The dissipated energy causes a rise in temperature, whose magnitude of course depends on the heat capacity of the system. The temperature may reach a steady-state value for continuous sinusoidal deformation, depending on the rate of heat loss to the surroundings. Equation 19 can be used to estimate heat production in various experimental procedures, where the strains are often purposely kept very small at high frequencies to prevent temperature rise as well as to insure linear viscoelastic behavior. It can also be used to estimate heat production in practical situations of cyclic deformations, such as the performance of automobile tires. Values can be compared on a relative basis even though the stress distribution in a loaded tire is complicated and the strains exceed the limitations of linear viscoelasticity; and the cyclic deformation does not follow a simple sinusoidal pattern.

Since in a tire under operating conditions the peak stress is specified, J'' is the relevant function in equation 19. It has been pointed out [22] that, although minimum heat dissipation at the frequency of wheel rotation is desired, higher losses at low frequencies may be beneficial in providing a smoother riding vehicle. Thus it would be desirable to operate on the left side of the maximum in Fig. 13–3. The losses should be compared not at the ambient temperature but at the steady-state temperature during operation.

As an example of a numerical calculation, a lightly cross-linked natural rubber with $J'' = 1.0 \times 10^{-8}$ cm^2/dyne under a sinusoidal deformation at 10 cycles/sec. and a peak shear stress of 10^6 dynes/cm^2 would dissipate 0.0038 calorie per cc. per sec. Since the heat capacity is about 0.5 calorie/deg/g., the temperature would rise about 0.008 deg/sec. if no heat were lost by conduction.

2. Vibration Damping and Noise Abatement

In contrast to the situation described above where minimum loss is desired, when polymeric materials are used to suppress vibrations the loss should be maximal. The frequency range of interest depends on the characteristic frequencies of the vibrating system, which involve the storage modulus of the polymer as well as masses and elastic stiffnesses of other components of the mechanical system. No attempt will be made to refer to the very large literature on damping of vibrations, except to point out that knowledge of the form of the viscoelastic functions and use of the WLF equation can aid in designing devices for specific ranges of frequency and temperature. Such applications have been discussed by Snowdon.[23, 24]

Suppression of flexural vibrations in metal plates and bars by application of a thin layer of polymeric material, either spread directly or applied in the form of a tape, has become of great importance both for elimination of noise (especially in vehicles and airplanes) and for improving fatigue characteristics. It was mentioned in Chapter 7 that measurements of resonance frequencies and damping in such compound layered systems can be used for obtaining the viscoelastic properties of the polymeric stratum. Conversely, knowledge of the viscoelastic properties and their dependence on frequency and temperature (and plasticization, incorporation of fillers, etc.) aids in the selection of anti-damping materials for specific applications.

The theory for complex bending stiffness of composite plates has been developed by Oberst [25-27] for double layers (metal and polymer) and by Kerwin [28] for triple layers (polymer sandwiched between comparatively heavy substratum and thin outer constraining layer). The loss tangent for the composite system depends critically on the relative thicknesses of the layers as well as the properties of the respective materials. In practice, polymeric materials with loss tangents near or slightly greater than unity (probably the maximum achievable,[29] unless one is willing to limit the damping to a narrow frequency range) can provide loss tangents in the neighborhood of 0.1 for compound systems.

It may be noted that in the acoustic literature the symbol η is often used not for viscosity but for the loss tangent (equal to the relative response width $(\Delta\omega)'/\omega_0$ as defined in Chapter 6, Section E).

3. Friction and Tack

The frictional force involved in sliding a layer of polymeric material along a hard surface (e.g., of metal) is evidently related in part to the viscoelastic properties of the former. There have been some studies of this phenomenon in rubbers [30] and plasticized polymers,[31] and some qualitative conclusions have been drawn. When the forces of adhesion are sufficiently high, sliding does not occur, but the force required for separation can be measured by some sort of tensile [32] or peeling [33] experiment. Both friction and tack partake of the so-called ultimate properties of the polymer as described in Section E below, and the mechanisms underlying them are not fully understood. Nevertheless, they involve to some degree the same molecular motions that are reflected in the simpler viscoelastic properties.

D. STRESS ANALYSIS IN VISCOELASTIC BODIES

The classical theory of elasticity provides in principle for knowledge of the distribution of stresses and strains within a body of any shape provided the elastic constants (e.g., G and μ) are known and the magnitude and direction of surface forces are specified. For an isotropic viscoelastic body with $\mu = \frac{1}{2}$ (i.e., $K \gg G$), the pattern of stress distribution for small strains is the same as in the corresponding perfectly elastic body.[34] However, if K and G are of the same order of magnitude, and the compressive and shear stresses relax at different rates, a very complicated time dependence of the stress distribution may result. Such problems have been examined by Lee.[35, 36] In the presence of a thermal gradient, where the relaxation rates vary with position within the body, the situation is still more complicated.[37]

For numerical solutions of problems of this kind, it is convenient to replace the experimentally determined viscoelastic functions by simple approximate analytical expressions. It cannot be expected, of course, that the results will be applicable over more than a very limited range of time or frequency, since no simple formulation can represent the viscoelastic functions over wide ranges. Lee [38,39] has used a four-element model with two springs and two dashpots for this purpose (*cf.* Appendix F).

E. ULTIMATE MECHANICAL PROPERTIES

When a polymeric material is subjected to tensile or shear stress of sufficiently high magnitude, it ruptures, as do all solids and under certain circumstances liquids.[40,41] The values of stress and strain at the moment of rupture—the so-called ultimate properties—are far less reproducible than the relation between the stress and strain up to the breaking point, since the mechanical failure depends on quantities which are subject to statistical fluctuations; experimentally, the ultimate properties should more appropriately be expressed by distribution functions.[42]

In hard solids such as metals and inorganic glasses, a distinction is drawn [42-46] between brittle and plastic failure. In the former, the broken surfaces are perpendicular to the tensile stresses and relatively little deformed, whereas in the latter plastic or viscous flow occurs and the separation involves shearing deformations. In polymers, the cases of primary interest are of the nature of brittle fracture, including both polymeric glasses which resemble other hard solids and cross-linked rubbers which fail by tensile rupture. The process of brittle fracture involves structural inhomogeneities—for glasses, flaws or microscopic voids, and for rubbers, network strands carrying more than their share of the stress. Because of the essential role of such inhomogeneities, the breaking strength cannot be calculated in terms of chemical bond energies or intermolecular attractive forces, which predict strengths too high by several orders of magnitude.[42-45]

The voluminous literature on correlation of ultimate properties with polymer structure is primarily empirical, and cannot be adequately treated here; bibliographies are given in some of the references cited.[42-50] However, certain aspects of the ultimate properties and their dependence on the time scale of measurement and on temperature are closely allied to viscoelastic properties in small deformations, and these will be briefly discussed.

There is a basic difference between rupture above the glass transition temperature where the polymer chain backbones have an opportunity to change their configurations before the sample fails, and below T_g (or somewhat above T_g with very rapid stressing) where the backbone configurations are essentially immobilized within the period of the experiment.

1. Rupture above the Glass Transition Temperature

It is generally recognized [42-51] that rupture of a vulcanized rubber involves breaking of network strands by mechanical dissociation of primary chemical bonds. In uncross-linked polymers of high molecular weight, the same mechanism will be operative provided rupture occurs within a time too short for slippage of the entanglement coupling. For high molecular weight uncross-linked systems under experimental conditions where slippage occurs, and for uncross-linked systems of molecular weight so low that there is no entanglement coupling, failure takes place by viscous flow, and is associated with substantial shear deformation; here the problem is hydrodynamic and outside the scope of the present discussion.

In accordance with the distribution of strand lengths and of strand configurations in a cross-linked network, a given macroscopic strain of the sample corresponds to varying elongations of individual strands, and some of these may momentarily be stretched almost taut—i.e., to the point where chemical bonds are substantially distorted.[52] If the force is not relieved by transfer of some of it to neighboring strands through configurational rearrangements, such a taut strand may break. Neighboring strands then suddenly experience an additional force, and if they in turn cannot transfer some of it in time, a cascade of fractures occurs with consequent sample rupture.[49,53]

Regardless of the detailed mechanism of the molecular breaking process, which may depend on a critical average extension of network strands[53] or a critical content of stored elastic energy, the important feature of relief of local stress by configurational rearrangements means that the breaking strength and elongation at break are functions of the rate of strain, and the effects of temperature and other variables are related to their familiar effects on the time scale of viscoelastic properties. For example, according to equation 13, if a change of temperature causes all relaxation times to change by a factor a_T, then a given stored energy

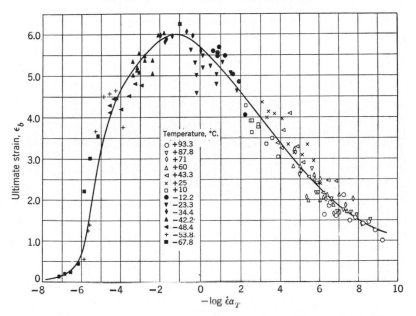

FIG. 19–2. Ultimate strain plotted against logarithm of strain rate (in sec⁻¹) reduced to 263°K. for a cross-linked GR-S rubber at 14 temperatures as indicated (Smith [54]).

is attained at an equivalent time t/a_T with a rate of strain $\dot{\epsilon}a_T$. The corresponding value of the critical strain, ϵ, is however unchanged. It would follow that ultimate elongation tests could be reduced to a standard temperature by plotting the strain at break against $\dot{\epsilon}a_T$.

A rather successful application of this principle is illustrated in Fig. 19–2, where data in extension for a cross-linked GR-S rubber, by Smith,[54] are given covering a temperature range from −68° to 93°C. The corresponding reduced plot for the tensile strength, where the coordinates are stress × (T_o/T) and − log $\dot{\epsilon}a_T$, is shown in Fig. 19–3. The deviations at the lowest temperatures are associated with cold drawing, where temperature gradients exist at the neck and the process is non-isothermal. The values of a_T in this case were determined primarily by the reduction of stress-strain curves at lower elongations as in Fig. 13–15, which could be performed with considerable accuracy; their temperature dependence followed the WLF equation, equation 36 of Chapter 11 with $T_s = 263°K$. Within the expected

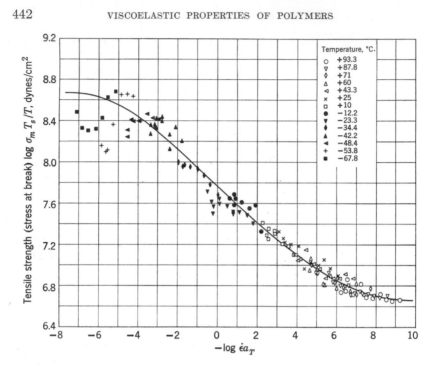

FIG. 19-3. Tensile strength plotted against logarithm of strain rate, both reduced to 263°K., for the material of Fig. 19–2 at the same 14 temperatures (Smith [54]).

large scatter of individual break-point measurements, composite curves are obtained. These would represent the ultimate properties at T_s over a very wide range of strain rates. In certain other studies of rupture of rubbers by tearing,[55] reduced plots of tear strength against rate of extension are obtained with a_T values which follow an equation of the WLF form but with different coefficients from those which characterize viscoelastic properties in small deformations. The differences may be associated with the high strains involved.[56]

In Fig. 19–3, the tensile stress increases monotonically with increasing strain rate. This dependence has been interpreted by Bueche [49] with the concept that the probability of rupture depends on the stored elastic energy per strand and the faster the deformation the higher the stress that can be reached before this energy is exceeded. Bueche's theory, however, would lead to a more rapid increase of tensile strength at very high strain rates than observed.[54] The elongation at break, on the other hand, goes through a substantial maximum with changing strain rate. At very high rates, the elongation is low because the stress rises so fast that chemical bonds are distorted to the point of rupture before there is time for extensive configurational rearrangements. At very low rates, the elongation is low because the finite breaking rate even with a small amount of excess stored energy leads to rupture—just as in a dead load test.

When the same polymer is cross-linked to different extents, the tensile strength and elongation at break for a given strain rate depend[51,57] on the number of network strands per cc., n_c. Usually[51] the tensile strength increases and the elongation decreases with increasing n_c. However, the distribution of strand lengths is also an important feature, since the shortest strands are the most vulnerable.

Since, at the present writing, there is extensive work in progress[51,55] on the ultimate properties of polymeric systems well above T_g, it is to be expected that further developments in the molecular interpretation of these phenomena will occur in the near future.

2. Rupture below the Glass Transition Temperature

When the chain backbone configurations are immobilized during the time of the experiment, ultimate properties do not involve long-range rearrangements and their relation to viscoelastic behavior in small deformations is more remote. Nevertheless, dissipation of energy by local relaxation processes appears to be important in determining the time required for a plastic below T_g to break under a dead load.[58,59] The rupture again involves breaking primary chemical bonds, and the energy of formation of cracks can be measured.[60] Flaws and adventitious cracks no doubt serve to initiate the breaking process.[46,61] Here, too, substantial advances in molecular interpretation may be anticipated from current investigations.

REFERENCES

1. P. J. Stedry and R. F. Landel, *Bull. Amer. Phys. Soc.*, II, **5**, 202 (1960).
2. W. P. Cox, L. E. Nielsen, and R. Keeney, *J. Polymer Sci.*, **26**, 365 (1957).
3. W. P. Cox and E. H. Merz, *J. Polymer Sci.*, **28**, 619 (1958).
4. H. H. Horowitz, *Ind. Eng. Chem.*, **50**, 1089 (1958).
5. F. Bueche and S. W. Harding, *J. Polymer Sci.*, **32**, 177 (1958).
6. E. N. Thrower, private communication.
7. R. H. Wiley and G. M. Brauer, *J. Polymer Sci.*, **3**, 647 (1948).

8. K. Schmieder and K. Wolf, *Kolloid-Z.*, **134**, 149 (1953).
9. H. Fujita and A. Kishimoto, *J. Polymer Sci.*, **28**, 547 (1958).
10. P. J. Flory, *J. Amer. Chem. Soc.*, **62**, 1057 (1940).
11. S. E. Lovell and J. D. Ferry, unpublished work.
12. J. D. Ferry, L. D. Grandine, Jr., and D. C. Udy, *J. Polymer Sci.*, **8**, 529 (1953).
13. F. P. Reding, *J. Polymer Sci.*, **32**, 487 (1958).
14. J. D. Ferry, *Rev. Mod. Phys.*, **31**, 130 (1959).
15. J. P. A. Tillett, *Proc. Phys. Soc.*, **B67**, 677 (1954).
16. E. Jenckel and E. Klein, *Z. Naturf.*, **7a**, 619 (1952).
17. D. G. Flom and A. M. Bueche, *J. Applied Phys.*, **30**, 1725 (1959).
18. D. Atack and D. Tabor, *Proc. Roy. Soc.*, **A246**, 539 (1958).
19. D. G. Flom, presented at the 137th Meeting of the American Chemical Society, Cleveland, Ohio, April, 1960.
20. D. Bulgin and G. D. Hubbard, *Trans. Inst. Rubber Ind.*, **34**, 201 (1958).
21. W. D. May, E. L. Morris, and D. Atack, *J. Applied Phys.*, **30**, 1713 (1959).
22. E. R. Fitzgerald, private communication.
23. J. C. Snowdon, *Brit. J. Applied Phys.*, **9**, 461 (1958).
24. J. C. Snowdon, *Noise Control*, March 1960.
25. H. Oberst, *Acustica*, **2**, Beih. 4, AB 181 (1952).
26. H. Oberst, *Acustica*, **4**, Beih. 1, 433 (1954).
27. H. Oberst, *Ber. Ver. Deuts. Ing.*, **8**, 100 (1956).
28. E. M. Kerwin, Jr., *J. Acoust. Soc. Amer.*, **31**, 952 (1959).
29. G. W. Becker and H. Oberst, *Kolloid-Z.*, **148**, 6 (1956).
30. A. Schallamach, *Kolloid-Z.*, **141**, 165 (1955); *Trans. Inst. Rubber Ind.*, **32**, 142 (1956).
31. D. I. James, R. H. Norman, and A. R. Payne, in *The Physical Properties of Polymers*, Soc. Chem. Ind. Monograph No. 5, London, 1959, p. 233.
32. P. Thirion, *Rev. Gen. Caoutchouc*, **35**, 441 (1958).
33. D. H. Kaelble, *Trans. Soc. Rheology*, **4**, 45 (1960).
34. T. Alfrey, Jr., *Mechanical Behavior of High Polymers*, Interscience Publishers, New York, 1948, Appendix III.
35. E. H. Lee, J. R. M. Radok, and W. B. Woodward, *Trans. Soc. Rheology*, **3**, 41 (1959).
36. E. H. Lee, in *Viscoelasticity—Phenomenological Aspects*, Academic Press, New York, 1959, p. 1.
37. L. W. Morland and E. H. Lee, *Trans. Soc. Rheology*, **4**, 233 (1960).
38. E. H. Lee, *J. Applied Phys.*, **27**, 665 (1956).
39. E. H. Lee, *Quart. J. Applied Math.*, **13**, 183 (1955).
40. H. N. V. Temperley and L. G. Chambers, *Proc. Phys. Soc.*, **58**, 420 (1946).
41. T. H. Bull, *Phil. Mag.*, **[8], 1**, 153 (1956); *Brit. J. Applied Phys.*, **7**, 416 (1956).
42. F. Schwarzl and A. J. Staverman, in H. A. Stuart, *Die Physik der Hochpolymeren*, Vol. IV, Chapter III, Springer-Verlag, Berlin, 1956.
43. R. Houwink, *Elasticity, Plasticity, and the Structure of Matter*, Second Edition, Harren Press, Washington, 1953.
44. T. Alfrey, Jr., *Mechanical Properties of High Polymers*, Interscience Publishers, New York, 1948, Chapter F.
45. R. N. Haward, *Strength of Plastics and Glasses*, Interscience Publishers, New York, 1949.

46. P. W. Bridgman, *Studies in Large Plastic Flow and Fracture,* McGraw-Hill, New York, 1952.
47. G. R. Taylor and S. R. Darin, *J. Polymer Sci.,* **17,** 511 (1955).
48. A. M. Bueche, *J. Polymer Sci.,* **19,** 275 (1956).
49. F. Bueche, *J. Polymer Sci.,* **24,** 189 (1957).
50. A. M. Bueche, in *Fracture,* edited by B. L. Auerbach, D. K. Filbeck, G. T. Hahn, and D. A. Thomas, Technology Press and John Wiley and Sons, 1959.
51. T. L. Smith, unpublished work.
52. W. Kuhn and H. Kuhn, *Helv. Chim. Acta,* **29,** 1095 (1946).
53. F. Bueche, *J. Applied Phys.,* **26,** 1133 (1955).
54. T. L. Smith, *J. Polymer Sci.,* **32,** 99 (1958).
55. L. Mullins, unpublished work.
56. R. D. Andrews, *Bull. Amer. Phys. Soc.,* **30,** 24 (1955).
57. L. M. Epstein and R. P. Smith, *Trans. Soc. Rheology,* **2,** 219 (1958).
58. F. Bueche, *J. Applied Phys.,* **28,** 784 (1957).
59. F. Bueche, *J. Applied Phys.,* **29,** 1231 (1958).
60. J. J. Benbow and F. C. Roesler, *Proc. Phys. Soc.,* **B70,** 201 (1957).
61. B. D. Coleman, *Trans. Soc. Rheology,* **1,** 153 (1957).

Additional References

62. W. N. Findley, *Soc. Plastics Eng. J.,* **16,** 2 (1960).
63. W. N. Findley and G. Khosla, *J. Applied Phys.,* **26,** 821 (1955).
64. J. K. Knowles and A. G. Dietz, *Trans. Am. Soc. Mech. Eng.,* **77,** 177 (1955).
65. W. N. Findley and J. J. Poczatek, *J. Applied Mech.,* **22,** 165 (1955).

APPENDIX A

List of Symbols

To avoid introducing unfamiliar and exotic symbols, it has sometimes been necessary to use the same symbol with two or more different meanings. However, the context should always make the identification clear. The following list does not include all the various subscripts which are used in certain special applications.

a	root-mean-square end-to-end distance per square root of number of monomer units
a_T	ratio of relaxation times at two different temperatures
a_c	ratio of relaxation times at two different concentrations
a_P	ratio of relaxation times at two different pressures
a_S	ratio of relaxation times at two different stresses (or strains)
b	sample coefficient or form factor
c	concentration (g. polymer per cc. solution), *or*
	width (sample)
$c_1{}^0, c_2{}^0$	coefficients in WLF equation referred to T_0 as reference
$c_1{}^g, c_2{}^g$	coefficients in WLF equation referred to T_g as reference
d	thickness (sample)
e	electromotive force, *or*
	base of natural logarithms
f	force, *or*
	fractional free volume
f_g	fractional free volume at the glass transition temperature
f_0	translational friction coefficient of a submolecule
h	height
i	current, *or*
	$\sqrt{-1}$, *or*
	intercept of linear plot
j	number of chain backbone atoms in a monomer unit

k	Boltzmann's constant, *or*
	arbitrary constant in various equations
l	length
m	mass (sample), *or*
	slope of logarithmic plot
n	number of molecules per cc.
n_c	number of network strands per cc.
p	summation index
q	number of monomer units in a submolecule
r	radius, *or*
	wave damping parameter, *or*
	other dimensionless ratios
$(\overline{r_0^2})^{1/2}$	root-mean-square end-to-end distance of a macromolecule (unperturbed)
s	running time variable, *or*
	slope of linear plot
t	time
u	running time variable, *or*
	shear displacement
v	velocity, *or*
	specific volume
v_f	free volume per g.
v_o	occupied volume per g.
w_i	weight fraction of component i
x	linear displacement
x_0	critical damping distance
A	area, *or*
	numerical factor in approximation calculations, *or*
	real component of complex propagation constant, *or*
	empirical constant in various equations
B	bulk compliance, *or*
	numerical factor in approximation calculations, *or*
	magnetic flux density, *or*
	imaginary component of complex propagation constant, *or*
	empirical constant
$B(t)$	bulk creep compliance
$\mathbf{B}^*$	complex dynamic bulk compliance
B'	bulk storage compliance
B''	bulk loss compliance
B_e	equilibrium bulk compliance
B_g	glasslike bulk compliance
B_n	numerical coefficient (vibrations of bars)
C_1, C_2	characteristic constants in various equations
C'_1, C'_2	characteristic constants in various equations
C_v	heat capacity at constant volume
D	tensile compliance
$D(t)$	tensile creep compliance

$\mathbf{D}^*$	complex dynamic tensile compliance
D'	tensile storage compliance
D''	tensile loss compliance
D_e	equilibrium, pseudo-equilibrium, or steady-state tensile compliance
D_g	glasslike tensile compliance
D_0	diffusion coefficient at vanishing concentration of diluent
E	Young's (tensile) modulus
$E(t)$	tensile relaxation modulus
$\mathbf{E}^*$	complex dynamic tensile modulus
E'	tensile storage modulus
E''	tensile loss modulus
E_e	equilibrium or pseudo-equilibrium tensile modulus
E_g	glasslike Young's modulus
G	shear modulus
$G(t)$	shear relaxation modulus
$\mathbf{G}^*$	complex dynamic shear modulus
G'	shear storage modulus
G''	shear loss modulus
G_e	equilibrium or pseudo-equilibrium shear modulus
G_g	glasslike shear modulus
G_i	modulus contribution of model element
$\widetilde{G}$	shear wave rigidity modulus
H	relaxation spectrum (shear)
H_l	relaxation spectrum in extension
I	moment of inertia
J	shear compliance
$J(t)$	shear creep compliance
$\mathbf{J}^*$	complex dynamic shear compliance
J'	shear storage compliance
J''	shear loss compliance
J_e	equilibrium, pseudo-equilibrium, or steady-state shear compliance
J_g	glasslike shear compliance
J_i	compliance contribution of model element
K	bulk modulus, *or*
	transducer constant, *or*
	characteristic constant
$K(t)$	bulk relaxation modulus
$\mathbf{K}^*$	complex dynamic bulk modulus
K'	bulk storage modulus
K''	bulk loss modulus
K_e	equilibrium bulk modulus
K_{ad}	adiabatic bulk modulus
K_{is}	isothermal bulk modulus
L	retardation spectrum (shear), *or*
	depth

L_l	retardation spectrum in extension
M	modulus for one-dimensional extension in infinite medium, *or*
	numerical factor in approximation calculations, *or*
	mass, *or*
	molecular weight
$\mathbf{M}^*$	complex dynamic longitudinal bulk modulus
M'	bulk longitudinal storage modulus
M''	bulk longitudinal loss compliance
$\bar{M}_n$	number-average molecular weight
$\bar{M}_w$	weight-average molecular weight
$\bar{M}_z$	z-average molecular weight
M_0	molecular weight per monomer unit
M_e	average molecular weight between entanglement coupling points
M_c	average molecular weight of a network strand
N	numerical factor in approximation calculations, *or*
	number of submolecules in a macromolecule
N_0	Avogadro's number
P	pressure
Q_e	entanglement coupling factor
R	radius, *or*
	electrical resistance
R_M	mechanical resistance
S_M	mechanical elastance
T	absolute temperature
T_0	reference temperature for reduced variables
T_s	standard reference temperature for WLF equation in form of equation 37, Chapter 11
T_g	glass transition temperature
T_M	temperature of mid-point of transition from rubberlike to glasslike consistency (under arbitrary conditions of time or frequency)
V	volume
W	work of deformation, *or*
	load
X	electrical reactance
X_M	mechanical reactance
Y_M	mechanical admittance
Z	degree of polymerization
$\mathbf{Z}$	electrical impedance
$\mathbf{Z_M}$	mechanical impedance
Z_e	average degree of polymerization between entanglement coupling points
Z_c	average degree of polymerization of a network strand
$\mathfrak{f}$	ratio of the numbers of entanglement network strands per cc. at two different temperatures

$\mathcal{E}$	differential Young's modulus
$\mathcal{E}_{st}$	stored energy per cc.
$\mathcal{E}_d$	dissipated energy per cc. (in a quarter cycle)
$\dot{\mathcal{E}}$	rate of dissipation of energy per second
$\mathcal{R}_M$	characteristic mechanical resistance
$\mathcal{S}$	torque
$\mathfrak{T}$	shear stress
$\mathfrak{T}_{ss}$	stress following cessation of steady-state flow
$\mathfrak{X}_M$	characteristic mechanical reactance
α	angle of deformation, *or*
	thermal expansion coefficient, *or*
	attenuation of propagated wave, *or*
	distribution parameter (Cole-Cole equation)
α_f	thermal expansion of free volume relative to total volume
α_l	thermal expansion coefficient above T_g
α_g	thermal expansion coefficient below T_g
β	coefficient of compressibility, *or*
	parameter characterizing isothermal contraction, *or*
	parameter in Andrade creep equation, *or*
	parameter relating free volume to weight concentration of diluent
β'	parameter relating free volume to volume concentration of diluent, *or*
	parameter in Andrade creep equation in terms of strain
γ	shear strain
$\dot{\gamma}$	rate of shear strain (velocity gradient)
δ	phase angle between stress and strain, *or*
	small increment, *or*
	Dirac delta
ϵ	tensile strain, *or*
	dielectric constant
ϵ'	real component of complex dielectric constant
ϵ''	imaginary component of complex dielectric constant
ζ_0	translational friction coefficient per monomer unit
ζ_E	monomeric translational elastic coefficient
ζ_1	translational friction coefficient for small foreign molecule
η	viscosity (shear)
η^*	complex dynamic shear viscosity
η'	real part of complex viscosity
η''	imaginary part of complex viscosity
η_l	tensile viscosity
η_v	bulk (volume) viscosity
η_i	viscosity contribution of model element
η_s	viscosity of solvent
η_a	apparent viscosity in non-Newtonian flow
η_e	effective local viscosity
$[\eta]$	intrinsic viscosity

$[\eta']$	real component of intrinsic dynamic viscosity
θ	angle
λ	wavelength, *or*
	summation index, *or*
	numerical coefficients (Zimm theory), *or*
	relative length (in simple extension), *or*
	coefficient of rolling friction
μ	Poisson's ratio
ν	frequency in cycles/sec.
ρ	density
σ	tensile stress, *or*
	root-mean-square end-to-end distance of a submolecule
τ	relaxation or retardation time; argument of H or L
τ_i	relaxation or retardation time of element of mechanical model
ϕ	phase angle, *or*
	volume fraction (of filler)
$\varphi(M)$	distribution function of molecular weights
ϕ_1	volume fraction of diluent (solvent) in solution
ϕ_2	volume fraction of polymer in solution
ψ	numerical factor in approximation calculations
ψ'	numerical factor in approximation calculations
ω	frequency in rad./sec.
ω_0	resonance frequency (forced oscillations)
ω_c	characteristic frequency (free oscillations)
Γ	gamma function, *or*
	complex propagation constant
Δ	differencing symbol, *or*
	logarithmic decrement
ΔH_η	apparent activation energy in viscous flow
ΔH_a	apparent activation energy for relaxation or retardation processes
Φ_1, Φ_2, etc.	dimensionless reduced theoretical functions (Appendix E)
Θ	coefficient of restitution

Applicability of Various Dynamic Methods for Viscoelastic Measurements

The methods are classified here according to the loss characteristics and magnitude of the impedance (in the acoustic sense—a measure of $|\mathbf{G}^*|$ or $|\mathbf{E}^*|$) of the materials to be studied. Examples of the six classes are given in the footnotes for illustration. For the transient methods, X denotes applicability; for the dynamic methods, letters are used to denote approximate frequency ranges, as follows: VLF, <1 cycle/sec.; LF, 1 to 10^2 cyles/sec.; MF, 10^2 to 10^4 cycles/sec.; HF, 10^4 to 10^6 cycles/sec.; VHF, $>10^6$ cycles/sec.

Method	Chapter	Ref.	High Loss (tan δ ≫ 1)		Medium Loss (tan δ ≃ 1)	Low Loss (tan δ ≪ 1)		
			High Imp. a	Low Imp. b	Med. Imp. c	High Imp. d	Med. Imp. e	Low Imp. f
Creep	5	1	X		X			X
	5	3	X		X			X
	6	1	X		X			
	6	7	X		X			X
	6	8			X			X
	6	9			X		X	
	7	1–5				X		
Stress relaxation	5	19	X					
	5	20	X					
	6	13–16			X	X	X	
	7	6–8				X		
Direct measurement of stress and strain	5	28	VLF			VLF		
	5	22	VLF				VLF	
	5	24	LF		LF		LF	
	6	19			VLF		VLF	
	6	20					LF	
	6	21–25			LF		LF	
	6	26			VLF	VLF	VLF	
	7	16				VLF, LF		
	7	17				VLF		
Transducer measurements of stress/strain ratios	5	27	LF					
	6	5, 29			MF	MF	MF	MF
Compound resonance measurements (forced)	6	31–35					LF	LF
	6	36, 37						
	6	38	LF					
	6	39			MF		MF	
	6	40–41	MF					
Compound resonance measurements (free)	6	8					VLF	VLF
	6	44–46				LF	LF	
	6	47					LF	
Shear, extensional, and flexural wave propagation	5	36, 37			MF			
	6	47					MF, HF	
	6	48					MF, HF	
	6	53, 54				VHF		
Longitudinal bulk wave propagation	8	12–15				VHF		
	8	15				HF		
Characteristic impedance measurements	5	39		MF				
	5	38, 40		HF				
	5	41	HF		HF			
	5	42		MF, HF				
	5	45	VHF	VHF	VHF		VHF	VHF
Resonance vibration measurements	7	18–27				MF		

[a] E.g., uncross-linked polymers of high molecular weight and their concentrated solutions in the terminal zone.

[b] E.g., dilute polymer solutions.

[c] E.g., most systems in the transition zone between glasslike and rubberlike consistency.

[d] E.g., glassy and highly crystalline polymers, or soft polymers at such high frequencies that the moduli approach glasslike magnitudes.

[e] E.g., soft cross-linked polymers in the pseudo-equilibrium zone, or uncross-linked polymers of high molecular weight in the plateau zone.

[f] E.g., soft gels in the pseudo-equilibrium zone.

Form Factors and Maximum Stresses and Strains for Various Deformation Geometries

VALID ONLY FOR SMALL STRAINS

Type of Geometry	Form Factor (b) and Units	Equation No. and Chapter	Maximum Stress	Maximum Strain
Simple shear sandwich	$A_1/h_1 + A_2/h_2$ (cm) or $(m_1/h_1^2 + m_2/h_2^2)/\rho$ (cm)	1, 7–9, 11, 12, Ch. 6	$\mho = f/(A_1 + A_2)$	$\gamma = x/h$
Pochettino	$2\pi L/\ln(R_2/R_1)$ (cm)	1, Ch. 6	$\mho = f/2\pi R_1 L$	$\gamma = x/R_1 \ln(R_2/R_1)$
Annular pumping	$2\pi L(R_2^2 + R_1^2)/(R_2^2 - R_1^2)$ (cm)	4, 6, 7, Ch. 6	$\mho = \dfrac{f(R_2^2 - R_1^2)}{2\pi R_1 L}$	$\gamma = \dfrac{(R_2^2 + R_1^2)\ln(R_2/R_1)/(R_2^2 - R_1^2) - 1}{x/R_1}$
Torsion between coaxial cylinders	$\dfrac{(R_2^2 + R_1^2)\ln(R_2/R_1)/(R_2^2 - R_1^2) - 1}{4\pi L}$ (cm³)	1, Ch. 5	$\mho = \mathcal{S}/2\pi L R_1^2$	$\gamma = 2R_2^2\alpha/(R_2^2 - R_1^2)$
Torsion between cone and plate	$2\pi R^3/3\theta$ (cm³)	1, Ch. 5	$\mho = 3\mathcal{S}/2\pi R^3$	$\gamma = \alpha/\theta$
Torsion of circular cylindrical rod	$\pi R^4/2h$ (cm³) or $m^2/2\pi h^3\rho^2$	1, Ch. 6	$\mho = 2\mathcal{S}/\pi R^3$	$\gamma = \alpha R/h$
Simple extension	A/L (cm)	2, 3, Ch. 6	$\sigma = f/A$	$\epsilon = x/L$
Flexure (cantilever, one end clamped, rectangular cross-section)	$cd^3/4L^3$ (cm)	5, Ch. 7	$\sigma = 6fL/cd^2$	$\epsilon = 3\,dx/2L^2$
Flexure (cantilever, one end clamped, circular cross-section)	$3\pi R^4/4L^3$ (cm)	8, Ch. 7	$\sigma = 4fL/\pi R^3$	$\epsilon = 3Rx/L^2$
Flexure (two ends clamped)	$16cd^3/L^3$ (cm)	3, Ch. 7	$\sigma = 3fL/4cd^2$	$\epsilon = 12\,dx/L^2$
Flexure (knife edge loading)	$2cd^3/L^3$ (cm)	4, Ch. 7	$\sigma = 3fL/2cd^2$	$\epsilon = 3\,dx/L^2$

c width	A area	γ shear strain
d thickness	L length	ϵ tensile strain
f force	R radius	θ angle (between cone and plate)
h height	$\mathcal{S}$ torque	ρ density
m mass	α angular displacement	σ tensile stress
x linear displacement		

Examples of Numerical Data
for Dynamic and
Relaxation Moduli

The shapes of the various viscoelastic functions have been abundantly illustrated graphically, especially in Chapters 2, 12, and 13. However, no numerical data have been cited (except in Table 4–I). Indeed, such data are very rarely given in the literature, where space restrictions usually limit the presentation to graphical form. Thus the material for derived calculations such as those in Chapter 19 is difficult to obtain. A compendium of numerical data would be of considerable value. A few examples are given here for dynamic and relaxation moduli reduced to standard reference temperatures as described in Chapter 11.

1. Storage and Loss Moduli for Polyisobutylene, Poly-n-octyl Methacrylate, Unvulcanized Hevea Rubber, and Lightly Vulcanized Hevea Rubber

The data for polyisobutylene refer to a sample with weight-average molecular weight 1.56×10^6 and a broad molecular weight distribution, distributed by Dr. R. S. Marvin of the National Bureau of Standards.[1] They are based primarily on dynamic measurements by Fitzgerald, Grandine, and Ferry,[2] Plazek, Vrancken, and Berge,[3] and Philippoff.[4] The reduction temperature is 25°C. The best coefficients for the WLF equation with $T_0 = 298.2°$K. based on the data of references 2 and 3 are $c_1 = 9.08$ and $c_2 = 209$. The a_T factors calculated from these coefficients are negligibly different from those used earlier [2] before the introduction of the WLF equation.

$\log \omega$	$\log G'$	$\log G''$	$\log \omega$	$\log G'$	$\log G''$
−3.5	6.02	5.67	3.0	6.76	6.71
−3.0	6.12	5.66	3.5	6.96	7.03
−2.5	6.21	5.64	4.0	7.20	7.37
−2.0	6.25	5.60	4.5	7.49	7.69
−1.5	6.30	5.48	5.0	7.83	8.02
−1.0	6.35	5.45	5.5	8.16	8.34
−0.5	6.38	5.44	6.0	8.49	8.64
0	6.42	5.40	6.5	8.81	8.92
0.5	6.44	5.42	7.0	9.11	9.16
1.0	6.47	5.49	7.5	9.40	9.36
1.5	6.48	5.75	8.0	9.64	9.50
2.0	6.51	6.05	8.5	9.82	9.51
2.5	6.61	6.38	9.0	9.93	9.39

The data for poly-n-octyl methacrylate [5,6] are those presented in Figs. 2–3 and 2–4. They appear in part also in Table 4–I. The reduction temperature is 100°C. The data have been reduced for the f-shift described in Chapter 11, Section D4, as well as with the usual a_T factor.

$\log \omega$	$\log G'$	$\log G''$	$\log \omega$	$\log G'$	$\log G''$
−3.5 [a]	3.98	4.01	4.5	6.20	6.22
−3.0 [a]	4.30	4.30	5.0	6.45	6.58
−2.5 [a]	4.61	4.64	5.5	6.67	6.90
−2.0 [a]	4.89	4.76	6.0	6.98	7.26
−1.5 [a]	5.16	5.01	6.5	7.31	7.63
−1.0 [a]	5.38	5.14	7.0	7.68	7.98
−0.5	5.42	4.93	7.5	8.06	8.28
0	5.49	4.87	8.0	8.49	8.55
0.5	5.53	4.79	8.5	8.82	8.71
1.0	5.57	4.76	9.0	9.03	8.81
1.5	5.56	4.82	9.5	9.20	8.83
2.0	5.61	4.97	10.0	9.31	8.77
2.5	5.68	5.19	10.5	9.39	8.73
3.0	5.77	5.42	11.0	9.44	8.67
3.5	5.89	5.68	11.5	9.48	8.74
4.0	6.05	5.98	12.0	9.44	8.87

[a] Calculated indirectly from creep measurements by the methods of Chapter 4.

The data for unvulcanized and lightly vulcanized Hevea rubber are those of Payne,[7] which have appeared in part in Fig. 13–1. The molecular weight of the unvulcanized sample is not specified, but must have been very high. The reduction temperature for the reduced frequencies given in this table is 0°C.

	Unvulcanized		Vulcanized	
$\log \omega$	$\log G'$	$\log G''$	$\log G'$	$\log G''$
−4.0	6.46	5.62	6.67	5.27
−3.5	6.49	5.62	6.68	5.28
−3.0	6.50_5	5.61	6.68	5.28
−2.5	6.54	5.61	6.69	5.28
−2.0	6.60	5.59	6.71	5.28_5
−1.5	6.67	5.57	6.72	5.29
−1.0	6.73	5.54	6.73	5.33
−0.5	6.78_5	5.46	6.74	5.37
0	6.83	5.39	6.76	5.42
0.5	6.86	5.38	6.77	5.48
1.0	6.88	5.42	6.79	5.53
1.5	6.90	5.53	6.81	5.64
2.0	6.91	5.65	6.85	5.79
2.5	6.94	5.83	6.89	6.06
3.0	6.96	6.01	6.93	6.35
3.5	6.97	6.20	7.01	6.65
4.0	7.00	6.44	7.13	6.98
4.5	7.06	6.73	7.28	7.33
5.0	7.16	7.03	7.45	7.70
5.5	7.31	7.38	7.70	8.11
6.0	7.54	7.80	8.03	8.49
6.5	7.89	8.28	8.53	8.88
7.0	8.37	8.72	9.07	9.18
7.5	8.91	9.13	9.53	9.53
8.0	9.39	9.47	9.82	9.42
8.5	9.71	9.61	9.97	9.37
9.0	9.91	9.59	10.07	9.27
9.5	10.00	9.45	10.14	9.14
10.0	10.06	9.24	10.15	8.98
10.5	10.10	9.03	10.15	8.81
11.0	10.12	8.81	10.16	8.62

2. Relaxation Moduli for Polyisobutylene, Polyvinyl Acetate, and Polystyrene

The data for polyisobutylene refer to the same sample as described above, and are quoted from stress relaxation measurements by Tobolsky and collaborators.[8] The reduction temperature is again 25°C. The modulus is *Young's* modulus, and the units of time are *hours*.

$\log t$	$\log E(t)$	$\log t$	$\log E(t)$	$\log t$	$\log E(t)$
−14.4	10.48_5	−8.4	8.05_5	−2.4	6.79_5
−14.0	10.46_5	−8.0	7.80_5	−2.0	6.75_5
−13.6	10.44_5	−7.6	7.58_5	−1.6	6.71
−13.2	10.41	−7.2	7.38_5	−1.2	6.65_5
−12.8	10.37	−6.8	7.21	−0.8	6.59
−12.4	10.30	−6.4	7.08_5	−0.4	6.50_5
−12.0	10.20_5	−6.0	7.00_5	0	6.39_5
−11.6	10.07_5	−5.6	6.96	0.4	6.26
−11.2	9.88_5	−5.2	6.92_5	0.8	6.08
−10.8	9.65_5	−4.8	6.90_5	1.2	5.85
−10.4	9.39_5	−4.4	6.89_5	1.6	5.54
−10.0	9.12_5	−4.0	6.88_5	2.0	5.18
−9.6	8.86_5	−3.6	6.87_5	2.4	4.5
−9.2	8.60_5	−3.2	6.85_5	2.8	−∞
−8.8	8.33	−2.8	6.82_5		

The data for polyvinyl acetate [9] are those presented in Fig. 2–2 as the plateau and terminal zones of Curve II, expressed in their original form as Young's modulus in relaxation. The reduction temperature is 75°C., and the units of time are seconds.

$\log t$	$\log E(t)$	$\log t$	$\log E(t)$
−1.0	7.02	3.5	5.85
−0.5	6.90	4.0	5.59
0	6.80	4.5	5.25
0.5	6.72	5.0	4.85
1.0	6.65	5.5	4.37
1.5	6.55	6.0	3.51
2.0	6.43	6.25	2.99
2.5	6.28	6.5	2.37
3.0	6.09		

The data for polystyrene refer to a sample with weight-average molecular weight 0.20×10^6, investigated by Fujita and Ninomiya.[10] The reduction temperature is 135°C., the modulus is Young's modulus, and the units of time are seconds.

log t	log $E(t)$	log t	log $E(t)$
−8.0	10.22	−1.5	6.91
−7.5	10.17	−1.0	6.84
−7.0	10.05	−0.5	6.65
−6.5	9.89	0	6.54
−6.0	9.64	0.5	6.45
−5.5	9.26	1.0	6.34
−5.0	8.82	1.5	6.20
−4.5	8.43	2.0	6.01
−4.0	8.12	2.5	5.77
−3.5	7.85	3.0	5.49
−3.0	7.59	3.5	5.11
−2.5	7.33	4.0	4.62
−2.0	7.10	4.5	3.95

It will be recalled from Chapter 12 that in the transition zone the values quoted in tables such as these are essentially independent of molecular weight and molecular weight distribution, and therefore characteristic of the chemical structure of each polymer. In the plateau and terminal zones, however, the viscoelastic properties reflect the molecular weight distribution in the particular sample investigated as well as its chemical structure.

REFERENCES

1. R. S. Marvin, *Proc. Second Intern. Congr. Rheology*, 1954, p. 156.
2. E. R. Fitzgerald, L. D. Grandine, Jr., and J. D. Ferry, *J. Appl. Phys.*, **24,** 650 (1953) ; **24,** 911 (1953).
3. D. J. Plazek, M. N. Vrancken, and J. W. Berge, *Trans. Soc. Rheology*, **2,** 39 (1958).
4. W. Philippoff, *J. Appl. Phys.*, **24,** 685 (1953).
5. W. Dannhauser, W. C. Child, Jr., and J. D. Ferry, *J. Colloid Sci.*, **13,** 103 (1958).
6. J. W. Berge, P. R. Saunders, and J. D. Ferry, *J. Colloid Sci.*, **14,** 135 (1959).
7. A. R. Payne, in P. Mason and N. Wookey, *Rheology of Elastomers*, Pergamon Press, London, 1958, p. 86.

8. A. V. Tobolsky and E. Catsiff, *J. Polymer Sci.*, **19**, 111 (1956).

9. K. Ninomiya, *J. Colloid Sci.*, **14**, 49 (1959).

10. H. Fujita and K. Ninomiya, *J. Polymer Sci.*, **24**, 233 (1957).

Additional Reference

Tabular data for time-dependent properties are given for a number of amorphous, crystalline, and filled polymers in Report No. 101 from Chesapeake Instrument Corporation to the Office of Naval Research under Contract Nonr-2678(00), by E. J. Cook, J. A. Lee, E. R. Fitzgerald, and J. W. Fitzgerald (1960).

Theoretical Viscoelastic Functions Reduced in Dimensionless Form

1. Rouse theory for uniform molecular weight with no entanglements, in the transition and terminal zones (equations 4 and 5, Chapter 10).

Dimensionless parameters: $\omega_R = \omega\tau_1$; $\Phi_1 = G'/(cRT/M)$; $\Phi_2 = (\eta' - \eta_s)/(\eta - \eta_s)$; $\Phi_3 = G''/(cRT/M)$; $\Phi_4 = J'M/cRT$. For undiluted polymers, replace c by ρ and set $\eta_s = 0$.

$\log \omega_R$	$\log \Phi_1$	$\log \Phi_2$	$\log \Phi_3$	$\log \Phi_4$
-1.0	-1.97	0.00	-0.78	-0.40
-0.8	-1.58	0.00	-0.58	-0.40
-0.6	-1.17	-0.01	-0.39	-0.40
-0.4	-0.72	-0.03	-0.21	-0.40
-0.2	-0.50	-0.09	-0.07	-0.41
0	-0.24	-0.17	0.05	-0.45
0.2	-0.05	-0.27	0.15	-0.50
0.4	0.10	-0.37	0.25	-0.57
0.6	0.24	-0.47	0.35	-0.66
0.8	0.36	-0.57	0.45	-0.75
1.0	0.47	-0.67	0.55	-0.85
1.2	0.58	-0.77	0.65	-0.95
1.4	0.69	-0.87	0.75	-1.05
1.6	0.80	-0.97	0.85	-1.15
1.8	0.91	-1.07	0.95	-1.25
2.0	1.02	-1.17	1.05	-1.35

2. Marvin theory for uniform molecular weight with entanglements (assumed of uniform spacing), in the transition plateau, and terminal zones (equation 71, Chapter 10).

Dimensionless parameters: $G'_R = G'M_e/C'_1 \doteq G'(6M_e/5\rho RT)$; $G''_R = G''M_e/C'_1$; $p_R = i\omega C'_2 M_e^2 \doteq i\omega(3a^2 \zeta_0 M_e^2/50M_0^2 kT)$. (Symbol $\doteq$ refers to identifications made in equations 36 and 37 of Chapter 10.)

Calculations made by Dr. Stuart E. Lovell * for the following values of $M/2M_e$: 3, 4, 6, 9, 20, 40.

	$M/2M_e = 3$			$M/2M_e = 4$		
$\log p_R/i$	$\log G'_R$	$\log G''_R$	$\tan \delta$	$\log G'_R$	$\log G''_R$	$\tan \delta$
−3.00	−2.88	−1.54	21.78	−1.87	−1.09	6.03
−2.80	−2.48	−1.34	13.74	−1.48	−0.90	3.81
−2.60	−2.08	−1.14	8.68	−1.13	−0.75	2.42
−2.40	−1.69	−0.95	5.48	−0.83	−0.63	1.55
−2.20	−1.32	−0.78	3.47	−0.60	−0.59	1.02
−2.00	−0.97	−0.62	2.20	−0.46	−0.61	0.71
−1.80	−0.68	−0.53	1.41	−0.38	−0.65	0.54
−1.60	−0.47	−0.50	0.93	−0.33	−0.67	0.46
−1.40	−0.34	−0.53	0.65	−0.28	−0.65	0.43
−1.20	−0.28	−0.58	0.49	−0.23	−0.63	0.40
−1.00	−0.24	−0.60	0.43	−0.18	−0.62	0.37
−0.80	−0.20	−0.57	0.42	−0.14	−0.61	0.34
−0.60	−0.15	−0.53	0.42	−0.11	−0.58	0.34
−0.40	−0.11	−0.47	0.44	−0.08	−0.52	0.36
−0.20	−0.08	−0.39	0.48	−0.05	−0.44	0.41
0.00	−0.04	−0.29	0.56	−0.03	−0.33	0.50
0.20	0.00	−0.17	0.68	0.01	−0.19	0.63
0.40	0.05	−0.03	0.82	0.05	−0.04	0.80
0.60	0.13	0.11	0.96	0.13	0.10	0.95
0.80	0.23	0.24	1.03	0.23	0.24	1.03
1.00	0.34	0.35	1.03	0.34	0.35	1.03
1.20	0.45	0.45	1.01	0.45	0.45	1.01
1.40	0.55	0.55	1.00	0.55	0.55	1.00
1.60	0.65	0.65	1.00	0.65	0.65	1.00
1.80	0.75	0.75	1.00	0.75	0.75	1.00
2.00	0.85	0.85	1.00	0.85	0.85	1.00

* H. Högberg, S. E. Lovell, and J. D. Ferry, *Acta Chem. Scand.*, in press.

log p_R/i	$M/2M_e = 6$			$M/2M_e = 9$		
	log G'_R	log G''_R	tan δ	log G'_R	log G''_R	tan δ
−4.00	−2.45	−1.44	10.20	−1.20	−0.94	1.82
−3.80	−2.05	−1.24	6.44	−0.95	−0.87	1.22
−3.60	−1.67	−1.06	4.08	−0.79	−0.85	0.87
−3.40	−1.31	−0.90	2.60	−0.70	−0.85	0.70
−3.20	−1.00	−0.78	1.67	−0.63	−0.82	0.63
−3.00	−0.77	−0.72	1.11	−0.55	−0.77	0.61
−2.80	−0.62	−0.72	0.78	−0.48	−0.72	0.56
−2.60	−0.53	−0.74	0.61	−0.40	−0.70	0.51
−2.40	−0.47	−0.74	0.54	−0.33	−0.68	0.45
−2.20	−0.41	−0.70	0.51	−0.27	−0.68	0.40
−2.00	−0.34	−0.68	0.46	−0.22	−0.69	0.34
−1.80	−0.28	−0.67	0.41	−0.18	−0.71	0.30
−1.60	−0.23	−0.67	0.36	−0.14	−0.73	0.26
−1.40	−0.18	−0.68	0.32	−0.11	−0.76	0.22
−1.20	−0.15	−0.69	0.28	−0.09	−0.79	0.20
−1.00	−0.11	−0.70	0.26	−0.07	−0.81	0.18
−0.80	−0.09	−0.70	0.25	−0.05	−0.80	0.18
−0.60	−0.07	−0.67	0.25	−0.04	−0.76	0.19
−0.40	−0.05	−0.60	0.28	−0.03	−0.68	0.23
−0.20	−0.03	−0.50	0.34	−0.02	−0.56	0.29
0.00	−0.01	−0.37	0.43	0.00	−0.41	0.39
0.20	0.01	−0.22	0.58	0.02	−0.24	0.55
0.40	0.05	−0.06	0.77	0.05	−0.07	0.75
0.60	0.12	0.10	0.94	0.12	0.09	0.94
0.80	0.22	0.24	1.04	0.22	0.24	1.04
1.00	0.34	0.36	1.04	0.34	0.36	1.04
1.20	0.45	0.45	1.01	0.45	0.45	1.01
1.40	0.55	0.55	1.00	0.55	0.55	1.00
1.60	0.65	0.65	1.00	0.65	0.65	1.00
1.80	0.75	0.75	1.00	0.75	0.75	1.00
2.00	0.85	0.85	1.00	0.85	0.85	1.00

	$M/2M_e = 20$			$M/2M_e = 40$		
$\log p_R/i$	$\log G'_R$	$\log G''_R$	$\tan \delta$	$\log G'_R$	$\log G''_R$	$\tan \delta$
-4.00	-0.63	-0.81	0.66	-0.35	-0.69	0.46
-3.80	-0.54	-0.76	0.61	-0.29	-0.68	0.40
-3.60	-0.46	-0.72	0.55	-0.24	-0.69	0.35
-3.40	-0.39	-0.70	0.49	-0.19	-0.72	0.30
-3.20	-0.32	-0.68	0.44	-0.15	-0.75	0.25
-3.00	-0.27	-0.69	0.38	-0.12	-0.80	0.21
-2.80	-0.22	-0.70	0.33	-0.10	-0.85	0.18
-2.60	-0.17	-0.73	0.28	-0.08	-0.91	0.15
-2.40	-0.14	-0.76	0.24	-0.06	-0.98	0.12
-2.20	-0.11	-0.81	0.20	-0.05	-1.05	0.10
-2.00	-0.09	-0.86	0.17	-0.04	-1.12	0.08
-1.80	-0.07	-0.92	0.14	-0.03	-1.19	0.07
-1.60	-0.05	-0.98	0.12	-0.02	-1.25	0.06
-1.40	-0.04	-1.02	0.10	-0.02	-1.28	0.06
-1.20	-0.03	-1.05	0.10	-0.01	-1.27	0.06
-1.00	-0.03	-1.05	0.10	-0.01	-1.23	0.06
-0.80	-0.02	-1.00	0.10	-0.01	-1.13	0.08
-0.60	-0.02	-0.91	0.13	-0.01	-0.99	0.10
-0.40	-0.01	-0.78	0.17	0.00	-0.83	0.15
-0.20	0.00	-0.62	0.24	0.00	-0.65	0.22
0.00	0.00	-0.45	0.35	0.01	-0.47	0.34
0.20	0.02	-0.27	0.51	0.02	-0.28	0.50
0.40	0.05	-0.09	0.73	0.05	-0.09	0.72
0.60	0.12	0.09	0.93	0.12	0.09	0.93
0.80	0.22	0.24	1.04	0.22	0.24	1.05
1.00	0.34	0.36	1.04	0.34	0.36	1.04
1.20	0.45	0.45	1.01	0.45	0.45	1.01
1.40	0.55	0.55	1.00	0.55	0.55	1.00
1.60	0.65	0.65	1.00	0.65	0.65	1.00
1.80	0.75	0.75	1.00	0.75	0.75	1.00
2.00	0.85	0.85	1.00	0.85	0.85	1.00

Use of Mechanical Models for Viscoelastic Properties and for Dynamic Response of Apparatus Systems

In the literature of viscoelasticity, mechanical models of springs and dashpots have been used for two quite different purposes: to represent the viscoelastic properties of materials, as in Figs. 1–1, 1–2, 3–1, 3–2, 15–13, and 18–2; and to describe the response of actual physical assemblies, such as apparatus used for measurements.

The latter application is less abstract, since some of the springs and dashpots correspond to real components of the apparatus (*e.g.*, Figs. 6–5, 6–6, and 6–7). In linear motion, the stiffness coefficient of a model spring has the same units as that of a real spring, force/displacement, or dynes/cm; in torsional motion, the units are torque/angle, or dyne-cm. The corresponding units of a model dashpot are dyne-sec./cm and dyne-cm-sec. respectively. The mechanical contributions of the sample itself also have these respective units. Such models usually include inertial elements.

In the representations of material properties, by contrast, the model parameters do not have the same units as real springs and dashpots, but rather those units divided by the appropriate sample form factor—cm for linear motion and cm^3 for torsion (Appendix C). Thus the model "springs" here correspond to elastic moduli (dynes/cm^2) and the "dashpots" to viscosities (dyne-sec/cm^2). Although the pictorial representation looks like simple extension, the moduli can obviously correspond to any type of deformation—shear, extension, or bulk compression. These models usually do not include inertial elements (with the exception of that used to interpret Fitzgerald resonances, Fig. 15–13).

In this Appendix, some examples of manipulation of both kinds of models are given.

1. Models Representing Viscoelastic Properties

For polymeric systems, the multiplicity of relaxation mechanisms ordinarily prevents representation of material properties by a small number of model elements, except for rough approximations as described in Chapter 19, Section D. The principles may be illustrated, however, by the theoretical viscoelastic behavior of dilute suspensions of macromolecular thin rigid rods and prolate ellipsoids, as calculated by Kirkwood and Auer,[1] Cerf,[2] and Scheraga.[3] These theories provide the following equations:

$$G' = G_1\omega^2\tau_1^2/(1 + \omega^2\tau_1^2) \tag{1}$$

$$\eta' = \eta_s + \eta_p + \eta_1/(1 + \omega^2\tau_1^2) \tag{2}$$

where η_s is the solvent viscosity, $\tau_1 = \eta_1/G_1$, and $\eta_s + \eta_p + \eta_1 = \eta$, the steady-flow viscosity. In terms of molecular parameters, $G_1 = 3cRT/5M$, where M is the molecular weight and c the concentration in g./cc. For thin rigid rods, $\eta_p = (\eta - \eta_s)/4$ and $\eta_1 = 3(\eta - \eta_s)/4$; for thin prolate ellipsoids, $\eta_p = 2(\eta - \eta_s)/7$ and $\eta_1 = 5(\eta - \eta_s)/7$. The magnitude of τ_1, and hence that of η_1, depend primarily on η_s and the molecular length, L. For rods, $\tau_1 = \pi\eta_s L^3/18kT \ln (L/b)$; for ellipsoids, $\tau_1 = \pi\eta_s L^3/9kT[2 \ln (2L/b) - 1]$. Here, b is the maximum lateral thickness.

Now, equations 1 and 2 can be easily shown to correspond to the behavior of the mechanical model illustrated in Fig. F–1A. There are several ways of calculating time-dependent behavior of such a model, and the methods for handling electrical analogs are extensively treated in books on network analysis (cf. Chapter 3).[4,5] For dynamic properties, the simplest procedure is probably to add complex compliances in series and moduli in parallel. The modulus of a dashpot is $i\omega\eta$, and its compliance is $-i/\omega\eta$. Thus, the compliance of the pair consisting of G_1 and η_1 is $1/G_1 - i/\omega\eta$, and its modulus is

$$\frac{1}{1/G_1 - i/\omega\eta} = \frac{G_1\omega^2\tau^2}{1 + \omega^2\tau^2} + \frac{i\omega\eta}{1 + \omega^2\tau^2} \tag{3}$$

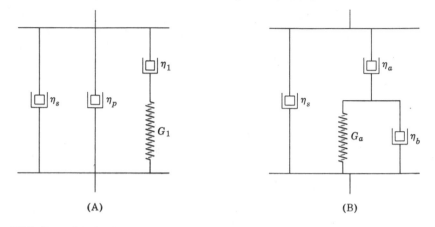

FIG. F–1. Mechanical models corresponding to molecular theories for the viscoelastic properties of dilute solutions of macromolecular thin rods [1] and prolate
ellipsoids.[2] A, equations 1 and 2; B, equations 6 and 7.

The modulus of the entire combination is obtained simply by adding
to the right side of equation 3 the moduli of the other two dash-
pots, $i\omega\eta_s + i\omega\eta_p$. Setting the sum equal to $G' + i\omega\eta'$ and equating
real and imaginary parts, equations 1 and 2 are verified.

Another arrangement of the model components would do just as
well to represent the frequency dependence of G' and η', though the
parameters are then less directly related to molecular theory. Thus,
let us calculate the behavior of the model in Fig. F–1B. First, the
modulus of the pair consisting of G_a and η_b must be expressed as a
compliance:

$$\frac{1}{G_a + i\omega\eta_b} = \frac{1/G_a}{1 + \omega^2\eta_b{}^2/G_a{}^2} - \frac{i\omega\eta_b/G_a{}^2}{1 + \omega^2\eta_b{}^2/G_a{}^2} \qquad (4)$$

To equation 4 must be added the compliance of the dashpot η_a and
the result expressed as a modulus:

$$\frac{1}{\dfrac{-i}{\omega\eta_a} + \dfrac{1/G_a}{1 + \omega^2\eta_b{}^2/G_a{}^2} - \dfrac{i\omega\eta_b/G_a{}^2}{1 + \omega^2\eta_b{}^2/G_a{}^2}}$$

$$= \frac{G_a\omega^2\tau_a{}^2}{1 + \omega^2(\tau_a + \tau_b)^2} + \frac{i\omega\eta_a[1 + \omega^2\tau_b(\tau_a + \tau_b)]}{1 + \omega^2(\tau_a + \tau_b)^2} \qquad (5)$$

where $\tau_a = \eta_a/G_a$ and $\tau_b = \eta_b/G_a$. Finally, adding the modulus of the dashpot η_s to the right side of equation 5 and equating the real and imaginary parts with G' and $i\omega\eta'$, we obtain [6,7]

$$G' = G_a\omega^2\tau_a{}^2/[1 + \omega^2(\tau_a + \tau_b)^2] \tag{6}$$

$$\eta' = \eta_s + \eta_a[1 + \omega^2\tau_b(\tau_a + \tau_b)]/[1 + \omega^2(\tau_a + \tau_b)^2] \tag{7}$$

Equations 6 and 7 are in fact the equivalent of equations 1 and 2 provided that $G_a = G_1(1 + \eta_p/\eta_1)^2$, $\eta_a = \eta_p + \eta_1$, and $\eta_b = \eta_p(\eta_p + \eta_1)/\eta_1$. Similar interconversions are encountered in dealing with the model of Fig. 18–2.

2. Models Representing Physical Assemblies

An example of a mechanical model to describe the response of an apparatus is shown in Fig. F–2. Here the springs represent elastances S_M (dynes/cm in linear motion) instead of moduli and the dashpots represent mechanical resistances R_M or frictances [5] (dyne-sec/cm in linear motion) instead of viscosities. There is also an inertance [5] M (for linear motion, simply a mass). This model corresponds to the dynamic resonance shear apparatus of Fig. 6–5. Here $S_M{}^0$ and $R_M{}^0$ are the small contributions associated with the motion of the apparatus itself, and S_M and R_M are those due to the sample investigated. The latter are drawn with slanting arrows to indicate that they vary with frequency, unlike the model components of Fig. F–1, which are by definition frequency-independent.

It is conventional, in dealing with such apparatus, to choose R_M

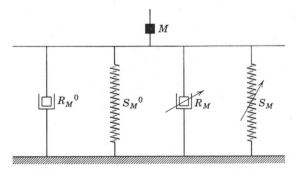

FIG. F–2. Mechanical model corresponding to the resonance dynamic shear apparatus depicted in Fig. 6–5.

as the real component and deal with the complex mechanical impedance (Chapter 5). The mechanical impedances of a dashpot, a spring,
and a mass are R_M, $-iS_M/\omega$, and $i\omega M$ respectively. Thus the total
impedance in Fig. F–2 is

$$\mathbf{Z_M} = R_M + R_M{}^0 + i(\omega M - S_M/\omega - S_M{}^0/\omega)$$

as given by equation 10 of Chapter 6, in which $R_M{}^0$ was omitted as
negligible. At one particular frequency, G' and η' can be obtained
from S_M and R_M by dividing by the sample coefficient b (Appendix C).

A somewhat more complicated example is represented by the Fitzgerald apparatus;[8] the total mechanical impedance depends on several components, some in series and some in parallel, as described in
Chapter 6, Section D. Other examples are given by Tschoegl.[5]

REFERENCES

1. J. G. Kirkwood and P. L. Auer, *J. Chem. Phys.*, **19**, 281 (1951).
2. R. Cerf, *Compt. rend.*, **234**, 1549 (1952).
3. H. A. Scheraga, *J. Chem. Phys.*, **23**, 1526 (1955).
4. H. F. Olson, *Dynamical Analogies*, Van Nostrand, New York, 1943.
5. N. W. Tschoegl, *Kolloid-Z.*, in press.
6. J. D. Ferry, W. M. Sawyer, and J. N. Ashworth, *J. Polymer Sci.*, **2**, 593 (1947).
7. J. D. Ferry and F. E. Helders, *Biochem. Biophys. Acta*, **23**, 569 (1957).
8. E. R. Fitzgerald, *Phys. Rev.*, **108**, 690 (1957).

Author Index

Subject Index